9 ⟩

POLYMER MIXING TECHNOLOGY

POLYMER MIXING TECHNOLOGY

GEORGE MATTHEWS

Principal Lecturer in Material Science and Technology,
Polytechnic of the South Bank, Borough Road,
London SEI, UK

APPLIED SCIENCE PUBLISHERS

LONDON and NEW YORK

APPLIED SCIENCE PUBLISHERS LTD
Ripple Road, Barking, Essex, England

Sole Distributor in the USA and Canada
ELSEVIER SCIENCE PUBLISHING CO., INC.
52 Vanderbilt Avenue, New York, NY 10017, USA

British Library Cataloguing in Publication Data

Matthews, George
    Polymer mixing technology.
    1. Polymers and polymerization
    I. Title
    620.1'92   TA455.P8

    ISBN 0–85334–133–8

WITH 4 TABLES AND 118 ILLUSTRATIONS

© APPLIED SCIENCE PUBLISHERS LTD 1982

Photoset in Malta by Interprint Limited
Printed in Great Britain by Galliard (Printers) Ltd, Great Yarmouth

Acknowledgements

The author first conceived the idea of a book on the present subject while he was with the Plastics Division of Imperial Chemical Industries Ltd and this book is largely based on his experience with that company from 1946 to 1964, expanded and conditioned by his subsequent experience as an academic and consultant. Consequently, many colleagues, customers and other associates have contributed information which has found its way into these chapters and it would be quite impossible to name them all, even if, indeed, it was possible to remember them. Their help, whether consciously or unconsciously given, is none the less greatly appreciated.

Many manufacturers and suppliers of mixing equipment and material aids to mixing responded to requests for technical information and this has been used freely in preparing the text. The companies concerned are listed in Appendix 2. Perhaps special thanks are due to those who provided information most generously but may not find this reflected in the text.

Thanks are also due to those companies who provided photographs, not only those that appear in the text and bear appropriate acknowledgements, but also those that, though informative to the author, were considered inappropriate for inclusion for one reason or another.

These acknowledgements would not be complete without a word of thanks to the referees for the constructive suggestions they offered and to John Brydson for several helpful comments on the script.

In spite of the obviously considerable help received from so many sources, the views herein are those of the author himself, and he accepts responsibility for them.

Preface

A large number of papers on the importance of mixing operations in the processing of polymers have already been published. It is surprising, therefore, that as far as the author is aware this is the first time that an attempt has been made to take the technology of polymer mixing as the sole subject for a book so that it may be treated in a reasonably comprehensive way.

The emphasis in this volume is technological, but in Chapter 2 theoretical aspects of mixing have been dealt with at some length without introducing much of the associated complex mathematics. This is partly because that part of the subject has been already admirably covered by John Funt in his *Mixing of Rubbers* (RAPRA, 1977). Also, in the author's experience the mathematics have generally been of little use to the average technologist involved with selecting and operating polymer mixing equipment. However, the basic theoretical concepts that the mathematics attempt to quantify are important, and an understanding, if only qualitative, is highly desirable for anyone concerned with mixing in practice.

Chapters 3, 4 and 5 deal with equipment and procedures for mixing of polymer compositions, while Chapter 6 is concerned with ancillary equipment and processes and how all the items are combined into a complete polymer mixing facility, concluding with a consideration of the all-important matter of costs. Finally, Chapter 7 attempts to deal with various aspects of polymer mixing that are concerned with specific materials.

The coverage is intended to be of value to all those concerned with production, development and research involving polymer mixing. The contents go well beyond the scope of undergraduate or postgraduate courses with polymer specialisation but should make useful reading for

vii

students in such courses either in their entirety or in selected parts. Each chapter has a list of references which should be good sources for those wishing to investigate in detail the literature on any particular aspect of the subject.

GEORGE MATTHEWS

Contents

CHAPTER 1

Introduction

1.1 HISTORICAL

In the manufacture of products from polymeric materials it is necessary to achieve not only the required shape, but also a suitable degree of homogeneity in composition and properties. The industrial utilisation of the polymeric materials with which we are mainly concerned here, namely plastics and rubbers, may reasonably be said to date from Goodyear's discovery of sulphur vulcanisation of natural rubber in 1839.[1] Since mixing of the sulphur and rubber are required to achieve satisfactory vulcanisation, the technology of polymer mixing may be said to have started at the same date, that is some 140 years ago.

From the earliest days of rubber technology 'kneaders' have been used for 'wet' mixing (i.e. with solvents) whilst roll mills have been used for mastication and compounding, and these types of machine are still in widespread use.[2] Indeed, the first roll mill seems to have been designed by Hancock as early as 1820,[3] although there is some disagreement as to whether Hancock's machine was a mill or an internal mixer,[4] and the first steam-heated two-roll mill has been ascribed to Chaffee (1835).[4] The first major development in mixing machinery was the development by Banbury, around 80 years later,[5] of the internal mixer, commonly though often erroneously known today as the 'Banbury mixer'. Various modifications in design features of internal mixers have taken place over the years but the basic principle is the same today as it was over 60 years ago.

Development of plastics during the early years of the twentieth century was not accompanied by major changes in designs of mixing equipment, and it was not until the requirements of the rapidly increasing scale of production of thermoplastics, particularly PVC and polyethylene, around the middle of the century, provided the required stimulus, that radically new types of mixing machines began to appear. Two-roll mills and internal mixers are basically operated as batch compounding machines and most developments during the past 30 years have been concerned with continuous machines. The other major development during the same period has been the introduction and proliferation of so-called 'high-speed' mixers, 'fluidmixers', or 'turbomixers', primarily intended for the production of dry powder or granulated blends without extensive softening, compaction or agglomeration of the polymer.

There is today a bewildering variety of shapes and sizes of machine available for the mixing of polymeric materials, and the main purpose of this book is to discuss the features of design and operation of these machines, in the hope that the reader will be better able to understand the principles of the different machines and so also be better able to select that which is most suited to his purposes, and once having made a selection to optimise its use.

1.2 TERMINOLOGY

As in most other areas of technology, in a consideration of polymer mixing we are faced with a dilemma of terminology. On the one hand, in order to avoid misunderstanding, it is desirable to be as precise as possible in the use of key words and indeed to define each one unequivocally. Once we do this, however, we commonly find that our definitions exclude certain cases that we would wish to include. If we try to modify our definitions to cover these cases we admit others that are not desired. The attempt to establish precise definitions becomes self-defeating. The fact is that knowledge often cannot be divided into clearly separated packages. It is more like a discontinuous spectrum with some clearly distinguished gaps, but as often as not a gradual transition from one situation through a series of closely related near neighbours. To add to the difficulty, technology has frequently progressed far in advance of its associated theory so that by the time an attempt is made to establish the scientific principles of the technology there already exists an associated terminology that grew up with it but which is often confused, uncoordinated, and commonly a matter for lack of consistency, disagreement or even dispute between the technologists and technicians concerned. This situation is as much the case with polymer mixing as it is with any other branch of technology. To illustrate by what is perhaps an extreme case, there are those who regard the word 'compounding' as applying to those mixing processes that involve shearing of the polymer in the 'melt' state, whereas to others the term has implied the writing down of the ingredients of a composition. Nevertheless, an attempt must be made to establish an agreed terminology, if only to avoid confusion and tiresome repetitive explanation in the chapters that follow.

The term 'mixing' is of course central to the main theme of this book. It may usefully be employed in two slightly different senses. In one sense it may be applied to a process or machine applied to a number of materials in order to mix them. From a somewhat different point of view mixing may refer to what happens to these materials as they become inter-mingled, whether this is the result of processing specifically or primarily intended for mixing or occurs adventitiously during a shaping process.

Depending on the nature and form of the polymer and any other materials with which it is to be mixed, and also depending on the nature of the shaping process and machinery, in some cases it may be necessary to submit the materials to shear conditions in the melt state prior to submission to the shaping process. In other cases an intermingling of the components of the composition without softening or melting of the polymer may be adequate. This will obviously require the polymer to be in a suitable form, e.g. powder, granule, dispersion, solution, or latex. It is convenient to distinguish between these two cases. Commonly, but not universally, the former case, i.e. where there is softening, melting and compaction more or less to a continuum of polymer with dispersed additives, is known as compounding and a machine that will effect this process is correspondingly referred to as a 'compounding machine'. This compounding process is sometimes called 'intensive mixing', though this expression is also used in a wider sense for any process where the degree of mixing is dependent upon the amount of shear, as distinct from 'extensive mixing', which depends on flow or development of new surface.[6,7] Even less agreement exists in respect of a word to describe mixing processes that do not involve compounding. The issue is some-times avoided by using the expression 'simple mixing'. Thus Palmgren[8] states that 'mixing in its restricted sense, also defined as simple mixing, is the process whereby the randomness or entropy of a mixture is increased without affecting the physical state of the com-ponents', but even this statement is not entirely free from confusion. Perhaps there is something to be said for the word 'blending', especially since the terms 'dry-blend' and 'powder blend' are commonly used to designate some of the products of this type of mixing process. Fisher and

Chard[7] defined blending as referring 'to all processes in which two or more components or ingredients are physically intermingled without significant change of physical state of the components being engendered'. They also differentiated 'milling' in which the mixing function is performed 'by a combination of smearing and wiping', possibly including 'a grinding action with a consequent reduction in particle size, thereby creating a dispersion'; 'kneading', where mixing is 'achieved by continually compressing and folding layers of material over one another'; and 'mulling' which involves 'a combination of a wiping action and a rolling motion'.

Palmgren[8] has designated four steps in mixing, namely 'subdivision', in which individual components are broken down into smaller elements; 'incorporation', in which elements of one component become dispersed in the space occupied by another; 'dispersion', in which elements of a component assembled in congregations or agglomerates become separated or segregated; and 'simple mixing', in which elements of a component move towards a random distribution amongst other components of a mixture. In an actual mixing process these steps may overlap, though some subdivision may be necessary before incorporation can commence, and clearly incorporation must occur before dispersion and simple mixing can take place. These are useful concepts but the difference between dispersion and simple mixing is not always clear.

As Mohr and coworkers[9] have said an 'inevitable problem in mixing work is to evaluate the quality of mixtures', or in Danckwerts' phrase,[10] the 'goodness of mixing'. Danckwerts has defined two properties that are useful in evaluating goodness of mixing: the 'scale of segregation' and the 'intensity of segregation'. Scale of segregation is a measure of the average separation between regions comprising the same component and may be correlated to the 'average striation thickness', which is the average distance between like interfaces in a mixture.[11] Intensity of segregation is a measure of deviation of concentration at any point from the mean concentration.[11]

Of the terms discussed the only ones that might lead to some confusion are 'mixing' and 'compounding.' As indicated earlier, the word mixing and its derivatives are conveniently applied to any process or operation where two or more components become more intimately intermingled, whether or not this involves changes in the physical nature of the components or processes specifically and primarily intended to increase the intermingling. This is the sense which will be employed throughout this book, except where the context indicates a departure, in which case an explanation will be given at that point.

The word compounding and its derivatives will likewise be used to apply to those cases where softening, melting, and compaction more or less to a continuum of polymer with dispersed additives occurs. Processes where there is intermingling of components without the characteristic features of compounding, as just stated, will be referred to as blending.

1.3 MIXING REQUIREMENTS WITH POLYMERIC MATERIALS

In the manufacture of polymers, materials mixing is generally not a major problem because the components of polymerisation systems are commonly soluble in the monomer phase or readily dispersed in the inert medium in which polymerisation is to be effected. In such cases the equipment used is typical of chemical engineering practice and further discussion here would be inappropriate. Some materials do, however, present mixing problems at the polymerisation stage. These are mainly thermoset materials produced by admixture of two or more components that react together to produce cross-linked structures. Such systems include some solid polyurethanes, polyurethane and urea–formaldehyde foams, and epoxy resins. Here the requirement is to achieve adequate mixing of the ingredients before the polymerisation and cross-linking reactions fix an appreciable proportion of the reactants, and thus restrict or prevent further mixing.

The largest bulk of polymeric materials, however, is processed in the melt state, either from the polymer itself or from a resinous intermediate. Very seldom is the polymer processed without additives, and even where it can be mixing of a sort may be required in order to ensure that as nearly as possible all parts of the product receive the same heat and shear treatment. In the majority of cases additives are incorporated with the polymer, and a list of possibilities indicates how formidable the task of mixing can be (Table 1.1). Not all these terms must be taken as precise and definitive of the functions of the various ingredients. It will sometimes be found that one term is used to describe different functions. More than one term may be used to describe what is essentially the same function. Moreover, although each ingredient may be selected for a particular specific function or effect it will almost invariably be found that other effects will also result.

Of course, no single polymeric material will contain representatives of all the above classes of ingredient, but for example, a nine-component

TABLE 1.1
POSSIBLE CONSTITUENTS OF A PLASTIC OR RUBBER

Polymer (or resin intermediate)	Filler(s)
Reclaimed polymer or	Plasticiser(s)
compound	Softener(s)
Vulcanising or cross-linking	Plasticiser extender(s)
agent(s)	Viscosity depressant
Vulcanising accelerator(s)	Stiffener
Vulcanising activator(s)	Blowing agent
Vulcanising retarder(s)	Foam promoter
Thermal stabiliser(s)	Slip agent
Anti-oxidant(s)	Anti-blocking agent
Anti-ozonant	Tackifier
UV absorber(s)	Anti-static agent
Colourant(s)	Anti-fogging agent
Toughening agent, impact	Fire-retardant(s)
modifier or reinforcing	Reodorant
resin	Bacteriostat
Lubricant(s)	Fungicide
Processing aid(s)	Peptising agent

composition is by no means atypical. Consider in addition to the possible number of ingredients the facts that they can vary very widely in proportions, i.e. from a fraction of a percent to a few hundred percent of the amount of polymer, and that their physical form can be anything from mobile or viscous liquid to a tacky, waxy or hard solid, and the task of achieving adequate mixing may appear daunting.

1.4 PLACE OF MIXING IN POLYMER PROCESSING

It is difficult to define mixing, and the objective of mixing without begging the question. Mohr's definition,[11] slightly amended, of the objective of a mixing process reads as follows:

'... to alter the original distribution in space of a non-random or segregated collection of components and thereby increase the probability of finding a particle or volume element of any one component at any particular point, such that an acceptable spatial probability distribution is achieved.'

This is something of a mouthful, but it does point to the statistical nature of mixtures and their assessment, to which matter we return in the

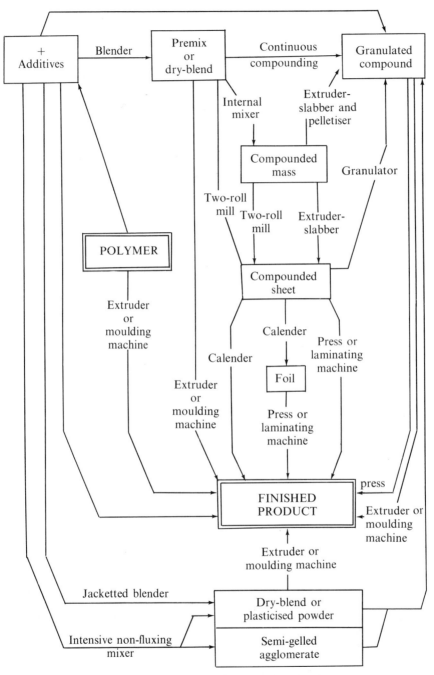

FIG. 1.1. Major routes for melt processing of polymers.

next chapter. A simpler but perhaps less scientific definition might be 'to increase the intermingling of the components of a mixture, at a molecular or some other appropriate level, to a degree that is acceptable'. There are theoretical and practical implications in both these definitions, to which a return will also be made in the next chapter.

As indicated previously, mixing may be effected in processes and machines designed specifically for the purpose of mixing alone, but may also occur in shaping processes. Figure 1.1, which is based on earlier efforts of the author and John Brydson,[12-14] is an attempt to summarise the major routes by which polymers are melt processed to finished products. Even though it does not include direct specific reference to some important related processes, such as blow-moulding and rotational moulding or casting, nor to curing, a glance will reveal that there is quite a variety of procedures in use, and the best choice between alternatives is not always obvious. Where mixing processes separate from the shaping are included, the requirements imposed on them depend on what happens in the other processes as well as on the requirements of the finished product. It may be assumed that processes like calendering, granulating and pressing will not contribute appreciably to mixing, but most other processes will, to an extent depending on the nature of the materials, the design of the machines, and operating conditions. Thus the requirements of mixing processes and machinery vary considerably. In general, of course, the greater the contribution to overall mixing made by the shaping process the less will be the demands on any associated mixing procedures. Conversely, the less effective a mixing procedure the more effective in mixing a shaping process has to be to compensate. An example of the situation where this is an important consideration is when considering a change to the use of dry-blend rather than compounded granules as feed stock for extrusion or injection moulding.

REFERENCES

1. LE BRAS, J., *Introduction to Rubber*, Maclaren, London (1965).
2. KAUFMAN, M., *The History of PVC*, Maclaren, London (1969).
3. KAUFMAN, M., *The First Century of Plastics*, Plastics Institute, London (1963).
4. TADMOR, Z. and GOGOS, C. C., *Principles of Polymer Processing*, Wiley, New York (1979).
5. KILLEFFER, D. J., *Banbury the Mastermixer: A Biography of Farnley H. Banbury*, Palmerston, New York (1962).
6. BOLEN, W. R. and COLWELL, R. E., *S.P.E.J.*, **14**(8), 24 (1958).

7. FISHER, E. G. and CHARD, E. D., *Int. Plast. Engng.*, **2**(2), 54; **2**(3), 113 (1962).
8. PALMGREN, H., *Eur. Rubb. J.*, **156**, 30; 70 (May/June 1974).
9. MOHR, W. D., SAXTON, R. L. and JEPSON, C. H., *Ind. Eng. Chem.*, **49**(11), 1855 (1957).
10. DANCKWERTS, P. V., *Appl. Sci. Research*, **A3**, 279 (1951/3).
11. MOHR, W. D., *Processing of Thermoplastic Materials*, Chapter 3, Bernhardt, E. C. (Ed.), Van Nostrand Reinhold, New York (1959).
12. MATTHEWS, G. A. R., *Advances in PVC Compounding and Processing*, Chapter 5, Kaufman, M. (Ed.), Maclaren, London (1962).
13. MATTHEWS, G. A. R., *Vinyl and Allied Polymers; Vol. 2: Vinyl Chloride and Vinyl Acetate Polymers*, Iliffe, London (1972).
14. BRYDSON, J. A., *Plastics Materials*, Newnes-Butterworth, London (1966, 1969, 1975).

CHAPTER 2

Principles

2.1 GENERAL

The object or aim of processing of polymeric materials is presumably to produce, at an economic cost, a product or products of the required shape and dimensions, with the morphological structure that will yield the required physical properties, and with the required intermingling of the component ingredients. As noted in the Introduction, this processing therefore involves shaping and mixing. At first sight one would assume that the aim should be to attain homogeneity or uniformity of morphology and composition, apart from any deliberate deviations therefrom for specific effects that are sometimes required, e.g. mottling or marbling in vinyl floor tiles.

Attainment of an acceptable degree of homogeneity or uniformity of composition and to some extent of morphological structure is the purpose of mixing. Indeed one might almost say that it is mixing.

Mixing processes constitute an important sector of processing polymeric materials, but, as indicated in the previous chapter, mixing in the sense of development of increasing homogeneity may also occur in processes primarily intended for shaping.

In any study of the fundamental principles involved in mixing, four separate but interrelated aspects demand consideration. First, there is the question of what features of the state of a material need to be taken into account in order to describe and assess its condition in regard to the mixing it has received. In other words what is 'mixedness' and how may it be assessed? Secondly, we will wish to study the mechanisms and kinetics of mixing processes. How do elements of one component of a composition intermingle with the other components, and how may the rate at which the intermingling occurs be assessed? This aspect of the subject cannot be completely studied without the foundation of the first, i.e. one can hardly describe mechanisms or kinetics of mixing if one has not previously established a scale and means of assessment of mixedness. Thirdly, the nature and behaviour of the components, for example particle size, softening or melting points, and melt flow behaviour, will have a more or less profound effect on the effectiveness of any mixing process. Finally, relationships between machine design and the three preceding aspects need to be considered.

A thorough theoretical mathematical analysis of polymer mixing has recently been admirably presented by Funt,[1] and no attempt will be made here to emulate or duplicate his excellent exposition. Any reader wishing to become fully acquainted with the mathematics of current theories of mixing is recommended to study Funt's work and the original papers referred to therein. Other good presentations appear in Chapter 12 of Middleman's *Fundamentals of Polymer Processing*,[2] Mohr's[3] and Bergen's[4] contributions to Bernhardt's *Processing of Thermoplastic Materials*, McKelvey's *Polymer Processing*,[5] and Chapters 7 and 11 of Tadmor and Gogos' *Principles of Polymer Processing*.[6]

Here the intention is to consider only those theoretical concepts that can help in the selection and efficient operation of commercially available mixing equipment. While basic fundamental theoretical studies are to be encouraged, it is a regrettable fact that up to the present time the mathematical approach has been of only very limited help to the practical design and operation of mixing equipment, and the practical aspects of mixing in general are still referred to, with a certain amount of justification, as the 'art of mixing'.[6] This is not so much a failing on the part of mathematics or the mathematicians but arises from the complex and varied nature of the materials and processes, and the tedium and other practical problems involved in analysing the states of admixture of most polymeric compositions of technological interest. Although computers obviously help with the calculations, the problems of measurement of state of admixture, as it varies throughout a quantity of polymeric material, have not generally been solved.

2.2 STATE OF ADMIXTURE

2.2.1 *Examination*

If the 'homogeneity of composition' that is usually the aim of mixing is taken to mean 'of constant composition or alike in all its parts no matter how small the parts', then strictly speaking this aim would never be attained, theoretically, let alone in practice, since at the molecular level composition will vary on passing from one molecule to another. With some additives in polymeric compositions, for example stabilisers and cross-linking agents, mixing on a molecular scale may be important, though its direct assessment at this level may be difficult or impossible. Assessment of the state of admixture will depend on the closeness of the examination, and it seems reasonable to suggest that perfect admixture might be defined as that state in which no variations in composition or morphology are observed at the relevant closeness or intensity of examination. To take a fairly obvious example,[3] incorporation of colourant may be assessed by a visual impression of homogeneity, the critical dimension being the resolving power of the eye, say 0·025 mm. By this method of assessment, provided there are no broad variations in hue or intensity, a mixture appears completely mixed when it exhibits no colour streaks or specks greater than 0·025 mm across. If, however, a spectrophotometer which integrates over a 25-mm circle, say, was used the streaks could perhaps be up to 2·5 mm without detection. Conversely, using a microscope can of course take the limits down well below the resolving power of the naked eye. Even when no specks or streaks appear, the impression of hue and intensity can depend on the level of dispersion of colourant at dimensions below the resolving power of the eye. Moreover, even if dispersed sufficiently to provide optimum effect in respect of hue and intensity, differences in concentration on a gross scale giving variations in hue or intensity may occur. In these situations assessment of state of admixture depending as it does on visual impression is difficult to quantify.

2.2.2 Scale of Scrutiny

All this indicates the fact that assessment of the state of admixture of a composition depends on the scrutiny to which it is subjected. Danckwerts[7] introduced the concept of 'scale of scrutiny', which he defined as 'the minimum size of the regions of segregation that would cause the mixture to be imperfect for the intended purpose'. It should include several particles of a component, and may be expressed as a length, area or volume. In the example of the colourant considered above, the scale of scrutiny depends on the resolving power of the eye and the distance of viewing, e.g. would be equal to a linear dimension of about

0·025 mm for close viewing by an unaided eye. It is clear that the more closely a mixture is scrutinised, i.e. the smaller the scale of scrutiny, the more likely it is to appear inhomogeneous or non-uniform. Application of this concept of scale of scrutiny is not limited to visual effects, since property requirements other than uniformity of product appearance also involve corresponding levels of mixing of any components of a composition whose dispersion affects those properties. In a sense the scrutiny may be equated to the demands that property requirements impose. Thus, for example, it might be assumed that for a stabiliser, or a plasticiser or a cross-linking agent to be fully effective it would need to be uniformly dispersed in the polymer on a molecular scale, and it might reasonably be supposed that the scale of scrutiny has molecular dimensions. In practice it would normally be difficult or impossible to measure the spatial distribution of additives of this kind, and assessment of their effectiveness, both in terms of intrinsic performance and adequacy of the mixing they have received, is likely to be based on evaluation of properties of the composition. Thus, in the case of a stabiliser one might ask such questions as: 'Is the composition under examination as stable as might be expected, having regard to the amount and nature of the stabiliser included and if not, is this due to deficiencies in the mixing?'

Tadmor and Gogos[6] discuss the concept of a 'scale of examination' which they define as 'the scale or size of the overall sample we are analysing for composition uniformity'. They go on to state that this scale of examination is imprecisely defined, but that in testing for gross uniformity, it 'is of the size of the object, system or overall sample examined for uniformity'. This concept appears to be related to sampling procedure and should not be confused with Danckwerts' scale of scrutiny, which is concerned with the intensity or closeness with which samples (or the whole) are scrutinised.

The impression that is obtained of the state of admixture of a composition depends not only on the scale of scrutiny but also on the sampling procedure. Consider, for example, a two-component mixture the components of which can be separately identified and quantified. If the whole mixture was analysed, i.e. if the scale of examination has the dimensions of the whole mixture, the composition (assuming there was no experimental error!) would be found to be identical to that from which the mixture was formed — *ipso facto*. Such an examination would tell us nothing about the distribution of the two components within the mixture, and it is obviously erroneous to conclude that the examination shows the mixture to be uniform or homogeneous. Dividing the mixture

into a number of portions and examining the portions separately introduces the possibility that their compositions will be found to differ
from the overall composition. The greater the number of portions into
which the mixture is divided the greater is the probability that portions
will be found to differ in composition, and the closer will the results be to
describing accurately the true state of admixture of the two components.
In the extreme, if the portions were made as small as the particles, or
more generally, 'volume elements', of the individual components, analysis
would show each portion to consist of one component or the other, i.e.
the system would appear to be unmixed or segregated. More realistically,
however, if the portions are large relative to the size of the volume
elements of the components, i.e. each portion contains a substantial
number of these volume elements, the analytical results will reveal a
distribution about a mean equivalent to the overall composition. In the
absence of any interfering specific interaction between the components,
complete uniformity of admixture, i.e. where every portion yields the
same analysis, will never be attained. The best that can usually be
expected is a statistically random distribution, and a mixture with such a
distribution is generally regarded as an ideal or perfect mixture.

Experimental studies of mixing apart, one would in practice, of course,
rarely if ever analyse the whole mixture, whether the analysis be by
examination of composition or some dependent property. Normally a
number of samples, usually amounting to a small fraction of the whole,
would be withdrawn for examination, thus introducing a statistical factor
into the relationship between the results and the actual state of
composition.

In general, from the foregoing it might be concluded that, within
obvious limits, accuracy of assessment of the state of admixture is
improved by increasing the number and decreasing the size of samples.
In practice, as indicated previously, taking and analysing samples for
evaluation of states of admixture is so tedious and time-consuming that
practical analyses are not carried out very frequently, even for theoretical
mixing studies, let alone for routine quality control purposes.

2.2.3 *Indices of Mixing*

Having obtained analyses of a number of samples taken from a
mixture, what use can be made of the data? A number of different
approaches to this question have been taken, all essentially based on

statistical and probability concepts. Apart from some special cases mentioned later, it is generally assumed that, however efficient the mixing process is, and however long it is continued, the best state of admixture that can be obtained will not be one that has a completely uniform distribution of components, but one that is statistically random. The 'goodness of mixing' or 'admixedness' of an actual composition is usually rated according to the closeness of its approach to the statistically random, the latter often being referred to as 'perfect mixing'. Various authors[8,9] have indeed defined a perfect mix as 'one in which the probability of any component appearing at any point in the mixture is constant'. Tucker and Suh,[10] however, have taken the quite reasonable view that the term perfect mixture should be equated to 'uniform mixture', and described a device that appears to be capable of producing states of admixture more nearly approaching uniformity than randomness. This is achieved by giving the particles of one component of a mixture an electrostatic charge of one sign while giving the particles of the other component a charge of the opposite sign. The particles are then brought together in streams metered at the required mixing ratio. Rotz and Suh[11] have described a device for mixing liquids based on a similar principle.

Lacey's original statistical analysis of particle mixing[12] high-lighted some of the problems of the statistical approach, some of which arise from the influence of sampling procedure to which reference was made in the preceding paragraph. The aim of a statistical analysis of a mixture is usually to allocate a value to a 'degree of mixing' that will define numerically the state of admixture of a composition. Lacey[13] originally proposed that the degree of mixing could be simply equated to the ratio of the standard deviation of a random mixture to the standard deviation of the mixture under consideration, i.e.

$$M = \frac{\sigma_r}{s} \tag{1}$$

where M is the degree of mixing, σ_r is the standard deviation of a random mixture, and s is the standard deviation of the actual mixture being examined. Kramers[14] suggested introducing a term σ_o for the standard deviation of the unmixed components:

$$M = \frac{(\sigma_o - s)}{(\sigma_o - \sigma_r)} \tag{2}$$

This expression was further modified by Lacey[14] by substituting variances for standard deviations:

$$M = \frac{(\sigma_o^2 - s^2)}{(\sigma_o^2 - \sigma_r^2)} \qquad (3)$$

on the basis that the additive properties of variances make this expression statistically more satisfactory. Note that in either of these expressions, if $s = \sigma_o$, i.e. the components are unmixed, $M = 0$, whereas if $s = \sigma_r$, i.e. the components are mixed to a statistically random distribution, $M = 1$. The degree of mixing is thus seen to change from zero to unity as unmixed components become transformed to a state of perfect admixture. Lacey[12] showed that for a perfect or ideal two-component mixture the most probable value of the variance is equal to the product of the proportions of the two components in the mixture divided by the number of particles in each sample, i.e. $\sigma_r^2 = P(1-P)/n$ where P is the overall proportion of one component and n is the number of particles in a sample. Since it is very readily shown that the variance for the unmixed, or completely segregated state is equal to the product of the proportions of the two components, i.e. $\sigma_o = P(1-P)$, it seems that it is only necessary to determine s for the actual mixture to permit the evaluation of a degree of mixing in accordance with one or other of the above equations. Note that for a completely uniform mixture $s = 0$ and eqn. (3) then reduces to

$$M_u = \frac{\sigma_o^2}{(\sigma_o^2 - \sigma_r^2)} \qquad (4)$$

$$= \frac{P(1-P)}{\left[P(1-P) - \frac{P(1-P)}{n} \right]}$$

$$= \frac{1}{\left(1 - \frac{1}{n} \right)}$$

$$= \frac{n}{(n-1)} \qquad (5)$$

so that for large values of n, i.e. large samples, the value of M for a completely uniform composition would be only slightly above unity, the value for a random distribution. For example, if $n = 100$, $M_u = 1 \cdot 01$.

These expressions were originally derived for mixing of particles, but there seems to be no reason why they could not be quite simply modified to describe other types of mixture. However, it is not clear that results based on this approach have much practical value. Experiments with the blending of commercial plastic granules in a simple tumble blender show that high values of degree of mixing are obtained in very short times.[15] This does not indicate that tumble blending is a surprisingly effective method of mixing, but that the numerical scale characteristic of these methods of calculation is not sufficiently extended at high values, e.g. >0.9, to yield a sufficiently sensitive measure of goodness of mixing.

Other indices of mixing have been defined,[6] and these have been reviewed[16] and analysed.[17] Tadmor and Gogos[6] select two in addition to those previously discussed as being of particular interest. These are

$$M = \frac{(\ln \sigma_o^2 - \ln s^2)}{(\ln \sigma_o^2 - \ln \sigma^2)} \qquad (6)$$

which, like the expression above due to Lacey (eqn. 3) yields values of mixing index between 0 and 1, and

$$M = \frac{(s^2 - \sigma_r^2)}{P} \qquad (7)$$

which yields values between 0 for the perfectly mixed state and a value of $M = (1 - P)(1 - 1/n)$ for the completely segregated or unmixed state. Tucker and Suh[10] use the ratio of the variance for the mixture to the variance of a random mixture:

$$M = \frac{s^2}{\sigma_r^2} \qquad (8)$$

which has the advantage that it provides a sensible numerical value for states of admixture that are more uniform than random, since if the mixture is worse than random $M > 1$, if it is random $M = 1$, and if it is more uniform than random $M < 1$. For a uniform or perfect mixture $M = 0$.

Buslik,[18] analysing particle size distributions, developed a formula that could be applied to statistical analyses of particle mixing to take account of variations in particle size that occur in many mixing operations. Adams and Baker[8] attempted to apply statistical methods to the evaluation of equipment for dry-blending small proportions of master-batch in granule form into natural polyethylene granules, and suggested that degree of mixing could be indicated by a probability function. Vance[19] drew attention to some common errors in applying statistical analysis to dry-blending, and presented a statistical procedure to provide a reliable indication of mixing by dry-blending, taking into account the effects of the size and numbers of samples examined.

2.2.4 Scale of Segregation — Striation Thickness

The concepts of scale and intensity or density of segregation have already been alluded to (Chapter 1, Section 1.2).[7,20] There appears to be some confusion over the precise meaning of these terms.

The difference between scale and intensity of segregation may be illustrated by considering how two separate components may become mixed together. If the two components are divided into smaller volume elements which are then intermingled, the scale of segregation is reduced. If, on the other hand, part of each component is progressively transferred into the space occupied by the other, the intensity of segregation is reduced. Both processes move the system towards uniformity. However, the difference between the two concepts of intensity and scale of segregation seems more apparent than real. Scale of segregation is the size of isolated component regimes, whereas intensity of segregation is the relative difference in concentration of the property of interest between the two regimes,[21] i.e. the purity of the two regimes. Since two different components cannot occupy identically the same space, in examining a system to determine its intensity of segregation one is really looking at scales of segregation within isolated component regimes. Mohr and coworkers[22] differentiate scale and intensity of segregation on the basis that, in general, the former is accomplished by mechanical energy, while the latter can be effected only by diffusion. Scale of segregation may be defined in terms of the average distance between like interfaces. It is a measure of the average distance between clumps of the same component, or as Mohr and coworkers[22] have put it, 'a measure of the size of undistributed portions of the components'. The average distance between like interfaces is also known as the striation thickness (Fig. 2.1). It has been shown[23] that average striation thickness, r, can be computed from the ratio of the interfacial surface area, S, between the components and the total volume of the system, V:

$$r = \frac{2}{S/V} \qquad (9)$$

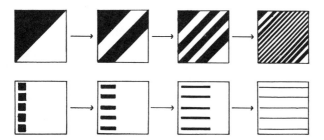

FIG. 2.1. Diagrammatic representations of mixing as a function of reducing striation thickness.

In many systems, e.g. in compounded compositions where particles are sub-divided or melted, it would normally be difficult to measure the interfacial surface area or striation thickness directly. Even for a solid particulate component whose structure is not changed during mixing, the external surface area, that is the surface area that will contribute to interfaces with other components of the mixture, is unlikely to be known with any great accuracy. Moreover, even if interfacial surface area can be calculated accurately the value of striation thickness derived from it may be correlated to good dispersion as defined by Palmgren,[24] but once this is attained will be constant whatever the degree of mixing. In other words, it could tell us something about the break-down of particle agglomerates but very little about the level of randomness of distribution of particles throughout the system.

2.2.5 Texture

Another approach that has been well discussed by Tadmor and Gogos[6] is by a consideration of 'texture'. This, again, is a visual concept but there is no reason why the basic principles underlying it should not apply to mixtures where the separate components do not differ in appearance and cannot, therefore, be differentiated by eye. The concept of texture is most easily understood in relation to the distribution of colourant in a viewed surface. As a result of non-uniform dispersion and distribution across the surface, specks, streaks, and variations in shade, hue and intensity, may occur and so produce a characteristic non-uniform pattern, or texture. The features that determine whether or not different textures will be distinguishable by the eye have been admirably discussed by Julesz.[25] He refers to systems having identical concentrations of components as having the same 'first order statistics'. Such systems may or may not be distinguishable. If the components are distributed differently in space, i.e. in Julesz' terms they have different 'second order statistics', they may be distinguishable, depending on the scale of scrutiny or examination. Successful differentiation of systems having identical first but different second order statistics may depend on the thoroughness of the examination, suggesting that higher orders of statistics are also involved in visual evaluation. Tadmor and Gogos[6] point out that this suggests that in attempting to characterise a texture quantitatively the scale of scrutiny or examination should also be 'varied over a range'. Thus, for a piece of coloured film or sheet the upper limit of the scale of examination is the size of the piece and the lower limit is the resolving power of the eye. However, if the distribution of components affects non-visual properties of the product, e.g. mechanical properties, resistance to degradation by UV light, the texture down to microscopic or even molecular scale may be relevant.

Danckwerts[20] suggested that his scale of segregation and intensity of segregation could be used to characterise texture quantitatively. Julesz proposed a 'dipole dropping' method in which a dipole (or needle) is dropped onto the surface whose texture is to be examined. The second order statistics of the texture would be related to the probability of the two ends of the dipole landing on regions of identical composition in any single throw. Tadmor et al.[6,26] showed how this approach can be used to characterise the dispersion of carbon black in blow extruded polyethylene film, and their technique could presumably be applied to other materials and forms of product. By carrying out measurements and calculations for varying sample sizes, they showed clearly how values of scale of segregation depend on scale of examination, and therefore they proposed that a scale of segregation profile, showing the relationship between the two variables, would give a more meaningful characterisation of texture than a single value.

As stated earlier (Chapter 1, Section 1.2) intensity of segregation is a measure of the deviation of concentration from the mean concentration, at any point throughout the system. It may be defined as the coefficient of variation of concentration in the system. Mohr[3] defines intensity of segregation as the quotient (I) of the standard deviation (s) of the concentration of a component in the mixture divided by the average proportion of that component in the mixture (P), i.e.

$$I = \frac{s}{P} \qquad (10)$$

Middleman,[2] Tadmor and Gogos,[6] offer a different expression:

$$I = \frac{s^2}{\sigma_o^2} \tag{11}$$

where the terms have the significance given previously. Defined in this way, $I = 1$ for the unmixed or completely segregated state, and $I = 0$ when the distribution of the component is uniform, and can be regarded as another form of index for degree of mixing.

2.2.6 Multi-Component Systems

Most of the methods for characterising mixedness that have been proposed have been related to systems of two components. Attempts have been made to develop procedures for deriving indices of mixing for multi-component systems, but they are complicated and may be said to be pointless, at least as far as polymeric systems are concerned. It seems probable that for each constituent of a mixture there will be a characteristic optimum degree of mixing, determined on the basis of a compromise between, on the one hand the desire to distribute the constituent as uniformly as possible so as to obtain its maximum effectiveness, and on the other hand technical and economic limitations on what mixing can reasonably be imparted. In a given composition the optimum degree of mixing for each constituent may well differ from those of other constituents, and it would be difficult to design a single mixing index that would indicate poor mixing in a composition where all but one of the constituents were adequately mixed, while the remaining one was so poorly mixed as to render the composition unsatisfactory. It is much more useful to consider each constituent in turn as one component in a two-component system in which the other component is made up of all the other constituents. Thus, one could obtain a series of indices of mixing, one for each constituent.

None of the indices of mixing that have been discussed can represent a complete description of the state of admixture of a composition of two or more components, but each one is a compromise between complete description and evaluation by some qualitative method or by measurement of some property that is dependent on mixing. As Tadmor and Gogos[6] point out, whatever mixing indices may have been calculated, or whatever other direct assessments of mixing one may have, it is impossible to decide whether a composition is well or poorly mixed unless the purpose of performing the mixing is known.

In industrial practice the adequacy of mixing of colourants is usually assessed visually on a qualitative basis, commonly by reference to previously prepared standards. Inadequate mixing of constituents that are visually indistinguishable from the rest of a composition will generally only be indicated by atypical results from physical or chemical tests.

2.3 MECHANISMS AND KINETICS OF MIXING

2.3.1 *Mechanisms*

Several authors have described mechanisms of mixing in broad conceptual terms and what follows is an attempt to distil the essence from their contributions. There is sometimes a tendency to obscure the general applicability of the broad concepts by referring to the 'particles' or 'ultimate particles' of the components of a mixture, thus apparently limiting the application of these concepts to mixing of solids. If the word particle is replaced by the expression volume element, taken to stand for granule, particle, drop, a fraction of volume within the whole, or even a molecule, many of these concepts are readily seen to apply to all kinds of system.

Thus translated, Mohr[3] and Bergen[4] suggest that mixing consists in altering the original distribution in space of a non-random or segregated mass, thereby increasing the probability of finding a volume element of any one component at any point, such that an acceptable spatial probability distribution is obtained. McKelvey[5] expresses essentially the same idea by describing mixing as increasing the randomness of the spatial distribution of the volume elements of the components of a mixture. A minor objection to this definition is that it would also include the 'unmixing' of a system that started off with a completely uniform spatial distribution of its components, and perhaps Tadmor and Gogos'[6] use of the expression 'to reduce non-uniformity' is to be preferred. McKelvey points out that since the volume elements of the system pass from a less probable to a more probable arrangement, mixing can be seen as increasing entropy to a maximum when the spatial distribution is random. He also differentiates between mixing in the general sense and simple mixing (Fig. 2.2) where the size of the volume elements is not reduced. This latter is seen to be equivalent to blending as defined in Chapter 1, Section 1.2.

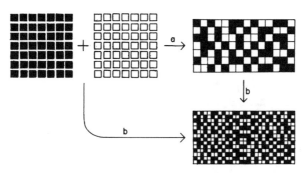

FIG. 2.2. Diagrammatic representation of (a) simple mixing and (b) dispersion.

An alternative way of regarding mixing to the concept of redistributing volume elements of the components in space, is to regard it as a process involving increase in the interfacial area between the components and distributing elements of the interfacial area throughout the system.[3] Since interfacial area is inversely proportional to the average striation thickness (Section 2.2; eqn. 9) this approach is the same as considering mixing from the point of view of reduction in average striation thickness.

Mixing obviously involves relative motion of volume elements of the components, or, to change a phrase from Lacey, transfer of volume elements from one location in the system to another. This motion may take a variety of forms. Lacey postulates three principal mechanisms utilised in machines for mixing particulate materials, though there seems to be no reason why these mechanisms should not apply to other systems. Thus he describes

(i) 'convective mixing' as the transfer of groups of adjacent volume elements from one location in the system to another;

(ii) distribution of particles over a freshly developed surface as a form of 'diffusive mixing'; and

(iii) setting up of slipping planes within the system as 'shear mixing'.

Convective mixing is the predominant mode of motion when mixing particles in a ribbon blender, where material is lifted and moved longitudinally and then released to fall under gravity. Diffusive mixing occurs in tumble blenders, i.e. rotating-drum type mixers, while shear mixing occurs in what Lacey refers to as 'geyser' type mixers, where an Archimedean screw draws material up a hopper while it descends in regions not influenced directly by the screw. It is not immediately obvious that the relative motions of volume elements that results in mixing really differs in these three modes of mixing, the differences lying rather in the means by which the motions are induced. Lacey describes his diffusive mixing in terms of the mixing of particles in a tumble blender where particles are repeatedly spread over a freshly exposed surface as the blender rotates, which he sees as clearly similar to ordinary molecular or thermal diffusion. As a particle rolls down the slope constituted by the exposed surface of the particulate bed of material, it has equal chances of being deflected to either side on each encounter with another particle. Thus, within the mixing plane the particle has random motion components at right-angles to the line of maximum steepness, closely analogous to the motions of the molecules of a gas. In a blender of this kind, frictional forces between the particles and the moving wall of the mixing chamber act to raise the particles until they begin to fall under the action of gravity, and it is thus the latter that produces the collisions of particles that result in changes in direction of motion and hence mixing. In a ribbon blender and the geyser type mixer, movement of the ribbons or screw replaces the frictional action of the mixing chamber walls, and the surfaces at which blending occurs are more complex. It seems likely that Lacey's diffusive mixing mechanism will also occur within the mass of particles, probably being very limited in a tumble blender and more significant in the other types of mixer. It could thus be suggested that the only differences between Lacey's three mechanisms lie in the means by which encounters between particles are induced. By replacing particles by volume elements, these concepts could be extended to include mixing of liquids or melts, with the added complication that shear encounters between volume elements may result in deformation, division or union. These features may not be entirely absent even in particle blending.

According to Tadmor and Gogos,[6] mixing involves three basic types of motion, designated by Brodkey[27] as

    (i) 'molecular diffusion';
    (ii) 'eddy diffusion'; and
    (iii) 'bulk diffusion'.

The first of these arises as a result of concentration gradients within the system, and is the dominant mechanism in mixing of gases and miscible low viscosity liquids. Molecular diffusion is only important in polymer systems in relation to low molecular-weight additives, and even with these its significance in mixing processes is dubious. Eddy diffusion occurs where turbulence is employed to induce mixing, and this is rare in polymer processing, so that bulk diffusion, or 'convective flow' processes are the dominant mixing mechanisms. Convective mixing can arise by two different mechanisms, one variously described as 'bulk-convective' mixing, 'plug-convective' mixing, 'distributive' mixing,[6] 'repetitive' mixing[23] or 'simple' mixing,[5] and the other as 'laminar' mixing,[5] 'laminar convective' mixing[6] or 'streamline' mixing.[23] The former involves simple bulk rearrangement of material by plug type flow and no continuous deformation of the material.[6] The repeated rearrangements can be ordered or random, the former being a major feature of so-called 'motionless' mixers, and the latter being characteristic of many solids blending machines. Laminar mixing, on the other hand, involves deformation of the system by laminar flow, and is characteristic of melt compounding, as defined in Chapter 1, Section 1.2 (Fig. 2.3). It is not

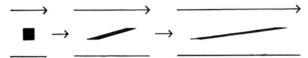

FIG. 2.3. Laminar shear mixing by reduction in striation thickness.

obvious, however, that mixing by laminar convective mixing should not occur to some extent even in particle mixing. Tadmor and Gogos,[6] following Spencer and Wiley,[23] state that generally for a liquid/liquid system 'to be mixed by a laminar convective mechanism, permanent deformation or strain must be imposed on the system'. In the sense that strain includes any changes in dimensions of the system or elements of it, the same might be said of any form of mixing, but the authors proceed to demonstrate the importance of strain in laminar mixing. They show that, for high values of strain, increase in interfacial area between components is directly proportional and striation thickness is inversely proportional to the total strain imposed on the system, but that low values of strain may in some circumstances decrease the interfacial area, thus effectively demixing or unmixing. Also, the initial striation thickness is proportional to the particle size and inversely proportional to the proportion by volume of a minor component, so that the larger the particles and the smaller the proportion of minor component, the greater is the total strain necessary to attain any particular required final striation thickness or degree of mixing; that is to say, the smaller the proportion and the larger the particles of a minor component in a composition, the more difficult is it to achieve adequate mixing, thus confirming the intuitive conclusion this author and no doubt many others have held for years.

The conclusion that the degree of mixing of a system depends on the total strain imparted to it, does not imply that rate of straining and stresses are not important. Both are significant factors in determining power requirements. Moreover, it is not uncommon for components of polymer compositions to possess yield points that need to be reached if volume elements are to be divided into smaller elements. Such components include granules or small volume elements of viscoelastic polymers, and agglomerates of very fine particle additives such as carbon black, some pigments, and precipitated calcium carbonate. With such components the stress distribution and its rate of development within the system may be critical if good dispersion is to be achieved. Mixing of such systems is commonly referred to as 'dispersive' mixing,[5] but a criterion for distinguishing between those systems that involve dispersive mixing and those that do not is not readily apparent.

In producing polymeric compositions we may be concerned with three broadly different types of system the mechanisms and kinetics of mixing of which may differ in kind as well as magnitude. These are:

(i) liquid/liquid mixing;
(ii) solid/solid mixing; and
(iii) solid/liquid mixing.

2.3.2 *Liquid Systems*

At one extreme the liquids may be low viscosity monomers, intermediates or non-polymeric additives, while at the other extreme they may be high viscosity polymer melts, and it would seem likely that these two extremes would involve quite different mechanisms and kinetics. In order to be satisfactorily mixed, solids will have to be either in powder or at least particle form, or broken down from large bulk to particles during the mixing process, or converted to the melt state. Effects of the nature of the components on their mixing behaviour is discussed in the next section.

As pointed out in Chapter 1, Section 1.3, where monomers are being polymerised to produce thermoplastic polymers destined for subsequent processing in the melt or softened state, mixing of the additives of the polymerisation system is generally not a problem since they are commonly soluble in the monomer or, in heterogeneous polymerisations, are readily dispersed in the inert medium, usually water, in which polymerisation is to be effected. Such component mixing as has to be done must usually be effected before or in the very early stages of the polymerisation. Subsequently, mixing is required in these systems in order to ensure uniformity of product, and, since the polymerisations are invariably exothermic, to promote sufficient circulation within the reactor to permit adequate heat removal across the walls of the reactor, so as to ensure effective control of temperature. The equipment used is typical of chemical reactors, and the mechanisms and kinetics are subject to normal chemical engineering theories, hence will not be discussed in detail here. The interested reader is referred to the standard chemical engineering text books for more detailed information.[28] However, it is worth noting that the four most important parameters of polymerisation reactors are usually:

(i) the ratio of the surface area available for heat-transfer to an external temperature controlling medium, to the volume of the polymerisation system;
(ii) the circulation of volume elements of the system over the inside surface of the walls of the reactor;
(iii) the distribution of turbulence within the system; and
(iv) the frequency and rate of circulation of volume elements of the system through zones of high turbulence.

The first two of these, and to a lesser extent the other two, constitute major factors in determining efficiency of control of temperature of the system. Other major factors are the heat-transfer characteristics of the walls of the reactor, the heat capacity and rate of circulation of any heat-transfer medium in the jacket around the reactor, and the temperature gradient across the walls of the reactor, the latter being dependent mainly on the temperature of polymerisation.

Systems involving mixing at the polymerisation stage that are more specifically in the domain of polymer processing rather than conventional chemical engineering, are those that produce thermoset materials *in situ* where required or in a form that may be shaped by subsequent machining but not melt processing. An example of the former is in the filling of cavity walls of buildings with insulating urea–formaldehyde or polyurethane foam, and an example of the latter is the manufacture of polyurethane foam slab stock or mouldings. In many of these cases the polymerisation and cross-linking reactions occur spontaneously on mixing at ambient temperatures without the need for applied heat. As these reactions proceed the viscosity of the system increases dramatically until the solid state is reached, so that it is vital to ensure adequate mixing very rapidly as the components of the system are brought together. This is commonly achieved by passing relatively thin streams of the components into and rapidly through zones of high turbulence and immediately into the forming space, e.g. cavity wall or mould. Clearly, the intensity of the mixing depends on the rates of flow, the extent and intensity of the turbulence, and the viscosities of the liquid separate and partially mixed components. Since viscosity is changing continually as mixing and reaction proceed, quantification of the mixing process on a theoretical basis is exceedingly difficult.

2.3.3 *Solid Systems*

Solid/solid mixing is involved where a solid polymer or resinous intermediate is to be blended with other solid components prior to melt compounding or shaping. A polymer will usually be in powder, granular, pelletised, or diced form, whereas resins and solid additives will usually be powders. If the solid/solid mixing is not coincident with mixing in the melt stage, the process is one of blending as defined in Section 1.2. Blending proceeds generally by random distributive mixing.

Where the polymer is produced more or less as a continuum, e.g. extruded strip, it will normally be granulated, pelletised, or diced by the manufacturer soon after it leaves the polymerisation vessel. Many polymers, however, are obtained directly as powders, and, while grinding of thermoplastic powders produced in block or sheet form is now rare, except for fluidised bed and like purposes, production of powders from thermosetting resin intermediates is still common.

2.3.4 *Solid/liquid Systems*

Solid/liquid mixing takes two distinct forms, namely

  (i) blending liquid additives with solid polymers without transforming the latter into the melt state, and
 (ii) compounding into polymers in the melt state solid additives whose melting points are above the compounding temperature.

Occasions arise where the melting point of a solid additive is close to the processing temperature and whether it melts or not, and consequently

how it mixes into the polymer melt, may depend on the precise processing temperature and the accuracy with which it is maintained. If there
are not specific interactions between a solid polymer and liquid additives,
mixing can proceed by some sort of shear mechanism breaking the liquid
down into thin layers so that it can be distributed uniformly over the
surface of the solid. Clearly, this is very difficult if the liquid is present in
a very low concentration, which is not uncommon in polymer processing,
and becomes relatively much easier as the proportion of liquid additive
reaches a level sufficient to provide a surface layer over all the solid
particles and also fill the space between them.

However, frequently specific quite rapid interactions occur between
solid particles and liquid additives. Thus, small quantities of liquid
additive may be totally adsorbed on the surfaces of a relatively small
proportion of solid particles. Quite large proportions of liquids can be
absorbed where the polymer (e.g. an EP PVC resin) or a filler (e.g. some
calcium carbonates) have a porous structure. In either case, if reasonably
uniform distribution of liquid throughout the solid particles is not
achieved very rapidly, the possibility of achieving it at all is virtually lost.
It is, therefore, often sound practice to introduce the liquid additive in
the form of as fine a spray as possible onto the exposed surface of the
vigorously agitated bed of solid particles. It is tempting to describe this
as distributive mixing. Experimentally, the problem has been overcome
by adding the liquid additive dissolved in a large volume of solvent that
is inert to the polymer, and then evaporating off the inert solvent, but
this would be expensive as a commercial operation. If the liquid component is in excess, once it has been distributed around the solid
particles, laminar mixing ensues.

2.3.5 Compounding Processes

A major part of polymer mixing involves solid/liquid and liquid/liquid
mixing where the liquid comprises polymer melt, i.e. compounding. In
most cases the polymer, and possibly other components, will start off in
the solid state and become converted to the melt state during the mixing
process, usually at an early stage thereof, so that solid/solid or solid/
liquid mixing may constitute an important part of the process before
true compounding commences. Laminar mixing is the dominant
mechanism in compounding processes, which are also characterised by
the existence of zones of high shear stress where dispersive mixing

occurs. The high shear conditions normally required in compounding are obtained by enclosing the composition in, or passing the composition through the space between two or more members between which there is relative movement and zones of relatively small clearance. Thus, in a two-roll mill (Chapter 4) the intensive shear conditions arise in the gap or 'nip' between two contra-rotating cylindrical rolls. In internal mixers (Chapter 4) the material is enclosed within a chamber where it is sheared by the action of two rotors. Continuous compounding machines are usually based on the screw extruder principle (Chapter 5), the material being intensely sheared by virtue of the rotation of the screw or screws. The precise pattern of the laminar mixing in a compounding machine depends on the particular geometry of the machine, the operating conditions and the nature of the composition being mixed (Section 2.4).

2.3.6 Rates of Mixing

It will be apparent that the mechanisms of mixing vary considerably depending on the type of materials to be mixed and the kind of mixing process that is required, and they have not been fully worked out qualitatively, let alone quantitatively, for more than a few specific cases. Measurement of kinetics of mixing is subject to the same problems as assessment of mixing indices, with the added factor that more measurements are required because it is necessary to assess mixing indices at a number of different times during the mixing process. There are implications, throughout the literature on mixing, of the rather obvious fact that degree of mixing improves with time of mixing. There are also some references to the possibility of unmixing or 'demixing' interfering with mixing processes and the rate at which this occurs also possibly increases with time. Very few quantitative theoretical or practical studies appear to have been reported, however. In his work on the theory of particle mixing Lacey[14] pointed out that any of the mechanisms he discussed, namely convective, diffusive and shear mixing (see Section 2.3.1), tend towards an equilibrium, so that the rate of change of degree of mixing is likely to be in accordance with a typical exponential rate equation:

$$M = 1 - e^{-kt} \qquad (12)$$

where M is degree of mixing as defined by eqn. (3), $t =$ time and k is a rate constant. It is interesting to note that if, as seems reasonable, a value of M greater than unity is allocated to a state of complete uniformity, a similar rate equation could describe the unmixing that a completely uniform array of components would receive if subjected to a conventional mixing process (Fig. 2.4).

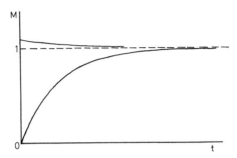

FIG. 2.4. Plot of $M = (\sigma_o^2 - s^2)/(\sigma_o^2 - \sigma_r^2)$ against time, t.

If eqn. (12) is rearranged and then transformed to log form we obtain:

$$\ln (1 - M) = -kt \tag{13}$$

and

$$k = -\ln \frac{(1 - M)}{t} \tag{14}$$

whence the value of the rate constant could be readily obtained from the linear plot of $-\ln(1 - M)$ against t (Fig. 2.5). However, as a mixing process proceeds some unmixing must be presumed to occur, so it might be more strictly correct to introduce a second rate constant to account

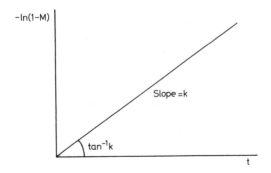

FIG. 2.5. Plot of $-\ln(1 - M)$ against time, t.

for this:

$$M = 1 - e^{-kt} - e^{-k't}$$ (15)

In practice, however, it would be exceedingly difficult to identify mixing and unmixing separately, and one would expect to obtain a value for the overall rate constant slightly different from the true value of k.

Brothman et al.[29] had previously attempted to develop an expression based on estimation of increase in interfacial area between components during mixing, postulating that the rate of increase in surface will be proportional to the difference between the actual S and the maximum possible area Sm, thus yielding an exponential equation:

$$S = Sm(1 - e^{-kt})$$ (16)

not unlike Lacey's rate eqn. (12), but even less amenable to practical evaluation.

Coulson and Maitra[30,31] obtained a somewhat similar expression using as criterion of mixing the fraction of samples containing both components, this being a measure of the interfacial area since a sample will only contain both components if its boundaries have intersected the interfacial surface.

Although mixing rates are obviously important, industrial cycles are commonly so short that numerical calculations of mixing rates or rate constants is rarely attempted. What is more usual is to measure times required to reach acceptable states of admixture. In this way, performances of different mixing machines can be compared, and throughputs can be calculated for plant design purposes.

2.4 RELATIONSHIPS BETWEEN THE NATURE OF THE COMPONENTS OF A MIXTURE AND MIXING PROCESSES

It will be apparent from the foregoing sections that the nature of the components may have significant effects on the progress of a mixing operation. In the mixing of reactive liquids, as in the production of polyurethanes, the most important properties in this connection will clearly be viscosity, surface tension wetting behaviour and chemical reactivity. It is not immediately obvious what magnitude of viscosity and what sort of variation of viscosity with shear rate are likely to be most conducive to good rapid mixing. Since higher viscosities lead to more intense shear it might be thought that high viscosities would be desirable. However, the shear conditions must be related to the yield behaviour of the liquid components, and it seems likely that high viscosity and high yield stress go together, and low viscosity and low yield stress likewise, thus according with intuitive predilection for low viscosity liquids where possible. Since the systems under consideration are almost invariably highly mutually reactive chemically, problems due to surface tension or poor mutual wetting behaviour are not likely to be serious, but in any case little, if any, work on these subjects appears to have been published.

2.4.1 Solid Components

Several properties of solid components are significant in solid/solid and solid/liquid mixing as well as in melt compounding. The most immediately obvious way in which solids differ is in their particle size, and, perhaps less obviously, their particle size distribution. Granules or pellets obtained by dicing and like processes from polymer produced in continuum form usually have relatively large particle size, possibly as high as an average particle volume of around $32\,\text{mm}^3$, compared to powders, which are unlikely to have particles with volume much above $0.04\,\text{mm}^3$, and which may have particles very much smaller than that, i.e. of the order of $0.00025\,\text{mm}^3$. Some solid additives may have particle sizes several orders of magnitude smaller still (e.g. as small as $5 \times 10^{-13}\,\text{mm}^3$). If there is no change in particle size during mixing and there are no processing limitations on the extent to which the particles can be intermingled, e.g. persistent agglomeration, it is clear that the smaller the particles the more intimate the admixture that can be obtained. Assuming as intimate an admixture as possible, the scale of segregation and striation thickness will be determined by the size of particles, as indicated previously. Indeed, as a first approximation these characteristics might be equated to the average diameter of the particles. However, although no quantitative data are available it is generally the case that difficulty of breaking down agglomerates increases as particle size decreases, i.e. agglomerates tend to be more persistent with decreasing particle size. This can provide quite severe problems particularly with average particle sizes below $1\,\mu\text{m}$. So much so that very fine particle, relatively cheap, additives, e.g. synthetic calcium carbonate, are commonly provided with costly surface coatings of lubricants that aid deagglomeration. Particle size, size distribution, and shape also have a profound influence on flow behaviour. This is most clearly recognised in relation to the flow of powders, or granules in hoppers feeding extruder screws[32] or other equipment where a screw can become starved due to bridging. It seems likely that particle flow is also significant in the feed zone of an extruder, and particularly from the present point of view of a compounding extruder. Particle flow behaviour is also likely to be a significant factor in solids blending, but this possibility does not seem to have been explored. From the more mundane practical point of view, very fine powders can constitute a dust problem with respect to good housekeeping and sometimes because of the possible hazard of dust explosions.

In melt compounding the size, size distribution, and shape, will also affect the way in which particles compact together, soften, and melt, ultimately to form a continuum, and hence will affect the shear vs time profile that a composition receives. As long ago as 1955, Kennaway showed that so-called 'caviare cut', spheroid polyethylene granules were extruded twice as fast as 'rough cut' disintegrated material, using both single- and twin-screw machines, while cube-cut and so-called spaghetti or lace cut granules exhibited only slightly less significant advantage over the rough material.[32] No further work on this subject appears to have been published.

It seems likely that in many mixing operations the total surface area of a particulate component is important, but this is a difficult property to measure, particularly with very fine powders where it is likely to be particularly significant.

Particle size and size distribution of powders are commonly assessed by relatively simple sieve analyses using a stack of sieves of differing aperture sizes. Provided attention is paid to details of technique, this method can give reasonably reliable results with coarser powders but is of little value below about 75 μm. For very fine powders more refined techniques such as gas absorption or electron microscopy are necessary. It is commonly assumed, at least for calculation purposes, that powder particles are spherical, but this is certainly not invariably the case. Particles may be in the form of platelets, for example, or of nondescript shape, and may indeed possess a porous structure.

These features can normally only be revealed by optical microscopy for larger particle sizes, and electron microscopy for the finer particles. Flow and packing behaviour of powders are clearly related to particle size, size distribution, and shape, and to each other, but precise relationships are not well established. Both flow and packing tend to decrease with particle size, so from this point of view coarse powders are generally to be preferred. Powders with wide size distributions will generally pack closer than those with narrow ones. Packing behaviour is usually assessed by simple 'apparent powder density', 'bulk factor' and 'packing density' methods. Flow of powders is less readily characterised. Methods that have been used include determination of 'angle of repose' under standard conditions, and observation of variation in flow behaviour through a series of 'hour glasses' or 'egg-timers', having a range of capillary sizes. Related to the latter method is the observation of the extent and sharpness to which a ridge pattern is retained when a 'flow comb', comprising shaping grooves of different sizes, is drawn over the surface of a bed of the powder (Figs. 2.6 and 2.7). Flow and packing of granulated or pelletised polymers is not generally regarded as a problem, but it is probable that granule size and shape can significantly effect compaction and softening, and thus efficiency and rate of compounding. Further investigation of this subject might well be worthwhile.

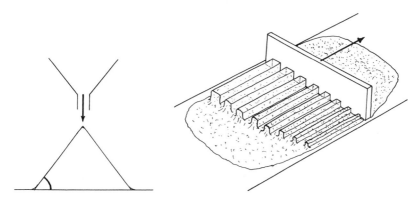

FIG. 2.6. Angle of repose.   FIG. 2.7. Principle of powder flow comb.

Density of solid particles, as distinct from their bulk and packing densities, becomes significant in solid/solid mixing where it can become surprisingly important when there are appreciable differences in this property between different components. These differences tend to promote segregation of the components, particularly where gravity has a major influence on the flow patterns.

Polymers, and some of the additives in polymer compositions, are exceedingly poor conductors of electricity, and consequently the relative movement of particles in contact with each other during solid/solid mixing, is liable to lead to the acquisition of electrostatic charges. This is said to be advantageous in some situations, e.g. dry-blending pigments with non polar polymers, or mixing components that have acquired opposite charges,[6,10,11] but the real value of this effect is doubtful except in processes where the charging is organised with the specific objective of improving mixing in view.[10,11]

Other materials properties that may have a significant effect in solid/ solid mixing are hardness or softness, friability, and stickiness of particles, but no theoretical studies of these factors have appeared. Hard particles will presumably tend to fracture other particles when the latter are sufficiently fragile, and incidentally may also tend to wear the internal and working surfaces of blending equipment to a sufficient degree to produce significant metallic contamination in some instances. Fragile, or friable, particles will tend to be relatively readily broken down into smaller particles, and this might be thought to aid mixing, since, as seen earlier, the smaller the particle size, the smaller becomes the ultimate possible striation thickness or scale of segregation, i.e. the better the mixture. However, very small particles are sometimes found to be more difficult to disperse than larger ones, and it should not always be assumed that the former are preferable. Also, the absorptivity of particles for liquid additives may be affected by fracture of particles and hence changes in particle shape. Thus, the manufacture of highly plasticised PVC dry-blends depends on absorption of plasticiser within the pore structure of EP suspension polymer, and if the particles of the polymer are broken down some of the absorptivity is lost. A sticky additive may create mixing problems not only because it will possibly be difficult to divide it and spread it around the composition, but also because it will tend to promote agglomeration of particles of polymer and other additives.

2.4.2 Compounding

Melt compounding is invariably preceded by introduction to the compounding machine of solid polymer either with or followed by other additives, so that the factors discussed already in relation to solids blending, may also be significant in compounding. In addition, the softening or melting behaviour, and compaction and adhesion properties of the polymer and additives, and melt flow behaviour will be important. Obviously, this means that compounding requires not only that appropriate relative motions are imparted to the components in order to achieve mixing, but also that heat has to be supplied to the system. Sometimes some of this heat is supplied by external sources such as heated jackets or electric resistance heaters, but frictional heating within the system, due to the movement of components in close contact with each other, invariably occurs and may constitute the sole source of heat. This not only avoids the necessity to provide external heat, but also constitutes a means of ensuring the maximum uniformity of heating and softening of the materials.

Softening and melting behaviour will clearly depend directly on chemical structure in that this will determine the transition temperatures of the polymer and additives, and indirectly in that chemical structure determines thermodynamic properties such as specific heat, latent heat, and thermal conductivity and diffusivity. Coupled with these material properties, the geometry and physical properties of the particles are significant. Polymers are poor conductors of heat, and for a given shape the larger the particles the more difficult it will be to heat them uniformly by conduction. On the other hand, variation in particle size will generally permit the particles to pack more closely together, and thus increase the contact surface area available for heat transfer from one particle to another. This increase in contact surface area will also tend to increase the rate of generation of frictional heat. The shape of the particles, too, will affect both heat transfer and development of frictional heat, though detailed analysis would be difficult. This is particularly so because the shape and dimensions will be changing in complex fashion under the action of compression and shear forces in accordance with stress/stain behaviour as it depends on temperature and shear conditions that change with time and location. The magnitude and distribution of shear forces within the mass of softening particles will also depend on the adhesion between the particles, as will the readiness or otherwise of the softened particles to 'gel' or congeal together to form a continuum. Not much appears to be known quantitatively about adhesion properties of polymers or additives, but additives of low compatibility with the polymer, particularly those with surface active properties, such as lubricants, antistatic agents and slip agents, may well tend to concentrate on the surfaces of the particles and to interfere with adhesion between them.

2.4.3 *Melt Flow Behaviour*

Once a continuum of softened polymer or melt has developed, melt rheological behaviour becomes an important factor in determining the pattern and intensities of shear within the system. Once again, full analysis is complicated by the changing nature of the system during compounding. When the melt stage has been reached the system will generally still be grossly inhomogeneous, and compounding will be continued until a satisfactory degree of admixture is attained. Once having attained this target there is no point in continuing the process, so throughout the process the system is changing in mixedness and consequently in rheological behaviour. Nevertheless, some general conclusions can be reached and a reasonably accurate detailed analysis is possible with some polymer systems. It is generally assumed that the more intensive the shear conditions, the more rapid and effective is the mixing. For compatible materials this is probably true, but with some additives of low compatibility high shear rates may cause segregation. This applies particularly to lubricants and fillers or pigments and fillers combined with lubricants. This phenomenon is difficult to predict and can be exceedingly troublesome in industrial practice. It is, however, frequently overlooked in compounding, only to become apparent upon subsequent processing by extrusion or some other shaping operation.

In introducing a theoretical treatment of mixing in laminar flow systems, Mohr *et al.*[22] expressed the view that goodness of mixing in such systems depends on the net amount of shear supplied to the material, the mechanism involving generation of new interfacial surface and consequent reduction in size of regions occupied exclusively by one component. They derived an expression showing that the ratio of the final to the initial striation thickness is inversely proportional to the amount of shear experienced by the system, and to the relative fluidity of the components. The amount of shear could be calculated as the product of the shear rate imposed on the major component and the residence time. This derivation expresses in mathematical terms what has long been realised qualitatively, namely that mixing is favoured by increase in shear rate and in residence time in regions of high shear. It should be noted, however, that shear rate distribution within the system is extremely important since this determines the intensity of shearing at individual localities. For if a composition receives a high total amount of shear but experiences it only or mainly in a limited range of localities within the system, part of the composition may indeed become well mixed but other parts will be poorly mixed, if at all. Furthermore, the lower viscosity fluid in a two component fluid system tends to migrate to regions of minimum shear.

As Mohr et al.[22] stated 'It is evident, therefore, that not only the amount of work, but the manner in which it is expended, is important in quantifying mixedness'. Since polymer will usually constitute the major component in a compounding process, the detailed melt rheological behaviour of the polymer phase or phases is, therefore, clearly of great importance. The shear rate distribution within a polymer melt is directly dependent on the velocity profile, i.e. the velocity distribution within the melt. In melt compounding the shear is usually obtained by retaining the polymer within, or passing it between, two or more metal surfaces undergoing relative movement. The velocity profile therefore depends on

   (i) the geometry of the compounding machinery,
  (ii) the relative rates of movement of the members of the compound-
       ing machinery, and
 (iii) the rheological behaviour of the melt, in particular the extent of
       deviation of the latter from Newtonian.

For a Newtonian fluid, i.e. one for which shear rate is proportional to shear stress, velocity profiles display quite wide velocity distributions, but as behaviour departs more and more from Newtonian, flow becomes more 'plug-like' and, although the range of velocities may still be quite wide, the changes in velocity, and therefore the high shear rates, become more and more concentrated near the surfaces of the compounding machine, with only small variations of velocity and therefore low shear within the main body of the melt. The departure of polymer from Newtonian behaviour is conveniently expressed in terms of the well-known Power Law:

$$\tau = K\dot{\gamma}^n \tag{17}$$

or

$$\tau = K\left(\frac{du}{dr}\right)^n \tag{18}$$

where τ is the shear stress, $\dot{\gamma}$ is the shear rate, (i.e. du/dr), K is known as the consistency index and n is known as the flow-behaviour index, K and n being characteristic for each particular polymer. For a Newtonian fluid $n = 1$, K becomes viscosity and the equation reduces to the usual

Newtonian form. As n becomes smaller flow becomes increasingly plug-like, becoming markedly so at values of n lower than about 0·5, so that a knowledge of the value of flow-behaviour index for a polymer should provide a good indication of the kind of velocity profile and therefore the shear mixing it is likely to receive in a compounding operation. As might be anticipated, the value of n for a given polymer is temperature dependent, but, surprisingly, increase in temperature may sometimes produce a fall in n rather than the expected rise.[33,34] The value of n also tends to fall with increase in shear rate.

In spite of these considerations, it is difficult to correlate observed compounding behaviour with values of flow-behaviour index quoted in the literature, but of course it must be remembered that the actual magnitudes of shear rates are important as well as the distribution. In other words, the value of the consistency index K is also important. Since, at a given shear rate, apparent viscosity is proportional to K, this is equivalent to saying that apparent viscosity is important, another fact that has long been recognised intuitively. For any given system, apparent viscosity generally falls with increase in temperature, so low temperatures are clearly indicated if maximum viscosity and shear conditions are desired, but other effects of shearing may need to be considered. Thus, apparent viscosity itself generally falls with increasing shear rate. Also, under the action of shear polymer molecules tend to undergo scission into shorter chain molecules, and the more intense the shear the greater is the extent of chain scission likely to be. This may or may not be desirable. In some cases, e.g. rubbers, it may be a prime aim of the compounding process. The molecular fragments produced by chain scission may be highly reactive so that some may reunite in more or less random fashion, with a resultant change in molecular weight distribution. This may account for the improvements by so-called homogenisation that some polymers are said to undergo during compounding. In some ways, attempts to obtain high shear by using low compounding temperatures are self-defeating because the shearing produces heat with consequent rise in temperature and fall in apparent viscosity, unless the heat can be removed as rapidly as it is produced. Efficient cooling is therefore necessary. Attempts to obtain high shear by using high speeds for the moving parts of a compounding machine can also be, to some extent, self-defeating, since apparent viscosity also generally falls with increasing shear rate.

If, as a result of intensive shearing, localised 'hot-spots' arise, degradation of polymer and/or additives may occur. Thus, chemical stability of the components of the polymer system are generally of importance in compounding operations. Even where there is good control of temperatures, polymer or additive instability may place a practical limitation on residence time, which, as seen earlier, is an important factor in achieving good mixing. Moreover, it must be noted that a polymeric composition must retain, after compounding, sufficient stability to withstand subsequent shaping and service conditions, so that degradation during the compounding process must be contained well within the maximum permissible limits for the composition as a whole. The situation is even more severe where the composition is a thermosetting one based on a reactive cross-linking resin intermediate, or containing a cross-linking agent. In such cases the 'cure' must not be allowed to advance sufficiently far as to interfere with flow of the composition during subsequent shaping operations. Since cross-linking systems are commonly highly reactive under compounding conditions, a severe limitation is placed on residence times and thus on mixing cycle times.

The stability, cross-linking and degradation behaviour of a polymeric composition depend very much on the precise nature of the polymer, resin, and additives, and also on the processing conditions, e.g. presence or absence of oxygen, so that each system has to be considered individually.

2.5 GENERAL ASPECTS OF MACHINE DESIGN AND OPERATION

The design of a mixing machine will obviously depend on the nature of the materials to be mixed and on whether the mixing is to involve simple blending or melt compounding. In all cases the mixing is achieved by relative movement between volume elements of the composition and parts of the machine. In the vast majority of cases the relative movement is obtained by motions, usually rotational but occasionally also reciprocating, of one or more parts or members of the machine. In so-called 'static mixers' the relative movement is achieved by extruding the polymer melt through the somewhat complex flow channels of the mixers. Ultimately, of course, mixing depends on the relative movements of volume elements of the components of the composition, and the only function of the movement of parts of the mixing machine is to impart appropriate flow patterns within the composition for these relative movements to occur.

The effectiveness and efficiency of a mixing machine depend on the intensity of shearing action or turbulence in zones where these occur and the residence times of components in these zones. It is rare for the mixing action to be uniform throughout the operational volume of a mixer, and in some zones mixing may not occur at all, so that the frequency of circulation of components through zones of high shear or turbulence becomes important. Obviously, these factors depend on the shape and dimensions, i.e. the geometry, and on the relative speeds of movement of the members of the machine, as well as on the nature of the components of the composition. Where shearing is imparted to material between the surfaces of two or more members of the machine, effectiveness is generally the greater the smaller the clearances and the higher the relative rates of movement. Power requirements are obviously of importance in the design of a mixing machine but, as far as the mixing process itself is concerned, it is the total energy absorbed by the composition that is important. Effectiveness, in the sense of how good a mixedness is achieved, depends on residence time. From this point of view, a batch mixing machine may have a distinct advantage over a continuous one, in that the former operates on a 'captive' composition so that additives of low compatibility or which for some other reason are difficult to disperse cannot escape, and it may be possible to prolong the mixing process until a satisfactory dispersion has been attained. There will be severe limitations on this, of course, with thermosetting or otherwise unstable materials. In a continuous mixing machine, on the other hand, the average dwell time of material passing through it cannot usually be increased to any great extent without reducing the mixing action, unless the increase in dwell time is achieved by increasing back-pressure by imposing increased restrictions on flow, e.g. by means of a valved head or die. Also, in a continuous mixing machine there is often plenty of opportunity for additives of low compatibility to avoid regions of high shear. Indeed, as indicated earlier, passage through regions of high shear may induce separation of such additives, i.e. unmixing, without the possibility of re-mixing at a later stage.

The efficiency of a mixing machine, however, will be assessed, not only in terms of the ultimate level of mixedness it can produce, but realistically by the total cost of carrying out the required mixing action, taking all factors into account. Technically this depends on the rate at which it produces the required degree of mixedness.

The modes of operation of batch and continuous machines are somewhat different. In a batch process the composition starts in a state of relative unmixedness and proceeds more or less steadily towards the required level of mixedness, whereas in continuous mixing, while the materials themselves experience the same kinds of changes with time, the process is operated in a steady state or equilibrium fashion. From the machine's point of view mixedness changes with location within the machine rather than with time. Another difference between the two types of process arises from the fact that in a batch mixer any volume element of the batch of material being mixed is liable to be transferred to any part of the system, whereas in most continuous mixers circulation in directions other than the forward flow is limited. In other words, the 'scales of mixing' in the two types of process are different. Consequently, a continuous mixing machine generally requires a much better pre-blending of components or a very accurate metering of components to the feed zone, whereas a batch mixer will commonly operate on the totally unmixed components merely dumped separately in the machine.

2.5.1 Initial Orientation

An aspect of mixing process operation, that has received theoretical but little if any practical attention, is the significance of initial orientation of the components of a composition, yet in some industrial processes this could be of considerable importance. Very often the manufacturer of a mixing machine has little or no control over this aspect of the process and is unable to design the machine to take account of this fact. It then becomes important for production procedures to take it into account. For efficient operation, the initial interfacial surfaces between the components need to be oriented at an optimum with respect to the material flow paths within the system. The importance of this factor depends on the complexity or otherwise of these flow paths.

Consider two components being mixed in a simple cylindrical drum blender, rotating about its longitudinal axis in the horizontal position. Mixing occurs essentially by diffusion of elements of the components across the interfaces between them (Fig. 2.8). If the appropriate quantities of the two particulate components are placed inside the cylinder with the interface between them in a vertical plane at right-angles to the axis, mixing (in the earlier stages at least) is solely by longitudinal diffusion, i.e. parallel to the axis, and is consequently very slow. Transverse or radial diffusion, i.e. in planes at right-angles to the axis, is rapid, so that

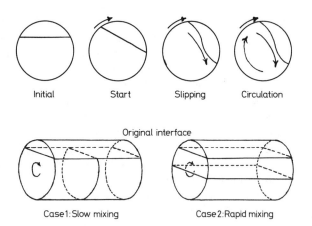

FIG. 2.8. Effect of initial location in a simple drum tumble blender.

very much more rapid mixing would be achieved by placing the components so that the interface between them is parallel to the axis of the cylinder. However, it must be remembered that mixing will only occur by relative movement of particles of the components, and if this is unduly restricted mixing may be slow. One possible source of restriction of movement consists in over-charging the mixing cylinder. In the extreme (if absurd) case, where the cylinder is completely filled with tightly packed particles, rotation will produce no movement of particles and hence no mixing. At the other extreme, with only a few particles of each component mixing might be extremely rapid. Somewhere between these two extremes lies the optimum charge capacity. It seems reasonable to suppose that this optimum would be the maximum charge that would not result in appreciable restriction on movement, by impingement or containment by the 'free' internal surface of the cylinder above the bed of particles being mixed.

With liquid/liquid blending and melt compounding the situation is somewhat different, since once the components, or a major part, are in the fluid state absence of free space within the mixing chamber may not seriously limit relative movements of the components. In practice, where the compounding machine comprises a mixing chamber with one or more internal moving members, the chamber is commonly filled with material. Indeed, in many cases, charging sufficiently to fill the chamber with material under pressure is a prime requisite for effective and rapid gelation and mixing. Initial orientation of the components with respect to each other and to the mixing machine may still be important. For rapid shear mixing to occur, it is necessary for the flow lines of movement to cut the interfaces between the components. This is illustrated[3] clearly by consideration of the effect of initial location of two components in a simple shear mixer similar in form to a rotational viscometer, i.e. comprising a circular cylindrical mixing rotor rotating within a concentric hollow mixing chamber (Fig. 2.9). If the two components are initially separated by a plane interface at right-angles to the

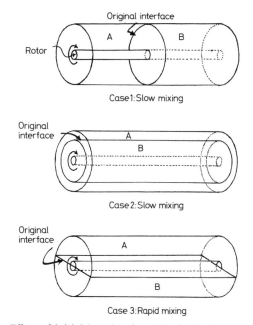

FIG. 2.9. Effect of initial location in a simple idealised shear mixer.

axis of the two cylinders, the situation is analogous to the first of those discussed previously in relation to solid/solid systems, and mixing is very slow. Likewise, if the components are disposed in the form of two concentric hollow cylinders, the interface between them also forming a concentric hollow cylinder, mixing will also be slow. For most rapid shear mixing, the two components should be located so that they are separated by two plane interfaces radial to the axis of the cylinders. Good design practice for mixing machines should include features that will tend to transfer material across shear planes, so that pre-location of components of a mixture becomes unimportant.

2.5.2 Effects of Shear on Structure

Reference has already been made to the side effects of degradation or cross-linking reactions that may impose limitations on the mixing process. Another factor that, while not always necessarily imposing limitations, is certainly frequently related to the mixing process, relates to possible structurisation and destructurisation of the polymer. Depending on its chemical nature, the molecules of a polymer will tend to be more or less entangled in the melt state. Rigid extended chain molecules will tend to entangle much less than flexible and branched-chain molecules. Since the melt flow behaviour of a polymer is affected by the amount of entanglement, anything that changes this is likely to alter the melt properties. Such evidence as is available suggests that high temperatures favour entanglement, while high shear conditions favour disentanglement. Compounding conditions can, therefore, affect the degree of entanglement of a polymeric composition, and thus in turn affect melt flow behaviour in subsequent processing such as extrusion.

Thus, with PVC, for example, extrusion behaviour is very dependent on previous shear and temperature conditions encountered.[35-38] High temperatures and low shear rates during compounding tend to produce relatively high melt viscosities and a predilection for melt fracture, while opposite effects tend to follow compounding at low temperatures and high shear rates. It is now generally accepted that PVC tends to retain some of its particle structure in the melt state,[39-42] and that this is the reason for the characteristic melt flow behaviour of the material. Depending on the method of polymerisation, the particles may be of three different dimensional orders[43] of around 10 nm, 0·1 to 2 μm and 100 μm, the smallest being formed by precipitation of polymer from the monomer phase, and the other two resulting from aggregation and agglomeration. The extent to which these particle structures are retained in the melt state depends not only on the shear and thermal conditions to which the polymer is submitted, but also on the firmness, or otherwise, with which the aggregates or agglomerates are held together. This in turn may depend on the polymerisation procedure and the conditions encountered during separation from the polymerisation system. The melt flow behaviour of PVC is, therefore, sensitively dependent on the conditions of the mixing process, and this may also apply to properties of finished PVC articles.[44] A continual awareness of these factors is a prime requirement for successful compounding of PVC on a production basis. It would be somewhat surprising if these phenomena were not exhibited by any other polymer.

REFERENCES

1. FUNT, J. M., *Mixing of Rubbers*, RAPRA, Shrewsbury (1977).
2. MIDDLEMAN, S., *Fundamentals of Polymer Processing*, Chapter 12, McGraw-Hill, New York (1977).
3. MOHR, W. D., *Processing of Thermoplastic Materials*, Chapter 3, Bernhardt, E. C. (Ed.), Van Nostrand Reinhold, New York (1959).
4. BERGEN, J. T., *Processing of Thermoplastic Materials*, Chapter 7, Bernhardt, E. C. (Ed.), Van Nostrand Reinhold, New York (1959).
5. MCKELVEY, J. M., *Polymer Processing*, Wiley, New York (1962).
6. TADMOR, Z. and GOGOS, C. G., *Principles of Polymer Processing*, Wiley, New York (1979).
7. DANCKWERTS, P. V., *Appl. Sci. Research, Hague*, **3**, 279 (1952); *Chem. Engng. Sci.* **2**, 1 (1953); *Research, London*, **6**, 35 (1953).
8. ADAMS, J. F. E. and BAKER, A. G., *Trans. Inst. Chem. Engrs.*, **34**, 91 (1956).
9. KING, G. T., *Industrial Chemist*, **40**(1), 20 (1964).
10. TUCKER, C. L. and SUH, N. P., *Polym. Engng. Sci.*, **16**(10), 657 (1976).
11. ROTZ, C. A. and SUH, N. P., *Polym. Engng. Sci.*, **16**(10), 672 (1976).
12. LACEY, P. M. C., *Trans. Inst. Chem. Engrs*, **21**, 53 (1943).
13. LACEY, P. M. C., *Chem. Age, Lond.*, **53**, 119, 145 (1945).
14. LACEY, P. M. C., *J. appl. Chem., Lond.*, **4**, 257 (1954).
15. Unpublished work. Polytechnic of the South Bank, London.
16. BOURNE, J. R., *The Mixing of Powders, Pastes, and Non-Newtonian Fluids*, Indl. Fellow Rep. No. 2, Inst. of Chem. Engrs., London (1969).
17. FAN, L. T., and WANG, R. H., *Powder Technol.*, **11**, 27 (1975).
18. BUSLIK, D., *Bull. Amer. Soc. Test. Mat.*, **165**, 66 (1950).
19. VANCE, F. P., *Ind. and Engng. Chem.*, **58**(6), 37 (1966).
20. DANCKWERTS, P. V., *Appl. Sci. Res. Sec.*, **A3**, 279 (1952).
21. BIGG, D. M., *Polym. Engng. Sci.*, **15**(9), 684 (1975).
22. MOHR, W. D., SAXTON, R. L. and JEPSON, C. H., *Ind. and Engng. Chem.*, **49**(11), 1855 (1957).
23. SPENCER, R. S. and WILEY, R. M., *J. Colloid Sci.*, **6**, 133 (1951).
24. PALMGREN, H., *European Rubber J.*, **156**, 30, 70 (1974).
25. JULESZ, B., *Scientific American*, **232**, 34 (1975).
26. NADAV, N. and TADMOR, Z., *Chem. Eng. Sci.*, **28**, 2115 (1973).
27. BROADKEY, R. S., *Mixing*, Vol. 1, Chapter 2, Uhl, V. H. and Gray, J. B. (Eds), Academic Press, London (1966).
28. STERBACEK, Z. and TAUSK, P., *Mixing in the Chemical Industry*, translated by Mayer, K. and Bourne, J. R., Pergamon Press, Oxford (1965).
29. BROTHMAN, A., WOLLAN, G. N. and FELDMAN, S. M., *Chem. metall. Engng.*, **52**, 102 (1945).
30. MAITRA, N. K. and COULSON, J. M., *J. Imp.Coll.Chem. Engng. Soc.*, **4**, 135 (1948).
31. COULSON, J. M. and MAITRA, N. K., *Industr. Chem. Mfr.*, **26**, 55 (1950).
32. KENNAWAY, A., *Brit. Plastics*, **28**(1), 18 (1955); in *Plastics Progress*, Morgan, P. (Ed.), Iliffe, London, p. 149 (1957).
33. WESTOVER, R. F., *Processing of Thermoplastic Materials*, Section 111, Bernhardt, E. C. (Ed.), Van Nostrand Reinhold, New York (1959).

34. SIEGLAFF, C. L., *S.P.E. Trans.*, **4** (2), 129 (1964).
35. BURKE, G. H. and PORTINGELL, G. C., *Br. Plast.*, **36**(5), 254 (1963).
36. DOWRICK, D., *Plastics*, **30**, 63, 328 (1965).
37. KHANNA, S. K. and POLLETT, W. F. D., *J. Appl. Polym. Sci.*, **9**, 1767 (1965).
38. MOORE, D. R., *PRI Int. Conf. on PVC Processing*, Eng. Royal Holloway College. PRI, London, pp. 11.1–11.11 (1978).
39. BERENS, A. R. and FOLT, V. L., *Trans. Soc. Rheol.*, **11**(1), 95 (1967); *Polym. Engng. Sci.*, **8**(1), 5 (1968); **9**(1), 27 (1969).
40. HORI, Y., *Japan Plast.*, **3**, 48 (1969).
41. SHINAGAWA, Y., *Plast. Ind. News*, May, 65 (1973).
42. FAULKNER, P. G., *J. Macromol. Sci. Phys.*, **B11**, 251 (1975).
43. GRAY, A., *PRI Int. Conf. on PVC Processing*, Eng. Royal Holloway College. PRI, London, pp. 10.1–10.9 (1978).
44. MENGES, G. and BERNDTSEN, N., *PRI Int. Conf. on PVC Processing*, Eng. Royal Holloway College, PRI, London, pp. 12.1–12.10 (1978).

BIBLIOGRAPHY

ANON, *Rubber J.*, **151**(10), 48 (1969). Analysis of rubber mixing.

BEAUDRY, J. P., *Chem. Eng.*, **55**(7), 112 (1948). Statistics of simple mixing.

BEST, W. G. and TOMFOHODE, H. F., *Soc. Plast. Eng. J.*, **15**, 139 (1959). Quick test for carbon black dispersion.

BOLEN, W. R. and COLWELL, R. E., *S.P.E. Tech. Papers*, **IV**, 1004 (1958); *S.P.E.J.*, **14**(8), 24 (1958). Mixing indices and shear stresses.

BOURNE, J. R., *New Scientist*, February, 334 (1967). Science of mixing.

BUTTERS, G., CROSS, J., DIXON, G. and TILLOTSON, J. F., *Plastics Pneumatic Conveying and Bulk Storage*, Butters, G. (Ed.), Applied Science Publishers, London (1981).

COULSON, J. M. and MAITRA, N. K., *Ind. Chemist.*, **25**(2), 55 (1950). Tumble blending.

DERRINGER, G. C., *Rubber World*, **167**(6), 33, 58; **168**(2), 43; **168**(3), 40; **168**(5), 149 (1973). Statistical methods in rubber technology.

FISHER, E. G. and CHARD, E. D., *Int. Plast. Eng.*, **2**(2), 54; **2**(3), 113 (1962). Principles of mixing.

GEHMAN, S. D., *Rubber Chem. and Technol.*, **35**, 819 (1962). Theory of random filler dispersion in rubber.

KING, G. T., *Ind. Chemist*, **40**(1), 20 (1964). Criteria of adequate mixing.

LANGTON, N. H., *Plast. Rubb. Wkly.*, 28 July, 149, 161 (1962). Mathematics of mixing.

MICHAELS, A. S. and PUZINAUSKAS, V., *Chem. Eng. Prog.*, **50**(12), 604 (1954). Uniformity index.

MOORE, W. R., *Trans. J. Plast Inst.*, **32**, 247 (1964). Mixing theory.

ORR, N. A. and SHOTTON, E., *Chem. Engr.*, January, 12 (1973). Mixing cohesive powders.

ROSE, H. E., *Trans. Inst. Chem. Eng.*, **40**, 272 (1962). Mixing model.

SKINNAR, R. and NAOR, P., *Chem. Eng. Sci.*, **15**, 220 (1961). Test for randomness.

SMITH, J. C., *Ind. Eng. Chem.*, **47**(11), 2240 (1955). Measures of mixedness.

STANGE, K., *Chem. Ing. Tech.*, **26**(3), 150; **26**(6), 331 (1954). Statistical assessment.
STUDEBAKER, M. L. and BEATTY, J. R., *Rubber Age*, May, 21; June, 21 (1976). Mixing factors affecting raw rubber stock.
VALENTIN, F. H. H., *Chem. Process Eng.*, April, 181 (1965). Review of mixing models.
WEIDENBAUM, S. S., *Adv. Chem. Eng.*, **2**, 211 (1958). Binomial distribution for particles.
WEIDENBAUM, S. S. and BONILLA, C. F., *Chem. Eng. Prog.*, **51**(1), 275 (1955). Mixedness measure.
WEYDANEZ, W., *Chem. Eng. Technol.*, **32**, 343 (1960). Mixing models.
WILLIAMS, J. C. and KHAN, M. I., *Chem. Engr.*, January, 19 (1973). Mixing and segregation of solids of different particle sizes.

CHAPTER 3

Blending and Blending Equipment

3.1 GENERAL CONSIDERATIONS

Surely the simplest forms of mixer must be the cocktail shaker, the medicine bottle shaken to ensure that every dose contains its proper amounts of each ingredient, or possibly the spoon or spatula in cup or beaker. Basic though these devices are, they can be remarkably effective, and many blending machines operate on essentially the same principles. As seen previously, all mixing involves relative motions between the components of a composition, and the differences between different types of mixing machine lie in the means by which the relative motions are achieved, and the flow patterns that the materials undergo as a consequence. In the treatment that follows, an attempt is made to classify blending machines in terms of their characteristic features that induce motion of the materials being mixed, as far as possible in order of increasing complexity, and to indicate the types of materials for which they are suited. Attention is also directed to considerations of limitations of the various types of machine and the selection of optimum operating procedures. In many cases, however, it is not possible to arrive at a precise, unambiguous conclusion as to what is the best form of machine and procedure to adopt. A tour of the polymer and other industries involved in mixing operations would reveal many instances of different types of machine being used to carry out, what is essentially, the same mixing operation, apparently with more or less equal success. Also, it is not uncommon for a machine to be used successfully for a mixing operation for which it was not designed, usually because the machine was available when a new mixing job came to be required.

Because of the confused state of terminology associated with mixing, clear unequivocal names for some types of mixer are not available, and it has been occasionally necessary in the following chapters to coin, borrow or select a name briefly to designate a particular type of mixer. It should be remembered that these names often carry no official approval, and that their usage around industry may vary considerably, so that in any commercial or technical negotiations, care should be taken to ensure that there is no misunderstanding.

3.2 VIBRATORY OR RECIPROCATING BLENDERS

What might be called 'the medicine bottle technique', that is, mixing by transference of the contents from end to end by a reciprocating action, only works because during separation the ingredients of a medicine tend to settle out in horizontal layers with major surface planes at right angles to the direction of reciprocation or shaking. Shaking in a direction at right angles to the vertical axis of the bottle, i.e. in the settlement planes, is not only difficult but is unlikely to produce rapid mixing. Horizontal vibration or reciprocation is also liable to lead to the separation of components as a result of density differences. For these reasons if for no others, reciprocation or vibration of the mixing chamber is rarely employed as the sole principle in the design of industrial mixers. It is, however, fairly commonly used for small-scale mixing in chemical laboratories when the length of mixing cycle is unimportant. Vibrational motion is also used as an adjunct to some other forms of mixing.[1-5]

In recent years ultrasonic vibration has been used increasingly for small-scale laboratory mixers but the technique does not appear to have been extended to industrial polymer mixing.

3.3 TUMBLE BLENDERS

In tumble blenders solid particles are made to move by pouring, rolling or falling. The common feature is that the particles are tipped beyond the angle of repose and continued tilting causes the particles to flow under the action of gravity.[6]

In its simplest form[7] the tumble blender consists of a drum previously used for transport of liquid or solid material, commandeered to act as a mixing chamber, the function of which is achieved by partially filling the drum with components to be mixed in the required proportions and then repeatedly turning the drum end over end or about its central axis aligned horizontally

(Fig. 3.1). Stands and drive mechanisms are commercially available to take one or two drums ranging in size from small cans to drums up to about $0.5\ m^3$ in total volume, i.e. to take a charge of up to about $0.4\ m^3$. This technique has proved to be so successful that tumble blenders of this type are now manufactured specially with removable and interchangeable drums of nearly $2\ m^3$ capacity (approximately 900 kg of material). An alternative to the 'end over end' motion is to position the drum on its side i.e. with its major axis horizontal, and to rotate or roll the drum about its horizontal axis. Commonly, the rolling action is achieved by placing the drum or two rollers, one or both of which are driven at an appropriate speed (Fig. 3.2). Larger

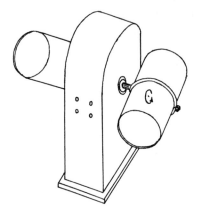

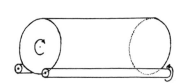

FIG. 3.1. Double drum tumble blender.   FIG. 3.2. Roller-driven drum tumble blender.

tumble blenders of this type may be driven directly. Sizes vary from the very small laboratory model taking only a few grams to large production blenders holding a few tonnes. Typical speeds of rotation vary from around 30 r.p.m. for small sizes down to around 12 r.p.m. for large sizes. This reduction in rotational speed with increasing size is less than proportional to the increase in diameter, so that it appears that the larger sizes of blender are likely to have higher surface speeds than smaller sizes. Power consumption is generally of the order of 0·04–0·08 W/kg.

Tumble blenders of the type described are commonly used for dry-blending polymer in powder or granule form with powdered additives such as pigments, with master-batches in powder or granule form, and also for blending successive batches of polymer or compounded granules, with the objective of smoothing out minor, possibly unknown, variations between the batches. When their mode of operation is taken into account, it is remarkable how effective these simple tumble blenders usually are for these kinds of mixing operations.

Consider a bed of particles in a rotating circular drum blender. If there was no friction between the particles and the internal surface the bed would remain stationary, so the whole action of a simple tumble blender is dependent on this friction, serving to rotate the bed in the same direction as the rotation of the blender and thus tilting the free surface of the bed of particles. At some critical point, gravity begins to move particles on the surface rather than contributing to their cohesion to the main body of the bed. The angle of tilt at which this occurs is related to the angle of repose of the solid, but is probably not constant but dependent on speed of rotation. In fact, in practice, an apparent oscillation of the free surface is frequently observed. The flow patterns of solids are also complicated, in that relative movement is probably not confined to particles on the free surface but a form of shear flow may well occur throughout a considerable part of the bed. However, whatever the precise nature of the flow patterns may be, there can be little doubt that while mixing may be rapid in transverse or radial planes at right-angles to the axis of rotation, mixing is very slow in the longitudinal direction, that is, parallel to the axis of rotation. In other words there is little 'cross-mixing'. For efficient mixing in this kind of tumble blender, therefore, it is necessary to spread the components evenly in the longitudinal direction before commencing (Chapter 2, Section 2.5.1). Where the axis of rotation is transverse to the longitudinal axis of the cylindrical mixing chamber, the flow patterns may be somewhat more complex but it seems unlikely that they would be markedly so, so that 'cross-mixing' is likely to be poor with this arrangement also. Most of the more sophisticated types of tumble blender have been designed to reduce this deficiency by introducing cross-mixing by one means or another.

3.3.1 Improving Cross-mixing

Conceptually, the simplest way of achieving this is to mount the cylindrical drum chamber so that rotation is skewed or eccentric, i.e. the axis of rotation is not parallel to any of the main axes of the cylinder (Fig. 3.3). This is done with fixed chamber and removable drum tumble mixers.[7] By this arrangement, a reciprocating tilting motion across the direction of rotation introduces an element of cross-mixing. A variant on the eccentric or skew arrangement is the well-known 'V' or 'twin-shell' blender (Fig. 3.4), manufactured in a range of sizes from small laboratory models up to capacities around 55 m³. Apart from symmetry, it is not obvious that the V-shaped mixing chamber offers any advantage over a simple cylindrical drum. It seems likely that the effectiveness of

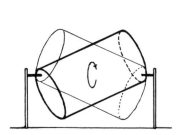

FIG. 3.3. Skewed or eccentrically rotating drum tumble blender.

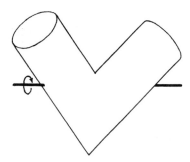

FIG. 3.4. 'V' or twin-shell blender.

mixing in blenders of these eccentric or skew types, is critically dependent on the relationships between the angle of inclination and the tilting and rotational motions, but few studies of the effects of varying these on mixing appear to have been published, apart from Coulson and Maitra's work[8] on simple drum tumble blending in which they found the optimum angle of inclination of the axis of rotation to be 14° to the horizontal. An angle of 40° to the vertical appears to be typical for the V-type mixer.[9]

Another variation, on what is essentially the same principle, is to give a rocking motion as well as the rotational motion to the mixing chamber.

3.3.2 Double-cone Blenders

Another way of achieving a measure of cross-mixing is to modify the shape of the mixing chamber or drum, so that gravitational flow of falling material is directed across the planes of rotational flow. A common arrangement is the double-cone blender (Fig. 3.5), in which the cylindrical section is surmounted at each end by a truncated conical section, though in some designs the central cylindrical section is almost absent. The cylinder and cones need not be of circular cross-section, and square and other sectioned double-cone blenders are available (Fig. 3.6). The relative merits of the different designs is not immediately apparent, and little appears to be known about the flow patterns and detailed mixing mechanisms in these blenders. Presumably, cross-mixing results from gravitational flow of material, directed towards the centre by the inclined surfaces of the lower cone when the blending chamber is at or near to the vertical position, coupled with outward flow as material is tumbled over by the rotational movement of the chamber. It might be interesting to try to observe the flow patterns in a mixer of the double-cone type, since it is not obvious how an outward flow to complement the inward flow due to inclined walls could arise, and one wonders whether, in the absence of additional deflecting devices, material would tend to be confined to the central region of the mixing chamber away from the points of suspension, leaving two outside regions virtually empty of material (Fig. 3.7). Some designs of double-cone blender avoid

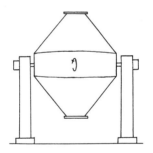 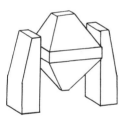 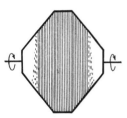

FIG. 3.5. Double-cone blender.   FIG. 3.6 Square-section double-cone blender.   FIG. 3.7. Possible poor circulation in a plain double-cone tumble blender.

this problem by having the mixing chamber rotate eccentrically. Data on tumbling speeds and power requirements in rotation to capacity are available for one range of double-cone blender. Tumbling speeds fall quite rapidly from 40 r.p.m. at a working capacity of 29 litres to around 21 r.p.m. at 1·4 m³ and then fall quite gradually as size increases to a working capacity of 4·25 m³.[10,11] At the same time, power requirements rise in a more linear fashion from 320 W to nearly 4 × 10⁴ W.

3.3.3 *Inclined Cube Blenders*

Another variant on the same theme is the tilted or inclined cube blender, which employs a mixing chamber shaped essentially like a hollow cube, rotating about an axis that passes through a point close to a corner of one face of the cube and a corresponding point near the opposite corner of the opposite face of the cube[7] (Fig. 3.8). This system

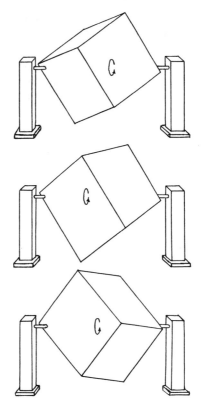

FIG. 3.8. Three positions in the rotation of a tilted cube blender.

seems likely to produce more effective cross-mixing than double-cone blenders, due to the variety of dimensions and inclinations of surfaces by which falling material is likely to be directed during rotation of the mixing chamber, and indeed Adams and Baker[12] found this to be the case in mixing natural and master-batch polyethylene granules.

3.3.4 *Ancillary Features*

In industrial tumble blenders of any size, the simple concept of mixing by a tumbling action is often complemented by additional features to make the machines more effective or versatile. The most important of these are members placed within the mixing chamber in order to deflect flowing material away from vertical flow paths,[13] or to break up agglomerates (Fig. 3.9). For the purpose of deflection, and hence improved cross-mixing, the arrangement usually consists of a number of

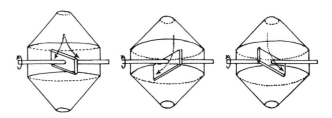

FIG. 3.9. Gardner deflector plate in double-cone blender.

deflector plates inclined at various angles, each attached by an arm to a central axle rotating with, or independently of, the mixing chamber. The breaking down of agglomerates can be aided by incorporating an agitator comprising a number of arms, pins, plain discs, or serrated discs projecting from a central axle rotating at relatively high speeds, i.e. as high as 1000 r.p.m. and upwards.[9] Canted discs running at tip speeds around 15 m/s are effective aids to dispersion.[9]

3.3.5 *Ball Mills*

Break-down of agglomerates or comminution of solid particles can also be achieved by having hard steel, stone, porcelain or the like, balls, tubes, rods or pebbles in the mixing chamber of a tumble blender, usually the circular cylindrical type rotating about its major axis. This is the essential characteristic of the well-known ball mill (Fig. 3.10), pebble mill, or pot mill widely used in the laboratory and in production for grinding resins, pigments and other solids to finer particle size, but also often suitable for the simultaneous blending of solid materials with each other

FIG. 3.10. Principle of the ball mill.

or with liquids. Some pot mills have the mixing/grinding action enhanced by the addition of a vibratory motion to the rotational movement.

3.3.6 Shaking Drum Mixer

In another variation on the tumble blender theme, the drum mixing chamber is submitted to a shaking/rotational action that promotes an intricate three-dimensional pulsating motion through regions of intense turbulence. This device is said to reduce mixing times to a remarkable extent without producing break-down of particles.[14]

3.3.7 Uses of Tumble Blenders

Although primarily used in the polymer industries for dry solids blending, tumble blenders, particularly those of the V-, double-cone, and vibratory types, are sometimes used for liquid/liquid and solid/liquid blending and dispersing. In the latter case, agitators to break down agglomerates may be desirable. For the better distribution of liquid additives, a double-cone blender can include a spray or atomisation system.[9]

Tumble blenders, particularly of the double-cone type, may also be provided with jackets for heating and cooling, and also with arrangements for applying vacuum to the mixing chamber. Both of these are mainly intended to permit removal of moisture from damp constituents, and indeed a blender fitted with these facilities can be used simply as a drier. However, a heating jacket can obviously be used to raise the temperature of liquid additives, thereby reducing viscosity and possibly increasing their rates of absorption by solid particles.

3.4 STIRRER MIXERS

This title is meant to embrace those mixers in which the requisite motions are imparted to the components of a mixture by a suitably shaped member rotating within the composition, usually about a vertical or near vertical axis. As such, it includes mixers known as paddle mixers, propeller mixers, dispersers, pony mixers, planetary mixers, turbine mixers, turbomixers, fluidmixers, intensive non-fluxing mixers, and sometimes just high-speed mixers. The title thus covers a wide variety of machines, whose modes of action are quite different and which may be directed at quite different types of materials. Nevertheless, these machines do possess common features and, although extreme examples may appear to operate in vastly different modes, there are so many minor variations on the theme between the extremes that there appears to be an almost continuous progression of designs from one extreme to the other. All the machines under this heading operate by the stirring or agitating action of an impeller, plate, propeller or some other device attached to a rotating shaft, usually dipping vertically downwards or projecting vertically upwards into the materials to be mixed in a suitable vessel. They differ mainly in the shape, dimensions and number of the devices used to effect agitation, and in the speed of rotation, though other features, such as the shape of the containing vessel, may also differ. As a consequence, mixers of this type vary considerably in the vigour of their mixing actions, the mildest being suitable only for relatively simple operations such as the mixing of two low viscosity liquids or solution of a solid in a low viscosity solvent; while the most intensive can be used for the most difficult of operations such as dry-blending solid and solid/liquid compositions, or dispersing solids into high viscosity liquids.

3.4.1 Paddle Mixers

The simplest and probably the oldest type of mixers within the classification of stirrer mixer, are paddle mixers, widely employed in the chemical industry for chemical reactors, including polymerisation vessels, and stirred mixing tanks. In its most elementary form, the paddle consists of a single plain oblong plate attached at its centre at or near the bottom of a vertical-driven shaft. Where the bottom of the mixing vessel is curved, the paddle may also be curved so as to be more or less parallel to it, this form being commonly known as an 'anchor stirrer'. In spite of the apparent crudity of these simple arrangements, they can be highly effective for many liquid/liquid mixing operations, generally up to viscosities of around $1 \, Ns/m^2$ (1000 cP),[15] and have been used for the preparation of quite complex solid/liquid blends, though in the latter case mixing cycles are rather long. The mixing action of a paddle mixer is dependent on the dimensions of the paddle and of the vessel in which it operates, clearances between paddle and vessel walls being particularly important, and on the speed of rotation. Typically, the paddle will extend to between 66 and 90% of the diameter of the vessel, and will rotate at between 15 and 45 r.p.m., though higher speeds are not uncommon. Mixing in a paddle mixer occurs mainly in eddies or regions of turbulence close to the edges and tips of the paddle blade, their intensity and extent depending on the rheological properties of the materials, the clearances between the paddle and the walls of the vessel, and the linear speeds of the paddle at different points along its diameter, the latter obviously being dependent on the diameter and speed of rotation of the paddle. There must also be some shear mixing of material between the stationary walls of the vessel and the moving paddle, but this does not appear to be considered to be a major factor in mixers of this type. Circulation of material largely arises from the pushing action of the paddle and consequent centrifugal movement of material diametrically outwards and upwards at the vessel wall, and then inwards and downwards near the surface of the material. At higher speeds of rotation, say over 100 r.p.m., this centrifugal action may become so intense as to develop a vortex. If this is undesirable the mixer may be fitted with one or more baffles, usually vertical oblong plates fitted to the vessel walls. Increased mixing and circulation may be provided by having more than one paddle blade. Thus, one or more additional blade may be attached to the drive shaft at locations above the main paddle. This is particularly desirable in large, tall vessels. Another arrangement is to have a number of blades placed at equal angles around the shaft at the same level.

Another variation on the paddle mixer theme is to have two shafts and paddles rotating in the same mixing vessel. Usually the latter will be in the form of a figure-of-eight, with one paddle rotating in each half of the mixing chamber. This arrangement is not merely a convenient way of scaling up, but offers the possibility of overlapping the paths of movement of the paddles so as to increase the mixing action by turbulence or shear (Fig. 3.11).

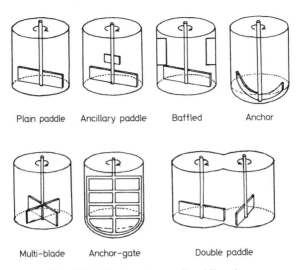

FIG. 3.11. Various types of paddle mixer.

3.4.2 Propeller Mixers and Dispersers

From the paddle mixer, it is only a short conceptual step to the idea of a propeller mixer (Fig. 3.12), in which a marine or aircraft type propeller is mounted at the lower end of a shaft rotating at speeds generally

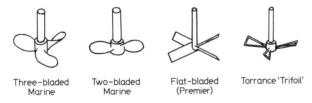

FIG. 3.12. Some types of propeller mixer impeller.

between 440 and 2400 r.p.m., corresponding to peripheral velocities of 5–15 m/s.[15] In some models, one or two additional propellers may be mounted on the same shaft. The mixing action results from axial flow of material actuated by the propeller, and helical turbulent flow of the components arising from a radial velocity gradient in strata at different distances from the propeller. It is very sensitive to shape and the location of the propeller within the mixing vessel, and a convex shaped bottom is preferred.[15] At high speeds, the whole of the materials being blended tend to swirl around the mixing chamber and a vortex forms. The depth of vortex is directly proportional to the speed of rotation and inversely proportional to the density and viscosity of the system.[15] Propeller mixers are suitable for rapid mixing of systems having viscosities up to $2 \, Ns/m^2$ (2000 cP), and for forming suspensions of solid particles up to about 0·5 mm in diameter, providing the solids content of the system is fairly low, i.e. not above 10%. Sometimes a propeller mixer is fitted with a 'draft' tube around the propeller, thus essentially converting it to a pump that circulates material through the agitated region around the propeller, and can be used to direct flow of material to regions of the mixing chamber that might otherwise tend to be stagnant.

The term disperser is applied somewhat indiscriminately to a wide variety of machines of greater or lesser complexity, and appears to be related more to the functions for which the machines have been intended rather than to details of design. However, the design of most dispersers (Fig. 3.13) appears to be derived from the basic principle of propeller

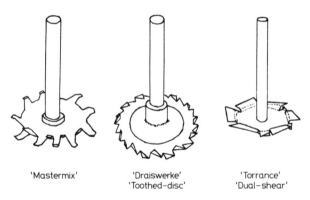

'Mastermix'   'Draiswerke'   'Torrance'
                     'Toothed-disc'   'Dual-shear'

FIG. 3.13. Some types of 'disperser' impeller.

mixers, but the theoretical basis, if any, on which a particular design has been arrived at is not usually obvious. Some, indeed, have impellers that are scarcely distinguishable from propeller blades. A common form consists of a circular disc with various appendages around the circumference, one particular design being essentially similar to a circular saw blade. Others ought to be called, perhaps more properly, turbine mixers (Fig. 3.14). These are supposed to have been developed from water

FIG. 3.14. Various types of turbine impeller.

turbines, acting similarly to a centrifugal pump working in a vessel against negligible back-pressure, and mixing by entrainment and discharge of material by the turbine blades.[15,21,22] One well-known form of disperser has a mixing impeller that is essentially a turbine impeller, rotating within a circular screen with holes that can be in a variety of forms.[23,24] Material is drawn up at the centre region of the impeller, thrown out radially, and expelled through the holes in the screen into the main body of material (Fig. 3.15). Rotational speed of turbine mixers is usually in the range of 120–200 r.p.m., with peripheral tip velocities around 3–10 m/s. Turbine mixers can be used for a variety of dispersing and mixing operations on liquids of a wide variation in viscosity, e.g. up to 200 Ns/m^2 (200 000 cP), and solids up to a particle size of 2·5 mm in diameter, but they are not generally so effective with pastes and doughs, though they can be used for these materials.[25]

3.4.3 Planetary Mixers

Planetary mixers (Fig. 3.16) are essentially paddle mixers in which the impeller shaft not only rotates in the normal way, but also moves in a circular path around the vertical centre line of the mixing vessel.

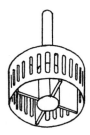

FIG. 3.15. Principle of the Silverson mixing head.

FIG. 3.16. Mode of agitator in a planetary mixer.

Commonly, the mixing vessel also rotates, in which case the mixer may be known as a pony mixer. A variety of types of agitator are available for planetary mixers and these are very often interchangeable on one machine, although selection of the most appropriate type of agitator often seems arbitrary and is determined by experience rather than on the basis of any basic scientific principles. Some models have two separate agitators on independent shafts, while others have a number of agitators on shafts carried on a single mixing head (Fig. 3.17). Planetary mixers are

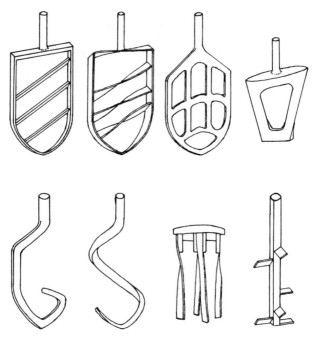

FIG. 3.17. Some types of planetary mixer agitator 'tool'.

commonly provided with a range of speed gears to that the mixing action, particularly generation of frictional heat, can be matched to particular mixing requirements. Planetary mixers are suitable for mixing dispersions, such as pastes and plastisols, but can also be used for solid/solid blending, provided that differences in density between the components of the composition are not too great. Power consumption for pastes and doughs is likely to be around 0·3 W/kg (40 h.p./ton).[6]

3.5 INTENSIVE NON-FLUXING MIXERS

Although this title[9] is not a widely used one for the type of mixer to be discussed in this section, it has been selected because it is less ambiguous or misleading than the commonly used terms, such as fluidmixer, fluidising mixer, turbomixer, high intensity mixer, dry disperser, high speed turbomixer, turbo rapid mixer, or merely rapid mixer or high-speed mixer. The lay-out of a mixer of this type is essentially the same as that of the paddle mixers, propeller mixers and turbine mixers of the previous section, but whereas the impeller shafts of these latter types are usually driven by geared or direct drive from above the mixing chamber, and may indeed be separable therefrom, in the present class of mixer the drive is almost invariably transmitted through the bottom of the mixing chamber (Fig. 3.18). However, the main difference is that the impellers of

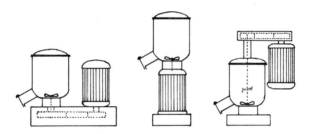

FIG. 3.18. Drive arrangements for intensive non-fluxing mixers.

intensive non-fluxing mixers are rotated at considerably higher speeds than is normal for stirrer mixers, with rotor tip speeds of between 20 and 50 m/s. Consequently, the flow and other conditions during the mixing processes differ markedly. Since the differences result in performance that has led to the widespread use of this type of machine for all types of blending operation in the polymer industries, fairly detailed discussion seems appropriate and justifies separate treatment.

The essential characteristic of intensive non-fluxing mixers (Fig. 3.19) is that movement of the ingredients is brought about by a rotor or impeller, rotating at such high speeds that the materials are thrown outwards centrifugally at high velocity, are forced upwards by impingement on the walls of the mixing chamber, and then flow downwards towards the centre of the rotor. Movement is so rapid that even particulate solids behave like liquids,[26] with a vortex forming at the

FIG. 3.19. Combined non-fluxing intensive mixer and cooler (courtesy of Dierks and Söhne, Osnabrück).

upper surface of the material (Fig. 3.20). Hence the names fluidmixer and fluidising mixer. Mixing rates are usually exceedingly high, and as a result of heat developed by friction the temperature rises progressively. Consequently, mixing cycles are quite short, varying generally from a few minutes up to 20 min or so depending on the nature of the composition. This necessitates precise control and rapid discharge. Although jackets for heating or cooling may be fitted, it is generally not good practice to cool the mixture while still in the mixer, and on any scale of production it is usual to discharge into a simple cooled paddle mixer at the end of the mixing cycle (Fig. 3.21). Control is usually based on temperature recorded by a thermocouple mounted in a probe mounted in the lid of the mixer and extending downwards into the circulating material. All but the simplest installations include an automatic control system that can be preset to open the discharge port pneumatically at a predetermined temperature. The discharge port is so located that the mixed material is thrown out centrifugally by the action of the impeller rotor and passes directly to the associated cooling mixer. Operation by hand is less reproducible and should only be used where the cost of an automatic

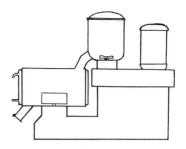

FIG. 3.20. Flow in an intensive non-fluxing mixer.

FIG. 3.21. Combined mixing and cooling unit.

control system would be prohibitive in relation to the scale of the operation.

The main difference between one model of intensive non-fluxing mixer and another is in the design of the impellers, agitators, or rotors, of which quite a variety has developed from the original propeller type (Fig. 3.22). Most manufacturers offer a range to suit the requirements of different compositions. Frequently, the single impeller is replaced by two or even more that may rotate as a unit, or in some cases independently in the same or in opposite directions. Thus, for dry colouring of granules the simpler forms (e.g. (b), (c) and (d)), possibly running at relatively slow speeds (e.g. only a few hundred r.p.m.), may be recommended because relatively low shear is called for. Nevertheless, other more complicated types of impeller may also be recommended for the same operation (e.g. (m) for dry colouring of nylon). In some models (e.g. (h), (i) and (j)), there is a scraper tool rotating close to the bottom of the mixing chamber with one or more impellers arranged above it. The horn-shaped upper impeller seen in some machines (e.g. (i), (j) and (k)) is said to improve vortex circulation, particularly with high charges, while the flat upper impellers seen on others (e.g. (h)) is claimed to be more appropriate for plastisols and powdered rubbers. A change in shape to a bent horn-shaped rotor (e.g. (i)) apparently offers the possibility of blending chopped film scrap. Sometimes the upper impellers serve to break down agglomerates, but the different modes of action of the various types of impeller are not always clear. The ring-shaped upper member of some models (e.g. (m)) for example is referred to as a 'vortex top rotor', or a 'rotary suction blade', but it is not obvious what its contribution is either to circulation

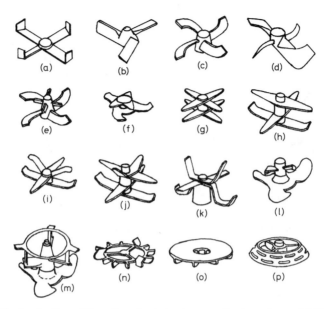

FIG. 3.22. A selection of impellers for intensive non-fluxing mixers. (a) Vaterland (Neuenrade). (b) Diosna (Dierks and Sohne) (Osnabruck). (c) Fielder (Eastleigh); Werner and Pfleiderer (Stuttgart). (d) Henschel (Kassel). (e) Fielder; Werner and Pfleiderer. (f) Meccanische (Busto Arsizio). (g) Diosna (Dierks and Sohne). (h), (i) and (j) Henschel. (k) Diosna (Dierks and Sohne). (l) Papenmeier (Detmold). (m) Papenmeier; Werner and Pfleiderer.(o) Ref. 2. (p) Chemica (Wohlen).

or to fluidisation, or indeed to vortex formation. Nevertheless, this design is claimed[27] to provide improved dispersion, particularly with ingredients that tend to 'ball-up'. It also permits more rapid temperature rises and hence shorter cycles, e.g. 20–130°C in 8–9 min.

In addition to interchangeability of impellers in some intensive non-fluxing mixers, the heights of the various members making up the impeller system can be adjusted in relation to each other and in relation to the bottom of the mixing chamber. Most models have lids that can be hermetically sealed so that vacuum can be applied in order to remove volatiles, such as monomers and water during mixing.

The operating procedure for an intensive non-fluxing mixer depends to some extent on the particular design, but depends very much on the nature of the components to be blended. Some illustrative cases are discussed in Chapter 7.

In recent years the use of intensive non-fluxing mixers has increased considerably, and there is no doubt that they can produce satisfactory blends in short mixing cycles from many types of solid/solid, and also solid/liquid compositions, e.g. plasticised PVC, both dry blends and plastisols. When dry-blending with liquid components, these are preferably introduced by means of a spray into the circulating solids. If large quantities of filler are also included, it is probably best to add them after the liquid has been thoroughly distributed throughout the bulk of solid polymer, otherwise appreciable proportions of liquid may be absorbed by the filler particles, and effectively prevent it from making its proper contribution to modification of polymer properties.

Power requirements for mixers of this type naturally depend on the size of machine, the design of the impellers, the nature of the components to be blended and on the charge size, but are typically in the region of 130–200 W/kg. Sizes are usually designated in terms of nominal and useful volumetric capacity, though for a given size the latter is dependent on the nature of the composition being blended. Nominal sizes range from small laboratory models of a few litres capacity up to as much as 2300 litres (2·3 m³). Useful capacity can be as low as 50 % and as high as 90 % of nominal, depending on the composition and on the estimation of the nominal capacity, and in any cost estimations it is vital that the true useful capacity for intended mixing operation should be known. The relatively small sizes of mixers of this type are, of course, compensated by the short cycle times, so that larger capacities would rarely, if ever, be of value.

Recent years have seen the introduction of less vigorous mixers of the intensive, non-fluxing type,[28] in which lower impeller speeds are employed, i.e. peripheral speeds of 6–12 m/s. These are particularly recommended for materials that are sensitive to shear and heat, especially some colourants used for dry-blending with granules. For blending high concentrations of pigment, this type of mixer may be fitted with an additional high-shear homogenising/granulating tool located at a position up the vertical side of the mixing chamber.[28]

3.6 RIBBON BLENDERS AND RELATED MIXERS

Ribbon blenders have long been used in the baking and agricultural industries, and were among the earliest machines to have been used for polymer/solid additive blending and for solid polymer blending with liquids where the liquid concentration has been sufficiently low for relatively dry mixes to result, but models are now available for blending pastes and slurries. In basic design, the ribbon blender (Fig. 3.23) comprises a trough-like mixing chamber inside which one or more ribbon-like blades, usually carried on a horizontal rotating shaft, agitate the contents of the chamber by a combined lifting and longitudinal

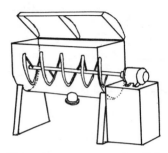

FIG. 3.23. General arrangement of a ribbon blender.

transfer action. As with other types of mixer, the main variation in design is in the shapes and arrangements of the agitators. In the simplest form, the ribbon blade consists of a single strip of metal held in a pitched spiral form around the drive shaft, i.e. something like the thread of a screw with a spiral of thrust face adjacent the root removed. For ease of construction, the spiral may be segmented into separate blades, but the principle remains the same. Because the spiral is pitched in relation to the drive shaft rotation, it imparts vertical and horizontal components of motion into material as it is lifted to a point at which gravity tends to return it vertically downwards. However, because the mixing chamber is generally charged to a level well above that of the drive shaft, material interaction leads to more complex flow paths that appear to lead to shear and eddies.[29] In order to increase the mixing action, two or more separate sets of blades may be provided, pitched so as to impart longitudinal movement in the opposite direction to that of the main blade.[7] There seems to be some logic in designing the ribbon blades (Fig. 3.24) so that there tends to be a net movement towards the outlet of the machine, so as to facilitate the discharge operation, but the outlet valve is commonly located at the centre of the bottom of the trough, irrespective of ribbon design. In some smaller models, the outlet valve is omitted and discharge is achieved by tilting the whole mixing chamber about an axis parallel to the ribbon drive shaft. A few manufacturers also offer

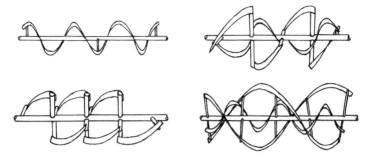

FIG. 3.24. Some ribbon blender blade arrangements.

machines with two sets of ribbons mounted on parallel drive shafts in a W-shaped mixing trough. As well as increasing the capacity, this arrangement can lead to more complex flow patterns and more efficient mixing by virtue of the interaction between the two sets of ribbons.

Ribbon blenders may be obtained with tight-sealing lids so that vacuum can be applied to remove moisture and other volatiles, and may also have jackets for heating and cooling. For heating purposes, the jacket may be located so that only the lower regions of the mixing trough are heated, thus reducing the risk of forming a crust of softened material on the inside surfaces near the upper surfaces of the blended materials. The mixing action of a ribbon blender is relatively gentle and consequently little frictional heat is generated. For this reason, cooling is rarely necessary unless the material has been previously heated either in a separate blender, e.g. an intensive non-fluxing mixer, or in the ribbon blender itself. Where heating and cooling is required, two-tier arrangements are available, comprising an upper blender for heating, discharging into a lower blender beneath it for cooling. A two-tier or 'piggy-back' arrangement is also appropriate for continuous blending, for, since mixing in ribbon blenders is usually relatively slow, a single trough would have to be inordinately long for a reasonable output to be attained. Nevertheless, single-trough continuous ribbon blenders are available and suitable for some operations because of their relatively low cost.

The working capacity of a ribbon blender in relation to the total capacity of its mixing trough depends on its geometry, and particularly on the height of its vertical walls in relation to the swept volume of the ribbons. Generally, it may be taken that the working volume is bounded at its upper surface by a horizontal plane just above the topmost reach of the swept volume, and may amount to as little as 40 or as much as 70% of the total capacity. Ribbon blenders are available in a very wide range of sizes, i.e. from as little as 1 to 14 000 litres (14 m^3). Power requirements vary with the nature of the materials and the size of machine, but are considerably less than that for similar sizes of intensive non-fluxing mixers. Ratings in relation to working volume vary from as little as 3 to as much as 40 W/litre or kW/m^3.

As competitors with other forms of blending machine, the main attraction of ribbon blenders is their generally relatively low cost. Longitudinal movement of materials tends to be limited and components of markedly different density to other components tend to congregate towards the bottom of the mixing chamber.[30] Ribbon blenders are also not too easy to clean, and this is particularly a problem with sticky materials such as some plasticised PVC compositions. Mixing cycles are liable to be comparatively lengthy with difficult compositions, particularly if heating and cooling are included.

3.6.1 *Inverted Cone and Screw Mixers*

Related to the ribbon blender, is the inverted cone and screw mixer,[6,7,29] in which the mixing chamber is essentially an inverted cone and the mixing tool is usually an Archimedean type screw or auger, rotating in such a way that it raises material up the inside surface of the cone. In the most common form used for blending polymers, the screw which is driven at its upper end, runs in a bearing which is mounted on a radial arm rotating in a more or less horizontal plane around the vertical axis of the mixer, so that the screw progresses in cycles around the inside inclined surface of the mixing chamber. Material raised by the screw eventually slides downwards over the surface of the material rising behind it, so that a constantly changing raised heap moves round the mixing chamber with the screw. Variants on the basic arrangement include constructing the mixing chamber in the form of two, or indeed more, interconnected inverted cones, each with its own screw, and, secondly, providing two screws in one conical chamber (Fig. 3.25). In another variation, the upper bearing of the screw is given an epicyclic movement so that the screw traverses the central as well as the outer regions of the mixing chamber. These types of mixer are used for dry-blending, pre-blending and plastisol production,[9] and are remarkably effective even with quite difficult compositions such as filled plasticised

PVC. Like other types of mixer, they can be provided with jackets for heating and cooling, and may have facilities for the application of vacuum and for spraying liquids onto the moving bed of solid particles. A form of cone and screw mixer that is perhaps more clearly related to the ribbon blender is the 'ribbon screw mixer', in which the Archimedean screw of the original type is replaced by two concentric ribbon screws spiralling in opposite directions, so that they have opposite directions of transportation (Fig. 3.26). This form of mixer is said to be particularly

 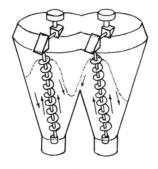 

FIG. 3.25. Single and double-cone and screw mixers.   FIG. 3.26. Cone and ribbon screw mixer.

suited for rapid mixing of viscous liquids and pastes, and for breaking down of agglomerates of fine particle solids such as fillers.

Cone and screw mixers require relatively low drive power, and come in a wide range of sizes from as small as 50 litres up to as large as 100 000 litres (100 m^3).

3.6.2 Auger Mixers

A mixer of somewhat similar principle to the cone and screw arrangement, originally used for agricultural purposes, but now developed for polymer blending, comprises a vertical auger (Fig. 3.27) which raises material up a tube that surrounds it. On reaching the top of the tube the material cascades down the side of the mixing chamber, eventually to re-enter the auger at the bottom of an inverted cone section of the mixing chamber. Additional agitation may be attained by 'booster worms' in the conical section near the bottom end of the vertical tube.

3.7 Z-BLADE AND RELATED DOUBLE-ARM MIXERS

'Z-blade' or 'sigma-blade mixers', or kneaders,[7] get their name from the shape of the two mixing blades of the original design. They have long been used for mixing dispersions, such as paints and pastes of viscosities up to several million centipoises,[9] but a variety of forms of mixing blade have been developed that make this type of mixer eminently suitable for dry powder and other blending. Several of the designs now available have rotor blades that bear little obvious resemblance to Zs or sigmas and are, therefore, sometimes referred to as 'double-arm mixers', or 'parallel shaft mixers',[31] but the fact that they are clearly based on the same principle makes it convenient to consider them as one class. This type of mixer has also occasionally been referred to as an internal mixer, but this term is best restricted to compounding machines, e.g. of the Banbury type.

In its basic form, a Z-blade mixer comprises a W-shaped or double trough, in each half of which rotates a Z-shaped or sigma-shaped rotor blade. Usually the blades rotate in opposite directions downwards into the region between the two troughs, but in some machines they rotate in the same direction (Fig. 3.28). Quite commonly, the blades rotate at

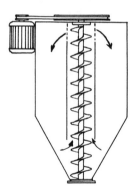 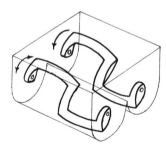

FIG. 3.27. Vertical auger in tube mixer.

FIG. 3.28. General arrangement of a Z-blade mixer.

different speeds up to a speed ratio of as much as 3:1. The blades may overlap or sweep tangential paths. In the former case, the blades usually rotate at equal speeds of necessity, although this restriction does not apply to some overlapping designs, e.g. 'multi-wing' and 'bear-claw'.[9] With tangential designs a speed ratio of 1·5:1 between the blades is typical. At first sight, it might be thought that overlapping designs should have a better mixing action than tangential, but this is not necessarily so because the latter form permits a higher ridge or 'saddle' between the two halves of the trough.

The various designs of blades have generally been developed with specific mixing operations in view, although any particular type is usually capable of mixing compositions differing quite markedly from those for which it was originally designed (Fig. 3.29). Thus, the basic Z- or

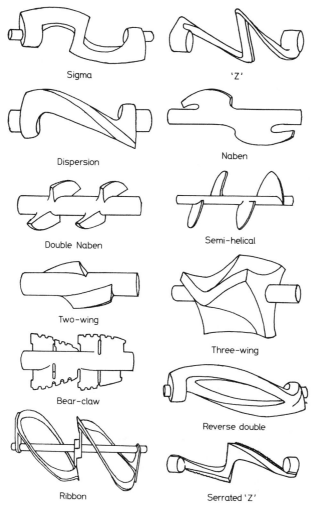

Sigma

'Z'

Dispersion

Naben

Double Naben

Semi-helical

Two-wing

Three-wing

Bear-claw

Reverse double

Ribbon

Serrated 'Z'

FIG. 3.29. Various types of parallel shaft mixer blades.

sigma[9,10,15,32-35] blade is commonly referred to as a 'general purpose' design. The 'single curve dispersion' blade[9,10,15,32,33] provides a shearing action across the face of the blades and between blades and side walls and bottom, and is reputed to be particularly suited to dispersing colourants in viscous media, and for production of aqueous rubber dispersions. Its action would normally be considered too intensive for powders. 'Naben' type blades[10,15] are recommended for heavy-duty mixing in small machines while 'double Naben' blades[9,10,15,33] perform the same function in large machines. A similar function is the intended purpose for the 'two-wing' blade.[10] The 'three-wing' rotor[10,15] bears little obvious resemblance to a Z or sigma and is more like the rotors of some internal mixers. Indeed, it is specifically intended for mastication of rubbers and mixing rubber stocks with fillers or solvents, and appears to be more commonly used in internal mixers (Chapter 4, Section 4.3.1). For mixing dry powders, slurries or low-viscosity pastes ribbon-like blades[10] may be used, although general-purpose Z-blades have been used satisfactorily for these purposes. The basic design has also been adapted to accommodate fibrous material by providing the blades with serrations,[33] or by having double blades on each rotor[10,15] also possibly provided with serrations to assist in shredding the fibrous material.

A superficially different design, that nevertheless seems to operate on essentially similar principles to the conventional Z-blade mixer, has two 'claw' type blades rotating in opposite directions at slightly different speeds on the same axis within a cylindrical trough.[33] This arrangement is said to be particularly designed for mixing of viscous pastes and slurries. With compositions that start with lumpy ingredients or tend to form lumps during mixing, one of the claw blades may be replaced by agitator bars to break the lumps down (Fig. 3.30).

The mixing chambers of Z-blade mixers may be jacketed for heating and cooling purposes, and in heavy duty machines the rotors may be cored for the same purposes. The lids may be sealable sufficiently for vacuum to be applied to remove moisture and other volatiles. Discharge arrangements are of three general types. Smaller models are generally discharged by tipping the whole of the mixing chamber about the axis of one of the rotors, and this arrangement is even used in some quite large machines. More commonly larger machines are fitted with discharge ports in the bottom of the mixing chamber. An alternative arrangement (Fig. 3.31) is to have an opening at the bottom of the mixing chamber leading directly to a discharge screw that runs in reverse during the mixing process, thus aiding the mixing process,[36] and runs forward to convey the mixed material away on completion of the mixing

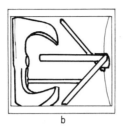

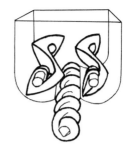

FIG. 3.30. (a) Claw type blades. (b) Claw and agitator bars.

FIG. 3.31. Z-blade mixer with extruder discharge.

cycle.[7,10,33,34] The screw may be a simple conveyor or may be designed to compress the mixture and force it out through a die.[33]

Machines of the Z-blade type are manufactured in a wide range of sizes from small laboratory models up to working capacities over $10\,m^3$ (10 000 litres). As well as variations in size, different machines of essentially the same type differ in the precise geometry of their rotor blades, in particular the areas of the thrust faces and their curvatures, and thus in the effectiveness of their mixing actions. Speeds also differ, being typically of the order of 35 r.p.m. in smaller models and becoming progressively slower with increase in size to around 10 r.p.m. or even less in the larger sizes. The drive power provided depends on the design of the blades and on the nature of the composition to be mixed, and may be as little as $10\,000\,W/m^3$ and as high as $300\,000\,W/m^3$.

3.8 PLOUGH MIXERS

There are a few single-shaft machines that bear a superficial resemblance to the ribbon blenders of Section 3.6, but whose action is more akin to that of the double-arm mixers of Section 3.7. This arises partly from the design of their mixing elements and partly by virtue of the speed of rotation. In the 'true' plough mixer (Fig. 3.32), plough-shaped shovels are attached to the rotor shaft by means of arms, in such an orientation that during their upward passage they throw material upwards and longitudinally into the space above the bulk of the mixing material.[9,37-39] A rate of 2 r.p.m. is typical. In other machines of essentially the same principle, the ploughs are replaced by skewed blades that perform a similar function. One such machine[40] has supports for the blades so arranged

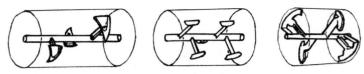

FIG. 3.32. Plough mixer and variants.

that they throw material outwards in a counter-current arrangement to the blades themselves. Some machines of this type include perforated plates through which material is forced by the action of the ploughs, thus increasing the shear mixing action and reducing agglomeration.[15,37,38] Other modifications that some machines of this type may have comprise stationary pegs or lugs on the inside casing of the mixing chamber, or dispersing blades rotating at high speeds, in similar locations. Both these arrangements increase the shear action and help break down agglomerates. Like most mixers discussed in previous sections, these machines may be provided with jackets for heating and cooling. They appear to be applicable to a variety of different types of composition including cold and hot blending of PVC; dry colouring and blending of lubricants into polyethylene, PVC, ABS and other polymers; blending of thermosetting compositions such as filled PF and UF; blending of reinforced thermoplastics; and even plastisol production. Mixers of this type come in a range of working capacities from under 3 litres to over 6 m^3 (6000 litres). Continuous versions are also available.

3.9 AIR AND FLUIDISED BED MIXERS

A number of different arrangements are possible for mixing liquids by agitation with air bubbles or using air-lift,[15] but these are only suitable where the liquids are not adversely affected by air, and where viscosities are relatively low[41] (0.2 Ns/m^2 or 200 cP). Solids, particularly powders, can, however, be blended by forms of fluidisation. This is accomplished either by means of a conventional porous plate or by air cyclones.[7] In the former case, the operation is batch-wise, and the air is supplied intermittently so that the powdered solids alternately fluidise and settle. Obviously, the solids have to be of size and density suitable for fluidising, and different components should not differ too much in these respects.

Where fluidisation is achieved by cyclone devices, the systems may be batch-wise or continuous. Typcially, the mixing cycle consists of a few blasts of air of 1 or 2 s duration, interspersed with settling intervals of a few seconds, and may be complete in under 1 min.[42] A development from the cyclone type mixer permits continuous metering of solid into a turbulent cyclone region with simultaneous continuous metered spraying of liquid additive.[42,43] Blending of solid particles with liquid alters their buoyancy characteristics so that blended material leaves the mixing chamber at its lower end.

A somewhat different arrangement[44] specifically designed for producing dry-blends from powders with liquid or solid additives, e.g. PVC with plasticisers and/or stabilisers and lubricants, consists of a continuous vertical tubular circuit into which solids are fed via a hopper, and around which the powder is circulated by turbulent air flow while any liquid is introduced through a separate pipe. Coarser particles tend to hug the outer wall of the tubular circuit while the finer particles tend to travel closer to the inner wall, whence they can be withdrawn via an outlet tube and into a cyclone or some other separator.

3.10 TOROIDAL MIXERS

A fairly recent innovation to polymer blending has been the introduction of the Evans and Ryder 'toroidal' mixer[45-47] (Fig. 3.33) previously used

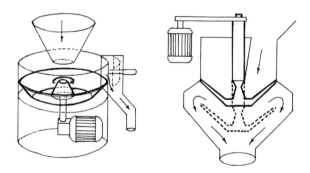

FIG. 3.33. Toroidal mixers.

for specialised treatment of feed grains, e.g. coating wheat and barley with fungicides and insecticides.[46] 'Toroidal' is intended to describe the spiralling, rotating motion imparted to the particles to achieve the mixing action. This is achieved by means of what is essentially a 'moat-shaped' dished rotor, rotating at high speed within a stationary circular cylindrical chamber. The mixing region is thus defined by the uninterrupted form of the rotor and the inner walls of the chamber, there being no blades or other tools in the working space to break up fragile particles or provide regions of stagnation. The centrifugal action of the rotor throws the solid particles outwards in much the same way as the rotor of an intensive non-fluxing mixer (Section 3.5). Indeed, it would be reasonable to include the toroidal mixers under the latter heading. Be that as it may, the particles impinge on the stationary wall of the cylindrical chamber to be deflected in a variety of directions and speeds. Within the spiralling, rotating mass, particles travel at different speeds and undergo changes in direction and speed as a result of collisions, so that mixing is very rapid. The rotor is usually kept in constant rotation during operation, the components to be mixed being fed in from above and the mixture being discharged by the centrifugal action on opening a door or port in the stationary wall. In an alternative arrangement, the whole rotor can be lowered so that mixed material is discharged into a receiving chamber below the mixing chamber. Because of the rapidity of mixing, the dimensions of a toroidal mixer can be relatively small for any given required rate of production. Thus, an output of over 15 000 kg/h has been claimed for a machine only 0·76 m in diameter.[46] For the same reason, a continuous mixer (Fig. 3.34) using the toroidal principle is eminently feasible, but accurate metering of the components is essential if they are to be metered in separately.

Toroidal mixers are claimed[46] to be effective with any free-flowing particles, irrespective of size, shape or density, including powder, masterbatch and dry-blending. They are particularly suited to compositions containing components whose particle structure needs to be preserved, e.g. glass fibre. They are also said to be particularly effective in distributing small quantities of solid or liquid additives uniformly throughout a composition, and there is no reason why they should not be equally effective with compositions including relatively large proportions of liquid, provided that absorption within polymer particles is sufficient to maintain free-flowing behaviour, e.g. plasticised PVC dry-blends. At the time of writing, these machines are available in sizes ranging from 25 to 100 kg/charge. Power consumption is up to 5 kW.

3.11 BUSS CONTINUOUS TURBINE MIXER

The manufacturers of the well-known 'Ko-kneader' have introduced what they term a 'mixing turbine type MT' developed for the production of solutions, suspensions and emulsions of viscosities up to $1000\,Ns/m^2$ $(10^6\,cP)$,[48,49] including polymer solutions for spinning, PVC plastisols and pigment dispersions in plasticisers. The design principle of this machine is extremely simple, a vertical cyclindrical mixing chamber with stator rings spaced up its inside wall (Fig. 3.35). A vertical shaft within

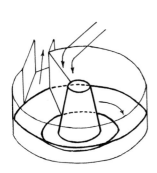

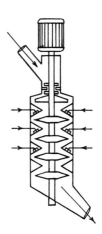

FIG. 3.34. Continuous toroidal mixer.   FIG. 3.35. Buss continuous
turbine mixer.

the mixing chamber, rotating at speeds between 2900 and 7500 r.p.m., carries circular discs that extend into the corresponding circular grooves between the stator rings. At the upper end of the mixing chamber, is a narrower cylinder with a rather similar arrangement of stator and rotor discs for fluidisation and milling of solid components. Liquid components are sprayed in through nozzles at the underside of the stator rings. Interaction between the rapidly rotating rotor discs and the stator rings is said to produce repeated acceleration and deceleration of the components, the consequent shear resulting in rapid dispersion and homogenisation without undue work on, or heating of the materials. Power consumption appears to vary from 26–30 kJ/kg for pigment/plasticiser and similar dispersions to 54–63 kJ/kg for PVC plastisols.

3.12 COLLOID, DISC AND PIN MILLS, ETC.

The terminology applied to the mixers under this loose heading is as confused as the details of construction of the machines is varied, but the main function for which they have been developed is generally the same, namely the dispersion of powdered solids into liquid media, especially pigment dispersions (Fig. 3.36). Colloid, disc and pin mills are usually continuous in operation, sharing the common feature that pre-blended material is fed into a dispersing zone of relatively small volume, where

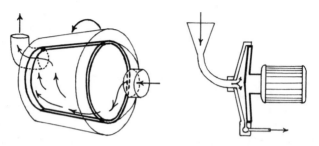

FIG. 3.36. Cylindrical and disc type colloid mills.

intensive shear is produced by rapid rotation of a rotary member in close proximity to a stator. One form of colloid mill comprises a hollow circular cylinder that rotates rapidly around a concentric cylinder.[7] Material is fed in at one end, experiences intensive shear by virtue of the small clearance between the rotor and stator cylinders, and is discharged at the far end. Intensity of shearing obviously depends on the speed of rotation, the clearance, and the viscous behaviour of the material under treatment.

The disc type of colloid mill[15] is based on essentially the same principle, but employs two circular discs instead of cylinders. Material is fed into the centre of the space between the discs and leaves tangentially under the action of the centrifugal forces arising from the rapid rotation of the rotor disc (e.g. 3000–15 000 r.p.m., 60–70 m/s peripheral speed). This arrangement is more versatile than concentric cylinders in that the discs can be flat or dished, or indeed of any other appropriate configuration not too removed from the circular disc form, and in that adjustment of the clearance between between the two discs is relatively easy to arrange. In pin mills and similar machines, projections resembling stubby pins or lugs are attached to one or both discs. A somewhat similar principle is used in the well-known 'Oakes' mixer,[50,51] which comprises a rotor carrying concentric rows of projecting blades rotating between two stators that also carry concentric rows of blades. By injecting compressed air into the feed stock just before it enters the mixing zone, this type of mixing mill can be used to produce mechanical foams from rubber latex or PVC plastisols.

The working volume of colloid mills is rather small, and they are reputed to have limited mixing action, but, as Fisher and Chard[7] have pointed out, these limitations do not apply when supplied with previously prepared bulk mixes. Moreover, it is possible to combine a disc or pin mill with a bulk container so that the mill is highly efficient in agitating and dispersing the bulk mixture.

3.13 BEAD MILLS, ETC.

Bead mills are superficially similar to ball mills[15] in that dispersion of solids in liquid media is aided by the grinding action of hard balls, but these are generally much smaller than those used in ball mills, and, indeed, are so small as to be generally designated as 'beads'. These may be of hardened steel, but are more commonly of silica-quartz or steatite. In other respects, bead mills scarcely resemble ball mills at all, differing in three major respects. Thus, the required motions are not achieved by rotation of the mixing chamber, which is stationary, but by rotation of agitators within the chamber and generally at much higher speeds (e.g. up to peripheral speeds of 20 m/s) than would be typical for a ball mill. Also, the grinding elements, or beads, may occupy a much higher proportion (up to 85 %) of the volume of the mixing chamber. Because of the resultant intensive shear, it may be necessary to remove heat generated by friction, and bead mills are therefore usually jacketed for circulation of cooling water. Like ball mills, bead mills are available as batch machines, but continuous models are possibly more common. Some forms of batch machines (Fig. 3.37) employ circulation systems.[20]

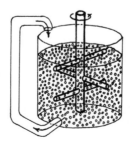

FIG. 3.37. Batch bead mill with circulation system.

In one such, material is forced from the bottom of the mixing chamber by the action of the agitator, passed up a conveying pipe and returned to the top of the mixing chamber. For larger batches, the material may be circulated between mill and a relatively large holding vessel. In continuous machines (Fig. 3.38), the material is usually pumped through the

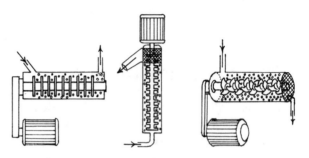

FIG. 3.38. Continuous bead mills.

mixing chamber, which may be mounted vertically or horizontally. Various forms of agitator are available,[18,20,40] and there is some scope for matching the design to the material to be processed. Thus, the agitator may consist simply of a shaft carrying spaced discs or projecting rods or lugs, but more complicated designs with propeller like agitators are also available.[18] The product is separated from the dispersion medium by passing through a screen or through a gap narrow enough to exclude passage of the beads.

Bead mills are suitable for solid in liquid dispersions, e.g. pigment dispersions and PVC plastisols, typically up to viscosities of around $5 \, Ns/m^2$ (5000 cP). Throughputs range from as little as 4 to over 5000 litres/h. Power requirements appear to depend widely on the particular design of machine and on the nature of the materials to be processed, varying from 0·5 to 4·5 J/m^3.

3.14 MULLERS AND PUG MILLS

These machines are primarily designed for dispersion of solids that tend to agglomerate, and are mainly of interest to polymer processers for the dispersion of pigments in liquid media. The basic design comprises a horizontal circular pan inside which there are one or two milling cylinders.[20] These cylinders may be located with vertical axes, in which case the machine may be referred to as a 'side-runner' mill, or with horizontal axes, when the term 'edge-runner' mill may be applied[12] (Fig. 3.39). Commonly, both milling cylinders and mixing pan rotate about their respective axes either in the same or in opposite directions. In

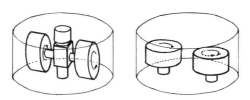

FIG. 3.39. Edge-runner and side-runner mills.

some models, however, the pan is stationary while the milling cylinders rotate, and alternatively the milling cylinders may be stationary while the mixing pan rotates.[15,52] In an edge-runner mill with two milling cylinders, these may follow the same path around the mixing pan or may move in concentric circles. Grinding and dispersion takes place between the edges of the milling cylinders and the inside surface of the mixing pan. The degree of shear may be controlled by adjustment of the location of the cylinders and hence of clearances between cylinders and pan. Edge-running milling cylinders tend to push material to the sides, and some mullers are provided with rakes or ploughs that return material into the paths of the cylinders and may also be used to aid discharge at the end of the milling process.

Mullers are generally batch operated machines, but continuous operating models are also available. One form of these comprises a double mixing chamber in the form of a figure-of-eight, each section having two edge-running mixing cylinders. Material to be processed is fed to one section and treated material is discharged frcm the other. This arrangement produces feedback from the second to the first section, thus tending to compensate for variations in composition of the feed stock.

Mullers are suitable for pastes and free-flowing solids, but are generally ineffective with compositions of low viscosity.[15] The conventional type of machine is not suitable for dry-blending of polymer with plasticiser because fusion tends to occur in the regions of high shear. This problem is overcome in one form of side-runner mill by passing air through the composition. If the temperature is carefully selected and controlled, such a machine can be used to produce plasticised PVC dry-blends.[7,53]

Mullers and pug mills are available in a variety of sizes from small laboratory models up to over $1 \cdot 7 \, m^3$ in capacity. Their power consumption does tend to be on the high side, so that their use, though widespread, tends to be limited to the dispersion of 'difficult' solids, particularly those that tend to form recalcitrant agglomerates.

3.15 ROLL MILLS

Though these machines are also commonly known as 'cylinder mills',[15] they are generally referred to as 'roll' or 'roller' mills in plastics and rubber processing (Fig. 3.40). They may possess one or more rolls in a

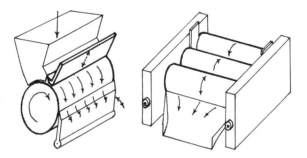

FIG. 3.40. Single- and triple-roll mills.

variety of arrangements,[54] of which the 'in-line' triple-roll mill is the most common. As blending machines, their main use is to produce high degrees of dispersion of solid materials in liquid media, e.g. chemical blowing agents in plastisols or resin intermediates. All roll mills achieve their dispersing action by passage of the blended components on the surface of a roll through a narrow gap or 'nip' between the roll and another surface. It has been suggested[55] that reduction of solid particles does not occur, but, while this may be true in respect of primary particles, surely it cannot be true for agglomerates of chemical blowing agents, for example. Single-roll mills differ from two- and multi-roll mills in that the second friction surface is provided by a stationary plate or bar parallel to the axis of the roll, and whose distance from the roll surface can be adjusted by mechanical screw or hydraulic means, whereas in other roll mills all the friction surfaces are provided by rolls. After passing through the nip, the treated material is removed by means of a scraper or 'doctor' blade that can be pressed tightly against the moving roll. Collected material may be returned to the roll and recycled as many times as is necessary to achieve the required degree of dispersion. Single-roll mills have been said to be suitable only for compositions of relatively low viscosity,[15] because their frictional effect is small compared with multi-roll machines. However, it is not clear why this should necessarily be true since the friction surface in a single-roll mill could be extended around a considerable arc of the roll, a possibility that is clearly not available when the second and subsequent friction surfaces are also provided by rolls. Such a design of single-roll mill does not appear to have been exploited commercially.[56]

Two-roll mills usually have one roll mounted in fixed bearings while the bearings of the second roll are mounted in slides, so that the nip between the rolls can be adjusted by mechanical screws or hydraulically. Most commonly, the rolls are in the same horizontal plane. They may rotate in opposite directions, downwards into the nip, or in opposite directions, and usually at different speeds to provide a 'friction ratio', typically between 1·5 and 3:1.

In a triple-roll mill, the rolls are usually arranged in one horizontal plane with the central roll in fixed bearings and the outer ones adjustable to provide control of both nips. Speed of rotation usually increases from the first to the third roll, and the second nip, which carries out most of the dispersing action, is set closer than the first.

The intention with mills having four or more rolls is to increase the friction surfaces, hence the dispersing action in one pass. In machines of this type the roll axes may be arranged in different planes so that axial movement of individual rolls is more simply provided for than is the case if the rolls are arranged in a single plane.

In all varieties of roll mill, actual nip settings depend on the nature of the components being blended and the degree of dispersion required, but obviously the smaller the nips the more intensive the crushing and dispersing action, but the lower the throughput. Typical settings for the final nip would be in the region of 0·05–0·1 mm.

The rolls are usually constructed of steel and may be cored for cooling or heating with circulating water. Cooling may be desirable to prevent or limit temperature rise due to frictional heating, in order to avoid reduction in viscosity of the media and hence frictional working, or to avoid premature reactions, such as solution of solid components, polymerisation of resin intermediates, or decomposition of blowing agents. Heating is less commonly required when blending (as distinct from compounding), but might occasionally be desirable in order to melt solid additives of low melting point so as to make them more readily dispersible. Stone rolls are available for milling corrosive substances, but this requirement is not common in polymer processing.

Sizes of roll mills vary from very small laboratory machines with rolls as little as 100 mm long and 5 mm diameter to larger production models, though there does seem to be a practical limitation to size resulting from the need to control roll clearances accurately right across the nip, and rolls much larger than 0·3 m are relatively uncommon. A typical output for a triple-roll mill of 0·3 m long rolls would be around 45 kg/h. Power consumption is likely to be of the order of 2·25 kW equivalent to about 180 kJ.

3.16 ELECTROSTATIC BLENDING

The possibility of using electrostatic charges to aid blending was alluded to briefly in Chapter 2, Section 2.4.1. Usually, the generation of electrostatic charges on particles during polymer processing is considered to be a nuisance, or even a hazard due to the possibility of sparking due to discharge. Tucker and Suh[57] make use of the attractive nature of unlike charges and repulsive nature of like charges, by deliberately supplying two powder components with opposite charges. They argued that unlike-particles would tend to be attracted and like-particles mutually repelled, so that combination of different particles in units of the required proportions of components might be obtained, thus leading to a uniform mixture or at least a mixture more uniform than the statistically random widely regarded as perfect admixture. On the basis of experiments reported at the 1976 Annual Technical Conference of the Society of Plastics Engineers, Inc., they concluded that a blender designed on these principles has low power consumption, need have no moving parts, avoids problems arising from over-heating of components, and provides better mixing than any conventional blending machine.

Rotz and Suh[58] investigating the possibility of using a similar principle as an aid to mechanical mixing of liquids, found a dramatic improvement in mixing efficiency, and suggested that an electrical–mechanical hybrid system could be used for full-scale polyurethane mixing.

3.17 CONCLUSIONS

The reader will not need to be told that a bewildering array of blending equipment is available, and it is surprising that, after over 30 years of development, so many of the types of machine originally produced for other purposes are still widely used for polymer blending, in spite of the introduction at fairly regular intervals of new types of machine that seem more aligned to the specific requirements of polymer blending.

In these circumstances it is exceedingly difficult, not to say imprudent, to pass judgment as to which form of machine is the best choice for any particular blending operation. Even machines that at one time appeared to be excluded from certain blending operations, because their modes of action were not suited to the physical form of the particular components, have a habit of proving at a later date, possibly after minor modification, to be eminently satisfactory.

Consequently, for any blending operation that is planned, the technical alternatives need to be thoroughly examined, preferably with the aid of full-scale plant trials, and the feasible alternatives should be costed as accurately as possible. Such considerations of blending are only a part of the whole subject of selection of machinery and processing intended to achieve the required overall mixing of polymeric compositions, and are discussed in more detail in Chapter 6. Some technical aspects related to individual materials are considered in Chapter 7.

REFERENCES

1. Rose, H. E. and Sullivan, R. M. E., *Vibration Mills and Vibration Milling*, Constable & Co. Ltd, London (1961).
2. Smith, E. A., *Chem. Processing*, **11**, 12 (1966).
3. Smith, E. A., *Chem. & Ind.*, 26 August, No. 34, 1436 (1967).
4. Smith, E. A., *Chemistry in Britain*, **8**(10), 425 (1972).
5. Pemberton, E. W. and Smith, E. A., *Processing*, **25**(3), 63 (1979).
6. King, G. T., *The Selection of Mixing Equipment*, Nautamix (UK) Ltd, Macclesfield.
7. Fisher, E. G. and Chard, E. D., *Int. Plast. Engng.*, **2**(2), 54, **2**(3), 113 (1962).
8. Coulson, J. M. and Maitra, N. K., *Ind. Chemist*, **26**(2), 55 (1950).
9. Scheiner, L. L., *Plastics Technology*, **13**(6), 39 (1967).
10. Baker Perkins Machinery Ltd, Hanley, *Oblicone Blender*, Technical Bulletin (1978).
11. Funt, J. M., *Mixing of Rubbers*, RAPRA, Shrewsbury (1977).
12. Adams, J. F. E. and Baker, A. G., *Trans. Inst. Chem. Engrs.*, **34**, 91 (1956).
13. Wm. Gardner & Sons (Gloucester) Ltd, British Patent 798085 (1958).

14. GLEN CRESTON LTD, London, *Turbula Shaker-mixers*, Trade Pamphlet (1979).
15. STERBACEK, Z. and TAUSK, P., *Mixing in the Chemical Industry*, Bourne, J. R. (Ed.), translated by K. Mayer, Pergamon, Oxford (1965).
16. PREMIER COLLOID MILLS LTD, Walton-on-Thames, '*Premier 7000*' Top Entry Mixer.
17. TORRANCE & SONS, LTD, Bristol, British Patent 1051692 (1966).
18. THE MASTERMIX ENGINEERING CO. LTD, Redditch, *H.V. S./H. S. High Speed Disperser*, Technical Information Sheets.
19. DRAISWERKE GMBH, Mannheim, *Drais Dispersers*, Technical Literature (1962).
20. TORRANCE & SONS LTD, Bristol, *Mixers and Dispersers*, Technical Literature.
21. LYONS, E. J., *Chem. Eng. Progress*, **50**, 629 (1954).
22. PECK, W. C., *Ind. Chemist*, **31**(2), 505 (1955).
23. ROTHMAN, N., *PRT Polymer Age*, **3**(5), 194 (1972).
24. AARONS, B. L., *Chem. Processing*, **20**(6), 65 (1974); *Pigment and Resin Technology*, November, 12, 17 (1976).
25. CLAES, G., Paper No. 6, *PINTEC 72*, Plastics Institute, London (1972).
26. WICK, G. and KOENIG, H., *Kunststoffe*, **46**, 583 (1956).
27. ANON, *Int. Plast. Engng.*, **6**(1), 14 (1966).
28. ANON, *Plastics Compounding*, May/June, 98 (1979).
29. PECK, W. C., *Trans. Instn. Chem. Engrs.*, **34**, 99 (1956).
30. KING, G. T., *Ind. Chemist*, **40**(1), 20 (1964).
31. BATTAGION S. P. A., Bergamo, *Parallel Shaft Mixers*, Technical Bulletin.
32. BUSS, A. G., Basle, *Buss Double Trough Kneaders*, Technical Bulletin (1973).
33. WINKWORTH MACHINERY LTD., Staines, *Pacemix Mixer*, Technical Bulletin, Leaflet No. P20/250/777.
34. WERNER & PFLEIDERER MASCHINENFABRIK, Stuttgart, *Universal Mixer with Screw Discharge*, Technical Bulletin (1969).
35. SCHNEIDER, A., *Kunststoffe-Rundachau*, **10**(7), 333 (1963).
36. BUSS, A. G., French Patent 1 271 333 (1960).
37. SHELLEY, F. N., *Plastics*, **21**, 171, 226 (1956); *Engineering*, **181**, 440, 4708 (1956).
38. MATTHEWS, G. A. R., *Advances in PVC Compounding and Processing*, Chapter 5, Kaufman, M. (Ed.), MacLaren, London (1962).
39. MORTON MACHINE CO. LTD, Wishaw, *Multimix*, Technical Bulletin.
40. DRAISWERKE GMBH, Mannheim, *Drais Special Machines for Mixing and Grinding*, Technical Bulletin (1964).
41. QUILLEN, C. S., *Chem. Eng.*, **61**(6), 178 (1954).
42. WM. GARDNER & SONS (GLOUCESTER) LTD, Gloucester, *Airmix*, Technical Bulletin (1961).
43. GRUN, G, British Patent 981605 (1965).
44. KEK LTD, British Patent 859 405 (1961).
45. EVANS, T. G. and RYDER, G. A., British Patents 1365685; 1365686; 1375943 (1974).
46. CRABTREE D. R., *Toroidal mixing*, paper to *3rd Ann. Intl. Bulk Solids Conference*, November, 1978. Oaktree Equipment Ltd, Faringdon (1978).

47. OAKTREE EQUIPMENT LTD, Faringdon, *Toroidal Mixer Type 25*, Technical Literature (1977).
48. BUSS, A. G., Basle, *Buss Mixing Turbine Type MT*, Technical Bulletin (1976).
49. BUSS, A. G., British Patent 1095628 (1967).
50. E. T. OAKES LTD, Macclesfield, *Continuous Automatic Mixer*, Technical Bulletins, Nos. 104, 501 and 508 (1969).
51. OAKES, E. T., British Patent 646591 (1950).
52. BULLOCK, H. L., *Chem. Eng. Progress*, **51**, 243 (1955).
53. FOSTER, J. L., *Powder Mixing Techniques for Polyvinyl Chloride Resins*, B. F. Goodrich Chem. Co., Brecksville, Ohio (1953).
54. FISCHER, E. K., *Colloidal Dispersions*, Wiley, New York (1950).
55. KRAPF, A. J., *Pigment and Resin Technology*, **5**(11), 7 (1976).
56. HEYES, J. and MULROY, *Plast. Rubb. Wkly*, 2 March, 6 (1979).
57. TUCKER, C. L., III and SUH, N. P., *Polym. Engng. Sci.*, **16**(10), 657 (1976).
58. ROTZ, C. A. and SUH, N. P., *Polym. Engng. Sci.*, **16**(10), 672 (1976).

CHAPTER 4

Batch Compounding Equipment

4.1 GENERAL CONSIDERATIONS

As discussed in Chapter 1 the words compound, as a noun or a verb, and compounding, do not mean the same throughout the polymer processing industries, and for the purposes of this text the words will apply to machines, processes and materials where softening, melting, and compaction of polymer more or less to a continuum with dispersed additives is involved. Laminar mixing involving deformation by laminar flow is characteristic of such melt compounding,[1-3] which is also characterised by zones of high shear stress where dispersive mixing occurs. In spite of the development and expansion of rubber and plastics processing, two types of machines, namely the heated two-roll mill and the internal mixer, have been dominant in batch compounding to the present time, and may indeed be fairly said to have dominated compounding as a whole until comparatively recently. As indicated in Chapter 1, there is some doubt as to the precise origin of the two-roll mill. According to Tokita and White,[4] Hancock's machine was a masticator comprising a spiked rotor moving inside a hollow tooth-studded cylinder,[5,6] which is perhaps more like an internal mixer. Evidently, this machine was used for mixing rubber compositions until it was ousted by Chaffee's steam-heated variable speed two-roll mill, introduced in 1835.[5,7] In due course, two-roll mills have become largely replaced by internal mixers[8,9] as manufacturing machines, though they are still widely used in research, development and control laboratories. This change arose partly from the introduction of carbon black (and other objectionable ingredients), with its accompanying well-known problem of house-keeping, and partly because the internal mixer is generally a much faster mixing machine and is more automatic in its operation. Other differences between the two types of machine include the fact that with a two-roll mill, or 'open roll mill' as it is sometimes called, the material being processed has surfaces exposed to the atmosphere, whereas the material processed in an internal mixer is largely enclosed except when the charging door is open, and on discharge at the completion of the compounding cycle. This is generally regarded as a disadvantage of two-roll mills, because of the risk of the possibility of oxidative break-down and of loss of more volatile constituents at processing temperatures. On the other hand, the open nature of a two-roll mill does mean that the progress of the compounding process can be observed relatively easily. This can be a distinct advantage with reactive compositions, such as thermosetting materials, where the onset of curing can often be detected from the surface appearance of the material being milled. It is also often useful in investigative work with materials whose compounding behaviour is not fully known.

Another major difference between the two types of machine is that, by the very nature of its operation, compounded material can usually be removed from a two-roll mill in the form of sheeting, suitable for direct granulation, lamination, compression moulding or cutting to produce specimens for testing. Indeed, with some materials, a really good quality two-roll mill can produce sheeting that is not so inferior to that produced by calendering. With the internal mixer, however, compounded material is discharged as a shapeless mass that necessitates at least one more processing step before the material can be put to normal use.

One thing that two-roll mills and internal mixers have in common is that, apart from relatively small (though admittedly sometimes important) changes in detailed design, the basic principles of operation of both types of machine have remained essentially the same since their inception, respectively, over 140 and 60 years ago.

4.2 TWO-ROLL MILLS

The only immediately obvious difference between the two-roll mills discussed in Chapter 2 (Section 3.15) and a two-roll mill used for compounding, is that the latter must be provided with means for heating and cooling the rolls, and this introduces design complications whatever means of heating is adopted, but whereas three or more rolls are much more common than two for dispersive blending, two are exclusively or almost exclusively used in compounding, three or more roll arrangements being reserved for calendering machines.

4.2.1 *General Design Features*

Depending on size, the rolls of a roll mill are carried in more or less massive end frames, or standards, of cast iron or steel, usually with a bed-plate of similar sturdy construction mounted on vibration insulators (Fig. 4.1). The 'fixed' roll, which is usually the 'back' roll (i.e. on the

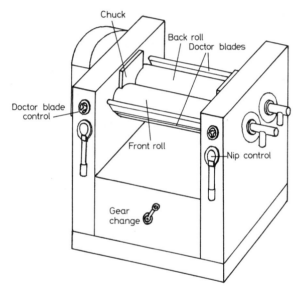

FIG. 4.1. General arrangement of a two-roll mill.

opposite side to the controls), rotates in bearings in fixed locations in the end frames, while the bearings of the movable roll are carried in horizontal slides in the end frames, so that the roll can be moved towards or away from its companion. The design of the bearings and their lubrication is rather important, and a modern heavy duty mill is likely to have roller bearings, with separate forced lubrication systems for each. Drive for the rolls is from an electric motor through reduction gears. Most commonly, a two-roll mill has a choice of two gear ratios between the rolls so that the rolls may be driven at equal speed, or with a friction ratio between the rolls, usually up to about 1·4:1, but possibly as high as

2:1, the back roll usually being the faster. Machines are available, however, in which the speed of one roll is continuously variable over an appropriate range (Fig. 4.2).

In the simpler designs, the positions of the movable roll bearings are adjusted manually towards the fixed roll bearings, by means of two

FIG. 4.2. Compact mill, 1500 mm (courtesy of Farrel Bridge Ltd, Lancs., UK).

independently operable 'lug' bars which turn robust screws in associated spiral grooves mounted in the end frames. The position of each bearing is indicated by a circular scale, but for some reason these are notoriously unreliable, on small machines at any rate, and the nip should be measured directly if a knowledge of its size is important. Movement to increase the gap between the rolls, in these machines with manually operated closing devices, is dependent on reaction by the material in the nip to the restraining forces of the rolls, pushing the movable roll as far as the adjusting screws will permit. More sophisticated modern machines have hydraulically operated nip adjustment in both directions.

The rolls themselves are commonly of ground and polished chilled cast iron, but machines with alloy steel and chrome-plated rolls are obtainable. Heating is achieved by circulating steam under pressure, hot water or heated oil through the rolls, or by electric resistance heaters, and cooling may be effected by circulating cold water. All these arrangements require some means of conducting heating or cooling medium from a stationary source to the inside of the rotating rolls. Fluid media may be passed into and taken from a roll through concentric pipes with a suitable gland arrangement. The fluid passes through passages that have been cored, bored or circumferentially drilled into the rolls. Electricity requires some form of rubbing contact arrangement. With steam heating, temperature is adjusted by two independent pressure control valves, one for each roll. Temperature control with liquid media, though perhaps more precise, requires heat exchange systems that may be more expensive. Cooling of rolls that are heated with direct steam tends to be rather imprecise. Three alternatives are open to the operator. Of the three, the gentlest is merely to turn off the steam entry valves to one or both rolls. Somewhat more rapid cooling results if, in addition, the exhaust steam traps are by-passed by opening the relevant stop-cocks. In practice, the cooling often needs to be much more rapid than can be achieved by these means, and then cold water may be passed through the rolls. This can certainly provide rapid cooling but tends to be rather vicious. Whatever the system, it is generally not advisable to rely on measurements of the heating or cooling medium to give accurate indications of roll temperatures. The most common way of obtaining these is by means of portable bow thermocouple pyrometers applied to the roll surfaces before commencing operations, but radiation pyro-meters can be used.

A perennial problem with two-roll mill compounding is the tendency of material to spread laterally along the rolls, over the edges, and down into the vicinity of the bearings. To control this spreading, two V-shaped chucks or chocks are located above the rolls, one towards each end of the nip. On some machines these are fixed so that the working volume is also more or less fixed, but it is more usual for them to be adjustable laterally so that they may contain varying quantities of material. It is not possible to have a very close fit of the chucks to the rolls because of the excessive friction and wear that would result, and because of the need to accommodate the horizontal adjustment of the movable roll, so almost invariably some material finds its way into the spaces between the chucks and the rolls, where it experiences intensive friction and is liable to degrade. Some of this material may also reach the edge of the rolls, and be forced on to the ends by the forces in the nip. It is not easy to see how this problem could be overcome completely, so regular inspection and cleaning are recommended.

For improving the mixing action and possibly for removal of compounded material, two doctor blades are provided, one for each roll. These are commonly operated manually, although hydraulic operation is usual on larger machines. Each doctor blade consists of a straight knife, held in a carrier frame which can be moved about an axis parallel to the roll axes, so that when not required the blade is held clear of the material on the rolls and can then be forced against its corresponding roll, cutting through the compounding material when required. A two-roll mill may also be provided with a strip cutter, which is similar to a doctor knife but is much narrower than the full length of the rolls, so that it can be used to cut into the compounded material and remove it from the rolls in the form of a strip.

Beneath the rolls there may be a removable tray, usually of stainless steel, which catches any material that falls through the nip or off the roll surfaces.

4.2.2 *Safety Precautions*

An unguarded two-roll presents obvious hazards and safety arrangements are all-important. There are three major sources of hazard, namely the possibility of clothing, hair, or even hands getting caught and drawn into the nip; the risk of burns by contact with hot metal parts of the equipment or with material being compounded; and evolution of gases and vapours from the hot material. With a small mill, it is a relatively simple matter to enclose the upper regions of the rolls by means of a metal grid, having a central charging opening that is sufficiently large to permit delivery of material to the nip but too small to pass a hand. On larger production mills this is not usually possible because of the quantity of materials that have to be charged to the rolls, but it is usually possible to locate the opening so that the possibility of anyone putting a hand in it is remote. The so-called 'Lunn Principles', laid down by the National Joint Industrial Council for the Rubber Manufacturing Industry, include the provision that a mill should be located so high in relation to the working position that an operative is unable to reach the danger region around the nip.

All two-roll mills have arrangements for rapid stopping in emergency.

Preferably, an emergency stop should also reverse the motion of the rolls through a small angle of rotation, so as to release anything that has been caught in the nip. Location and mode of operation of emergency stops is clearly important but does vary from one manufacturer to another. The rolls of one early type of two-roll mill were driven through a clutch controlled by a switch operated by a pedal-bar, so that removal of the foot from the pedal activated an emergency stop. This arrangement seems to have gone out of favour, but if updated in conjunction with modern instrumental techniques seems to have much to be said for it. Sometimes the emergency stop is operated by a sensitive press-button switch located in some position that renders it easily activated without using a hand, but it is difficult to decide on a location that is universally appropriate to all operatives. More satisfactory are trip-switches operated by bars mounted on sensitive rocker arms. The Lunn safety bar, required by the Lunn Principles referred to above, comprises such a bar at chest height parallel to the roll axes. On application of a predetermined pressure, it operates a switch, cutting off power and applying a brake to the driving shaft.[12] On smaller machines a similar bar-switch may be positioned at head height adjustable to individual requirements. Additionally, trip-switch operating bars may be located under the doctor blades.

In addition to the possibility of injury, there is also the risk of dropping inanimate objects such as spatulas, scoops, etc., into the nip, where they are not only liable to sustain severe damage but, what is usually more important and expensive, may also damage the rolls. For this reason, if hand tools are used in the vicinity of the rolls it is best to use only those made of wood or plastic material.

There is not much that can be done additionally in respect of machine design to prevent the possibility of burns. Operatives should certainly wear protective gloves and other clothing, but this does tend to introduce an element of clumsiness that is undesirable.

Any two-roll mill today, whether in a laboratory or in a production unit, should be provided with an effective extraction unit. This will usually comprise a hood over the mill and as close to the rolls as is practicable, with a sufficiently powerful extractor fan drawing any vapours off, to be conveyed through ducting for disposal as is appropriate for the particular location. Because dust and oily vapours tend to get drawn into, and deposited on, the inside surface of the hood, extractor systems constitute a potential source of contamination, and regular inspection and cleaning are essential.

4.2.3 *Speeds and Friction Ratios*

The matter of friction ratios between the two rolls was mentioned earlier. Actual roll speeds vary with the size, and for a given machine, speed of mixing will depend not only on the dimensions of the nip but also on the roll speeds. Increase in speed of rotation increases intensity of shearing in the region of the nip, and also increases the frequency with which a volume element of material passes through the nip, but the effect of these factors may be partially opposed by the accompanying reduction in dwell time in regions of high shear. On balance, it seems likely that increasing speed of mixing will be favoured by increasing roll speeds. However, quite apart from any mechanical limitations at very high speeds, a limitation on roll speed is imposed by the fact that handling of processed material becomes increasingly difficult above a certain point. For this reason, if for no other, roll speeds tend to decrease with increase in roll diameter. Thus, for a small laboratory mill with rolls 0·3 m long and 0·15 m diameter, speeds are usually around 30 r.p.m., corresponding to peripheral speeds of the order of 0·25 m/s, for the back roll, with the front roll rotating at a slower speed depending on the friction ratio. The faster roll of a 1·5 m by 0·56 m mill will probably rotate at about 16–20 r.p.m., corresponding to peripheral speeds of about 0·5 m/s. This seems to be approaching the limit for comfortable surface speed, since the speeds of rotation of larger two-roll mills seem to be usually reduced in relation to size, so that peripheral speeds are not generally much higher than 0·5 m/s.

4.2.4 *Sizes and Capacities*

The maximum batch size for a given two-roll mill is more or less proportionally dependent on the separation of the V-shaped chucks and the diameter of the rolls, but also depends on the nature of the material to be processed, particularly its density. Typical values are indicated in Table 4.1.

4.2.5 *Milling Procedures*

Procedures for compounding on two-roll mills depend to some extent on the nature of the materials to be processed, in particular on whether

TABLE 4.1

TYPICAL BATCH SIZES FOR TWO-ROLL MILLS
OF DIFFERENT SIZES

Size (m)	Volumetric batch capacity (m^3)
0·3 × 0·15	0·0006–0·0013
0·46 × 0·23	0·002 –0·003
0·6 × 0·3	0·004 –0·006
0·9 × 0·4	0·01 –0·013
1·05 × 0·4	0·011 –0·017
1·2 × 0·4	0·013 –0·02
1·5 × 0·56	0·03 –0·05
1·8 × 0·6	0·05 –0·08
2·1 × 0·66	0·1 –0·13

the composition is thermosetting or vulcanisable, or is thermoplastic. It is first necessary to ensure that the rolls are free to expand without mutual interference in the nip and consequent possible damage. This is achieved by withdrawing the movable roll, if the machine has hydraulic roll controls, or slackening off the lug bars if the operation is manual. The rolls can then be heated to the required temperatures. These depend on the nature of the material to be compounded, in particular on the softening range of the polymer but also on the nature and proportions of additives, whether the composition is thermoplastic or cross-linking, and to what extent shear degradation is required. For the common thermoplastics, temperatures will generally be between 130 and 180 °C,[10] whereas for thermosetting materials, such as phenolic moulding materials, a range of 70–130 °C is normal.[11] With natural rubber compositions, milling also serves to reduce molecular weight, and effectiveness of mastication in achieving this seems to be at a minimum around 105 °C, so temperatures below this (cold mastication) or above (hot mastication)[12] are indicated, depending on the amount of degradation in molecular weight required. Synthetic rubbers may be produced more closely to the molecular weight required, so with compositions based on these degradation will need to be minimised. As a general rule, in mill compounding it is desirable to persuade the material to form a continuous crepe or hide around the front roll, and to this end the two rolls are usually heated to different temperatures (Fig. 4.3). For thermoplastics, a temperature difference of 3–5 °C is usually sufficient, whereas for thermosetting materials the difference may be as high as 20–30 °C. Unfilled compositions will usually adhere to the hotter roll, so with such materials the front roll will be at the higher temperature. Some filled

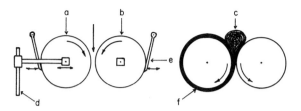

FIG. 4.3. Side elevations of a two-roll mill. (a) Movable roll, (b) 'fixed' roll, (c) rolling bank, (d) lug bar, (e) doctor blade, (f) crepe or hide.

compositions, however, may prefer to adhere to the colder roll, and then the temperature difference should obviously be reversed. In practice, particularly in the laboratory, material being milled may adhere to the unexpected roll. Sometimes it may even change its allegiance during the milling process, transferring its attachment from one roll to the other without warning. What is even worse is that material will sometimes adhere to both rolls, in different regions. This may be due to temperature differences across the face of the rolls, or, what is particularly often the case with laboratory machines where a variety of materials is processed, to contamination on the rolls left from previous batches. However, with a little patience and practice, it is usually possible to persuade material to adhere to the desired roll, once a reasonably complete crepe or hide has been formed.

Once the required temperatures have been attained, the rolls can be set in motion and the nip adjusted according to the physical form of the polymer or resin to be processed. The gap needs to be sufficiently small to limit the amount of material falling through the nip to within acceptable bounds, so that where the polymer or resin is a fine powder the gap needs to be quite small. Material that falls through can be collected and re-fed to the nip, but this is tedious and liable to lead to contamination. Powdered polymer or resin will usually have been previously blended with all or at least some of the required additives. The blended material is added to the nip in successive small portions, each portion being added when the previous material has softened and gelled to a more or less continuous crepe. Too rapid addition is likely to chill the material on the rolls, to the point where it loses its cohesion and adhesion to the rolls and so breaks up and falls off. As the amount of material in the crepe increases, the movable roll can be slackened off to increase the nip gap and hence the capacity of the rolls, and addition of further material can be speeded up. Once a continuous gelled hide or crepe has been formed, opening of the nip should be adjusted in relation to the rate of addition, so that a small rolling bank of material always remains at the entry region to the nip, i.e. on top of the rolls. This technique is reasonably straight-forward with a stable thermoplastic composition, but with thermosetting material care is necessary in order to avoid curing, and time is at a premium, so the procedure may be modified. Thus, the nip may be kept relatively small, no attempt made to form a true crepe, and material repeatedly re-fed to the nip. Since most thermosetting materials compounded on rolls will be subsequently ground to moulding powders, there is no absolute requirement to form a continuous sheet or crepe except for ease of handling. In any case, once the composition has reacted as far as is permissible in relation to cure, it must be removed from the rolls by application of the doctor blades. Milling of thermosetting compositions of this type is generally somewhat easier on a production scale than in the laboratory, if only because consistent conditions and procedures can be established. Indeed, on a large two-roll mill, it may be possible to operate continuously by feeding slowly at one end and removing compounded strip at the other.

Natural rubber and synthetic rubbers in bale form are processed somewhat differently.[13,14] First, the bales have to be cut into pieces sufficiently small to be picked up by the roll nip. The pieces are then fed re-fed to the rolls to form a continuous crepe until it has been sufficiently masticated, at which point the other ingredients are added to the rolling bank. Powdered rubbers are usually pre-blended, preferably in an intensive non-fluxing mixer (Chapter 3, Section 3.5), and may then be fed to the mill in much the same way as is usual for a thermoplastic composition like PVC. It is, however, preferable to compact the pre-blend into continuous strips that are then delivered to the mill at relatively wide nip settings. This is not only cleaner in operation but can also greatly increase throughputs.[15]

4.2.6 Mixing Action

A number of fundamental theoretical studies of two-roll milling have appeared, spanning a period of at least three decades.[2,3,16-27] They have mostly been concerned with calculations of forces between the rolls, and the magnitude and distribution of shear forces in and close to the nip. However, it does not require complicated mathematics to show

(i)   that as far as the nip region and the hide are concerned the streamlines are closed, and that there is no flow across streamlines through the nip because interfaces oriented along a given streamline will continue to follow that streamline, and

(ii) that this is true even when there is a friction ratio between the two rolls, although this increases shear deformation.[18]

Moreover, even in the rolling bank, where there is possibly some breakdown of streamlines, cross-mixing, i.e. at right-angles to the streamlines, will generally be very slight unless steps are taken deliberately to impose it. This tends to suggest that the simple two-roll mill is an inefficient distributive mixer,[18] though it may provide satisfactory dispersive mixing.[3] Much of the theoretical work that has been published is related to Newtonian behaviour, and it has been pointed out that for a power law fluid where the flow-behaviour index (see Chapter 2, Section 2.4.3) is less than one, the pressure gradient is everywhere lower than for a Newtonian fluid so that shear stresses are significantly lower and particle dispersion not so effective.[24]

If the feed stock to a two-roll mill comprises all the required components and has previously been thoroughly blended, in an intensive non-fluxing mixer, for example, dispersive mixing may be all that is required and, as can be the case with powdered rubber blend mentioned above, mixing can then be quite rapid. In other cases, i.e. where the pre-blending has been relatively cursory, or where the blending is carried out on the mill itself, steps need to be taken to ensure that the necessary cross-mixing occurs. Commonly, the operative will use the appropriate doctor blade repeatedly to cut the hide so that it begins to fold back on itself, retracting the blade in sufficient time for the folded material to be carried up into the rolling bank. This introduces the risk that the hide may have insufficient adhesion to the roll to withstand the gravitational pull of the released portion of hide, so that the whole may fall from the rolls before the operative can take preventative action. What is more important, however, is that this manner of cutting contributes little, if anything, to cross-mixing. The only effective manual action is to cut diagonally across the hide using a hand-held tool, such as a carpet knife or a triangular scraper, so that the cut portion folds back along a line inclined to the transverse and longitudinal directions (Fig. 4.4). This should be done from alternate sides of the hide, and the more frequent this operation, the more rapid the whole mixing operation.

The total time of compounding on a two-roll mill depends on the design of the machine, the composition, and on the procedure. In the laboratory, small pieces of hide can be removed with a knife from time to

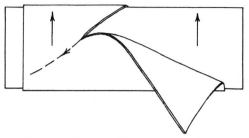

FIG. 4.4. Cross-cutting a crepe or hide.

time and the progress of mixing monitored by optical examination. In a manufacturing process, the procedure will usually be established by experience. Typically, for a thermoplastic, milling will continue for a specified time from the moment the whole of the batch has softened and gelled to a more or less smooth hide and rolling bank. This is likely to be of the order of 10–15 min. With thermosetting and vulcanisable materials, mixing time will be limited by the onset of cure. When compounding has been taken to the required point, the hide is removed in a form depending on the size of the hide and on the process to which it is to be submitted subsequently. First, it may be necessary to adjust the nip to give a specific thickness of hide. Then, on a laboratory mill, the whole hide is removed by hand after cutting right across it with the doctor blade. Generally, it will then need to be cooled, and as this is usually done in the air, care to avoid contamination is necessary. Probably the best arrangement is to hang the hide on a clean horizontal stainless steel bar. With some heavily filled thermosetting materials there may be some difficulty in obtaining a coherent hide around one roll and it may then be necessary to remove the compounded material, by using both doctor blades, and possibly to accept the product in the form of fragmented pieces which may nonetheless be satisfactory for subsequent disintegration.

4.2.7 *Strip Cutting*

Although the manual procedures just outlined have been used in production, they really are rather too crude for manufacture of any magnitude, and it is more satisfactory to employ a strip cutter that can be used, as its name implies, to cut into the hide, usually at one end, so that it may be removed as a strip of appropriate width to suit the next process. If the strip is to be granulated or diced, it can be cooled by passing through a water-bath of suitable length, dried on emergence from the bath and fed directly to the granulating or dicing machine (Fig. 4.5). If the compounding is to be followed by calendering or extrusion without intermediate disintegration, it will generally not be desirable to cool the

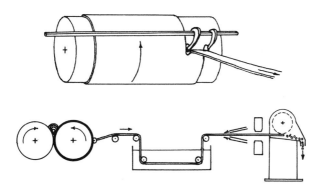

FIG. 4.5. Strip cutter, water-bath and granulator.

strip. The strip may be fed directly to the calender or extruder, preferably after passing a metal detector. In calendering, however, it seems more common to remove small portions of hide from the mill to be fed to the calender nip in separate doses, though why this should be preferred to continuous feed, which should be controllable to match the calender throughout, is not clear.

4.2.8 Cross-mixing Devices

Apart from mechanical arrangements associated with drive motors, gearing, bearings, etc., the main developments in design of two-roll mills have been aimed at removing the deficiency in respect of cross-mixing (Fig. 4.6). One rather obvious way of achieving this objective is to use plough-like separators or guides to cut into the hide and transfer its path forcibly across the roll at an angle. In one arrangement of this type, a number of these guides are carried on a supporting bar above the front roll, so that they project downwards towards the nip region.[28] The end guides need to direct the hide inwards, and may replace the usual guide chucks. Another method is to mount a so-called 'stock blending unit' above the two-roll mill.[29] This comprises a lower driven roll, an upper

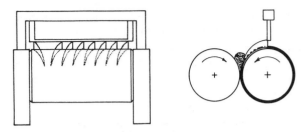

FIG. 4.6. Cross-mixing ploughs.

floating roll, and a traversing carriage (Fig. 4.7). To carry out cross-mixing with such a unit, the hide is cut to form a narrow strip which is fed manually between guides on the stationary carriage and into the nip of the stock blender rolls. The traversing carriage is then set in motion, and continues to traverse laterally to and fro over the nip of the two-roll

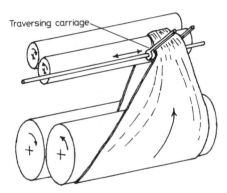

FIG. 4.7. Two-roll mill stock blending unit.

mill, drawing the full width of the hide into the blender and feeding it back into the mill nip at the diagonally opposite position. On completion of the desired cross-mixing, the hide is cut at a position before entry to the blender rolls, and can then be removed from the mill in the usual manner. This device has been specifically designed for rubber, and does require the hide to have sufficient hot strength to withstand the tension between mill and stock blender. Consequently, plastics may not be amenable to processing in this way because they tend to tear under relatively small tension. A possible design modification to two-roll mills that could improve cross-mixing, is to construct one or both rolls with helical grooves or ridges. Construction of rolls to such a design is likely to be expensive, and this may be why the possibility does not seem to have been explored thoroughly. One machine that does incorporate this idea is the Frances Shaw 'Mixer-Extruder Double R', but this is essentially a continuous compounding machine and is discussed in Chapter 5.

4.2.9 Power Consumption

Power requirements for two-roll mills naturally depend on the nature of the compounding job for which they are intended, but although manufacturers often refer to 'heavy duty' mills, presumably as distinct from 'normal duty' mills, power provisions do not seem to vary much for a given size of mill. In the normal way, the drive motor and gear arrangements are an integral part of a two-roll mill machine, and the processing technologist can usually safely leave their selection to the manufacturer. Typical drive motor sizes range from 7·5 kW for 300 × 150 mm rolls to 40 kW for 1000 × 400 mm rolls, being roughly proportional to the product of roll length and diameter from the latter size upwards, rising to around 250 kW for 2500 × 750 mm rolls. This implies that motor power is approximately proportional to volumetric capacity for production size machines, but it must be noted that the accuracy of this relationship also depends on the nip setting and on the volume of the rolling bank, and these both depend on the nature of the composition being processed. As an example, for a 1500 × 560 mm mill the power rating may vary from 1800 to 3700 kW/m^3. When purchasing a two-roll mill, therefore, it is necessary to specify as definitively as possible the nature of the materials with which it has to cope, and the production rate expected. As with many other production installations, if there is any doubt, it is usually advisable to install a machine that is larger and more powerful than the estimated requirements.

4.3 INTERNAL MIXERS

The internal mixer (Figs. 4.8 and 4.9) is related in design and action to the two-roll mill and the Z-blade mixer, the latter often being referred to as an internal mixer, though there are major differences in construction and applications between Z-blade mixers and the internal mixers used for melt compounding. The internal mixer as envisaged here was

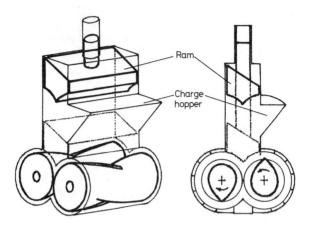

FIG. 4.8. Internal mixer—general arrangement.

originally designed by Banbury[8,10,30,31] for the compounding of rubber stocks. Indeed, machines of this type are frequently referred to as Banbury mixers or Banburys, though this is not strictly correct as many other makes and designs are now available, and the name should be applied only to the machines made by the limited number of manufacturers whose designs have descended directly from Banbury's original. Over the years since its inception, numerous modifications in design have been introduced, but the basic principle remains the same. Although originally directed at rubber compounding, internal mixers have been adapted and designed specifically for plastics compounding, and the machines are, or have been, used for the manufacture of most of the major plastics.

4.3.1 General Design Features

As previously suggested, internal mixers resemble Z-blade or sigma mixers, but they are much more intensive in their action and of necessity much more robust in construction.[10,32] Like a Z-blade mixer (Chapter 3, Section 3.7), an internal mixer comprises two parallel kneading rotors, each rotating within the corresponding region of a double trough or W-shaped chamber, but with the walls of the chamber continuing upwards over the rotors to constitute a closed mixing chamber, comprising a hollow regular cylinder most commonly with a cross-section in the form of a figure-of-eight on its side. In fact, the

FIG. 4.9. F370 internal mixer (courtesy of Farrel Bridge Ltd, Lancs., UK).

original Banbury mixer[31] appears to have had a mixing chamber more like a prone letter 'B' with a V-shaped region at the top unswept by the rotors, and some modern machines have similar design. The upper central region of the mixing chamber is constituted by a ram or 'floating weight', which, for a figure-of-eight chamber, is V-shaped at the bottom, so as to complete that figure. As well as the flat-bottomed rams already referred to, some machines have rams whose lower surface is more like a shallow 'U' in profile. The ram can be lowered or raised within a hollow vertical shaft, usually by hydraulic means, thus providing a charging entry when in the raised position, and sealing the mixing chamber when in the lowered position. Earlier models of internal mixers have one or both of the curved sides of the mixing chamber hinged at the top, and rotatable outwards and upwards, so that they can be opened to discharge the compounded material. Modern machines are usually designed for bottom discharge by having the inverted-V section at the bottom of the mixing chamber, in the form of a hinged 'drop-door' or a sliding unit operated hydraulically.[32,33] The drop-door discharge system generally permits total mixing cycles some 40–50 s shorter than those obtainable with sliding systems, and also requires less cleaning on changing from one material to another.[34] In another variation, instead of running in bearings at both ends of the mixing chamber, the rotors run in single bearings at one end in the so-called 'overhung' arrangement, leaving the other ends floating 'freely' unsupported by bearings. The end wall at the free end is then arranged as the discharge door with a horizontal hinge along its top edge[35-37] (Fig. 4.10).

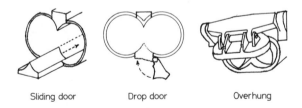

Sliding door   Drop door   Overhung

FIG. 4.10. Internal mixer discharge arrangements.

4.3.2 Rotor Designs

The rotors of an internal mixer are more robust and occupy a higher proportion of the mixing chamber than is usual with Z-blade mixers.

They are usually driven in a contra-rotating sense downwards into the nip in the same sense as a two-roll mill, but in some internal mixers the rotors rotate in the same direction.[35,36] The rotors and the side walls of the mixing chamber are cored or drilled for circulation of water, steam or heat-exchange oil, though frequently external heating may be dispensed with, the internally generated heat arising from the intense frictional working of the material being sufficient to induce the required degree of softening and gelation.

Externally, one internal mixer looks much the same as another in general shape and arrangement, but there is quite a variety of shapes of rotor, and there are detailed differences in motor power, bearing and drive arrangements. From the author's point of view, it is unfortunate that the shapes of internal mixer rotors are not easy to describe in words or to illustrate by simple diagrams. Even the manufacturers themselves find it necessary to resort to simple terms such as 'spiral-shaped'[38] that do not by any means fully describe the shape, or introduce terms such as 'nogs'[39] that are largely meaningless in the absence of explanatory diagrams. The rotors of the original Banbury mixer[30] appear to have resembled 'filled-in' Z-blade rotors. In modern internal mixers there are some variants[40,41] on the basic arrangement that are related to rotor shape. First, the rotors may or may not overlap. Second, if they do overlap they will generally of necessity have to rotate at the same speed, but if they do not they may rotate at different speeds. Finally, as mentioned earlier, the rotors may rotate in opposite directions, usually like a two-roll mill downwards into the nip between them, or in the same direction. Most rotors do, indeed, have some form of spiral, but the pitch is usually so large in relation to the length, that a complete turn is rarely, if ever, included, so that any similarity to an extruder screw is not very obvious. Nevertheless, the leading faces of the raised portions of the spirals do have functions in shearing and transporting material along the line of the rotor axes as well as peripherally. In the so-called two-wing, three-wing and four-wing varieties of rotor (see Section 3.7 and Fig. 3.29) one of the functions of the wings is to pump material from the ends towards the central region. The simplest form of rotor consists of what might be described as a 'lozenge' shape; that is, it is bounded by two curved surfaces, the axis of curvature of each of which lies on the far side of the central rotor axis, i.e. the radius of curvature is greater than half the thickness of the rotor—indeed it is usually greater than the thickness. The two curved surfaces meet along two lines parallel to the axis and defining the maximum diameter of the rotor, which is of such a size that there are only small clearances between these regions of the rotor and the inside wall of the mixing chamber. Imagine, now, that a twist is imparted to the lozenge to an extent approaching one half of a complete turn over the length of the rotor, and the resultant shape is beginning to resemble that of several common makes of internal mixer rotor. Usually, however, there is a break in the spiral so formed, rather beyond half way along the rotor, the remainder comprising a sharper spiral in the contrary sense or a more complex shape. When the rotor shape is asymmetrical in this way the two rotors are mounted in the mixing chamber in the opposite 'sense' to each other. In an older variation on this basic shape the lozenge is one-sided, so that in effect the rotor has a single ridge with steeply curved sides spiralling round a central core. In a variant of this design there are two of these 'half-lozenges', one starting from each end of the rotor, and each extending rather more than half-way towards the other end. The so-called 'four-bladed' rotor has this arrangement with two additional blades or wings, one each side of the central core in the regions between the blades formed by the two half-lozenges.

One well-known form of internal mixer[39] has rotors that perhaps do bear a superficial resemblance to short extruder screws. Each rotor comprises a circular cylindrical root or core carrying one relatively large helical projection that runs half-way round the root, and two small, roughly triangular projections, or nogs, one at each end of the rotor. The rotors are so arranged that the helices tend to transport material in opposite directions along the direction of the axes. The helices and nogs project sufficiently far for there to be quite small clearances between them and the root of the other rotor, so that movement between the rotors provides a friction ratio in the nip region due to the different peripheral speeds at the root and outside diameters. With all these arrangements there is shearing

  (i) in nip regions, which, where the rotors rotate in opposite directions, is somewhat akin to the action of a two-roll mill,
 (ii) between rotor surfaces and the inside surface of the mixing chamber, and
(iii) between surfaces of the rotors that are disposed at a variety of angles to the directions of rotation.

There is also an intense kneading or folding action in the regions corresponding to the rolling bank location in a two-roll mill. Additionally, there is transport of material towards the central regions of the rotors, and consequently also transport in the opposite direction, so that cross-mixing occurs.[42] Some more recent designs (Fig. 4.11) depart from the spiralling arrangement almost entirely. The rotor of one such[43] has two sets of separate projections, one located on each side of the central transverse plane of the rotor, and the two sets spaced in intermediate circumferential locations to each other. During rotation, the

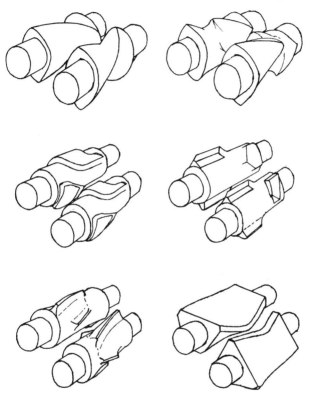

FIG. 4.11. Types of internal mixer rotors.

projections of one rotor overlap the projections on the other, so as to rotate in a similar fashion to cogs of gear wheels but without the close meshing. Transverse transfer of material is still achieved by inclined thrust faces on these projections. In another recent design,[44] each rotor is shaped like a triangular prism rotating about its main axis, the prisms being distorted by twisting the central section so that the edges form obtuse angles instead of straight lines. The two rotors are arranged so that during rotation, as a convex side of the edge of one passes into and out of the nip region it smears in close relationship to a concave side of the other rotor. Another design change introduced in the same machine is to incline the mixing chamber, so that the figure-of-eight is only about 30° from its upright position (Fig. 4.12). This arrangement does not

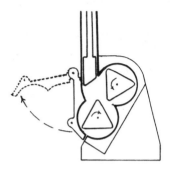

FIG. 4.12. Inclined-8 internal mixer.

appear to be inherently bound to the rotor design just described, but does permit the discharge door to be located at one side of the machine, in rather similar fashion but with a different orientation to that used with overhung rotors.

4.3.3 Control

Control of operation of an internal mixer is generally based on stock temperature[45] and possibly power consumption. An indication of the former is provided by a thermocouple probe, usually inserted in the central ridge at the bottom of the mixing chamber and coupled to an indicator and possibly an automatic controller operating the discharge door and ram. For an indication of power consumption, it has usually been necessary to rely on the ammeter normally provided in the motor supply circuit. Where more accurate measurements were to be made it has been necessary to install a wattmeter specially for the purpose. However, power consumption recorders, and controllers based on power vs time integration, are now offered as optional extras on some machines, and it is to be hoped that this will develop until such arrangements are standard, for there can be no doubt that quite small variations in compounding conditions can produce profound differences in subsequent behaviour of different batches.

4.3.4 *Power Consumption*

To the non-engineer, and possibly to the engineer as well, the most immediately impressive thing on first acquaintance with an internal mixer is the massiveness of the motor and drive arrangements in relation to volumetric capacity. This is, of course, a reflection of the relatively rapid input of work involved in compounding high viscosity materials in short mixing cycles. Clearly, power requirements depend not only on viscous behaviour of materials but also on the geometry of the mixing chamber and rotors, the speed of rotation of the rotors, and the pressure on the ram. Several attempts have been made, with varying success, to derive models for flow, power requirements, and mixing efficiency of internal mixers, in relation to the geometry of the rotors and mixing chamber, pressure on the ram, speed of rotation, and the nature of the material to be processed. For full details the reader is referred to the extensive literature on the subject.[3,18,24,45] Some useful empirical formulae have been derived, but they are usually too specific in respect of materials and machine design to be of general use.

A study of the technical literature relating to commercial internal mixers shows, as expected, a general increase in power provision with size, ranging from as little as 3·75 kW for a charge capacity of 0·0013 m^3 to as high as 3000 kW for a charge capacity approaching 0·5 m^3. At the same time, there is a general, but by no means uniform, trend for the speed of rotation of the rotors to be reduced as machine size increases. For small laboratory internal mixers, speeds may range anywhere between 45 and a few hundred r.p.m., while for the largest machines speeds between 16 and 60 r.p.m. are typical. At a charge capacity of the order of 0·1 m^3, rotor speed may be anywhere between 16 and 100 r.p.m., and at twice that charge capacity it may be anywhere between 20 and 80 r.p.m. There is a tendency to match the available power to the requirements of the particular compounding job for which the internal mixer is intended, and so two or three alternative motors and alternative speeds of rotation are sometimes offered, for a given size and model of mixer. If the batch size is known, the available power per unit mass or volume of composition can be calculated, and this, too, varies quite considerably, from under 600 to around 8000 kW/m^3. This compares with 600 to 2250 kW/m^3 for two-roll mills. While figures such as these may give some indication of the order of magnitude of power required, they are not very useful for the purpose of making comparisons between different machines. Since power consumption depends on speed of rotation of the rotors, a more meaningful quantity might be power per unit mass or volume per revolution. Even this varies quite widely, from 33 to over 280 kW/m³/revolution, but there is a slight tendency for the value to fall between 60 and 90 kW/m³/revolution, and some manufacturers appear to attempt to match similar models of machine of different sizes on the basis of this quantity. Of course, actual speeds of movement of the working surfaces of the rotors are more significant than rate of revolution, depending as they do on the geometry of the rotors and particularly the radii of the relevant parts. The necessary data are not readily available, though measurements on specific machines should not be difficult. Knowing the power consumption and the cycle time, or more precisely the integrated power–time relationship, for a known batch size, it is easy to calculate the total work done per unit mass or volume of material, and this is likely to be more relevant to estimations of amounts of mixing. For a number of reasons, however, it should not be assumed that degree of mixing will match work input per unit quantity of material. It might be possible to allow for energy dissipated as heat, but it is not obvious that even all the net energy absorbed by the material necessarily contributes to the forward movement of the state of admixture towards perfection.

As far as rubber mixing is concerned, it has been suggested[42,47,48] that energy of mixing is independent of machine design or size. This would seem reasonable for any composition. If all machines were perfectly or equally efficient in their use of energy supplied, and provided the compounding process follows the same path for a given composition, machine energy input could be taken as a measure of energy of mixing, but the first of these suppositions is highly suspect to say the least. A number of typical energy consumption values for rubber compounding have been published,[39,42,47,49-51] ranging in the region of 0·1–1 MJ/kg. This range should be compared with the range of values of power provision in commercial internal mixers indicated above. The latter corresponds to 0·09–1·2 MJ/kg for a specific gravity of 1 and a cycle of 2·5 min.

A number of studies of relationships between power consumption and progress of compounding processes have been published. Theoretical studies[18,24,42,52] have mainly attempted to relate power requirements to rheological properties, mixing chamber and rotor geometry, speed of rotation, ram pressure and charge size, and shear strains necessary for adequate mixing. While valuable in developing an understanding of the compounding process and as a basis for scale-up calculations,[24] for a variety of reasons the theoretical approach is of limited applicability to specific practical operations. For one thing, as indicated previously, the rheological characteristics of the kinds of composition that are submitted to internal mixer compounding are frequently ill-defined, and by the very nature of the process not uniform throughout the mass nor constant with time. Also, the geometry of the rotors is usually highly complex and not readily amenable to precise definition in mathematical terms. The greatest problem, however, is perhaps the determination of the total strain and strain rates required to produce the desired state of admixture. As indicated in the previous chapter, for high values of strain in laminar mixing, increase in interfacial area and decrease in striation thickness are directly proportional to total strain.[1,3] However, in practice, all volume elements within the composition need to experience the minimum strain required to attain the desired state of admixture, and this is not always simple to achieve or to take into account in calculations. Moreover, in many cases, even after the major proportion of the composition has reached a state of adequate admixture, there may remain undispersed agglomerates or particles that need to be broken down, dissolved, or melted, and their dispersal may be critical to the achievement of satisfactory product quality. An example of this is where the composition is destined for the production of thin clear film, where relatively very small numbers of undispersed particles of polymer or pigment show up disproportionately.

4.3.5 *Experimental Studies*

Experimental studies of internal mixer compounding have generally been devoted to PVC and rubbers. Some of these have used small-scale internal mixers of basically the same design as production machines, but there have been extensive studies using the Brabender 'Plastograph' (Fig. 4.13) or 'Plasti-Corder'.[53] Thus, Bergen and Darby[54] studied the compounding behaviour of PVC with various plasticisers, using a small internal mixer of the Banbury type (Fig. 4.14). They recorded temperature and power consumption, and noted 'fusion time', which was equated to the time to reach the 'power peak', i.e. the time to reach maximum power consumption. The significance of power peaks and temperature, in relation to compounding of plasticised PVC, was clearly demonstrated in work by Tughan,[10,35,55,56] who obtained photomicrographs of samples corresponding to various time intervals during the compounding cycle. Starting with a cold (25°) mixer and

FIG. 4.13. Brabender 'Plastograph' (Courtesy of Brabender OHG, Duisburg, West Germany).

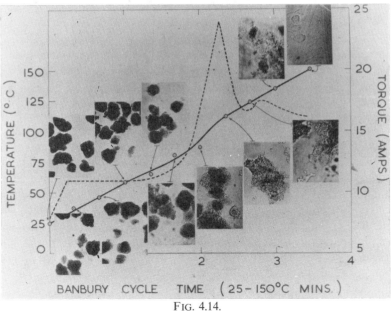

FIG. 4.14.

relying on frictional work to produce the heat required for softening and gelation, temperature rises regularly, apart from a marked increase in rate where a short break occurs when power consumption rapidly increases to the power peak. Power consumption stays sensibly constant during the early part of the cycle, and then rapidly peaks to a value typically more than twice its original value. The rapidity of this peaking is clearly dependent on the nature of the materials being processed and on the intensity of the shearing action of the rotors, but a major part of the rise in power consumption may take place in less than one-fifth of the total time to maximum power consumption. After peaking, power consumption drops steadily, presumably as a reflection of falling apparent viscosity as stock temperature continues to rise. So the compounding cycle for plasticised PVC may be divided into four sections, comprising

   (i) heating to a temperature at which plasticiser absorption becomes rapid,
  (ii) swelling of polymer particles by absorption of plasticiser,
 (iii) gelation of softened, swollen particles to form a continuum of 'molten' polymer, and
  (iv) continued shearing and heating of the molten polymer, with relatively slow dispersion of remaining pockets of undispersed polymer particles and additives, until the cycle is concluded by discharging the mass from the mixer.

Apart from the absence of swelling by plasticiser, there seems to be no reason why a similar analysis should not apply to internal mixer compounding of other polymer systems (Fig. 4.15).

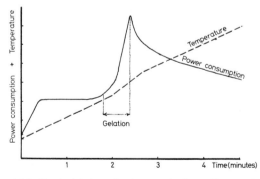

Fig. 4.15. Typical internal mixer cycle for a thermoplastic.

An examination of photomicrographs obtained from studies of the kind just described,[10,56] reveals some of the problems not only of assessing internal mixer compounding itself, but also of defining states of admixture in simple numerical terms. Shortly after the power peak, the bulk of the composition is seen to have gelled to a reasonably homogeneous mass, containing a relatively small proportion of undispersed solid or incompletely softened particles. Generally, at this level of dispersion, the composition will achieve its maximum potential of mechanical properties, and if the end-product is fairly heavily pigmented or if visual appearance is of no importance, the compounding cycle may be concluded at this point and the material discharged. If, however, the end-product is one in which undispersed components are inadmissible, e.g. transparent film, it is necessary to continue the cycle until an acceptable level of dispersion is reached. Thus, under favourable conditions, an internal mixer cycle for PVC may be as short as 1·5–3 min, whereas with some difficult compositions, e.g. containing plasticisers that are relatively inactive or additives that are difficult to disperse, cycles may have to be extended to 15 min or more.

Also using a small internal mixer, Bargellini[57] attempted to calculate total energy input during compounding of PVC with various plasticisers, by integrating the area under power consumption vs time curves, but the correct interpretation of his results is not immediately obvious. Energy consumption was found to be directly related to plasticiser reactivity, e.g. to the readiness with which a plasticiser penetrates a PVC resin particle and the polymer structure, and the opposite relationship might have been expected.[58] However, if, as has been suggested[58] for rubbers at any rate, internal mixing is an extremely inefficient operation, it should not be surprising if measurements of power consumption prove to be of limited value in interpreting mechanisms of compounding.

The previous literature on rubber compounding in internal mixing has been reviewed by Palmgren,[42] who also calculated shear strain rates and shear stresses for a variety of commercial internal mixers. As might be expected, his analysis of a compounding cycle is not dissimilar to the foregoing as discussed for PVC. Assuming that there is a fixed quantity of energy required to achieve complete dispersion over a wide range of conditions, and that this corresponds to a given number of rotor revolutions, it is clear that, for a given system, increase in rotational frequency reduces 'efficient' mixing time, but it might be expected that there would be a linear relationship between mixing time and rotational frequency over the same range of conditions, and not a non-linear one as Palmgren indicates.

4.3.6 *Scaling-up*

The subject of scaling-up results obtained with small internal mixers to production size machines has followed two alternative lines that have sometimes been confused. On the one hand, the designer wishes to know how to calculate the dimensions, rotor speeds and power provision necessary to achieve, as nearly as possible, the same compounding conditions in internal mixers of widely different capacities. On the other hand, the processing technologist may wish to know how to operate internal mixers of different capacities and designs, so as to achieve similar overall compounding on a particular composition. Palmgren[42] and Funt[24] have reviewed the various approaches to scaling-up. By the very nature of the design of machine and the materials being processed, exact scaling-up is impossible except within impracticably restrictive limitations. Nevertheless, some useful principles and equations have been presented. Bergen[18] concluded that valid scaling-up requires the clearance between rotor and mixing chamber wall to be the same for all sizes of internal mixer, and that frequency of rotation of the rotors should be inversely proportional to the width of their tips. McKelvey[2] concluded that scaling-up a mixer using the same linear scale factor for all dimensions, and using the same frequency of rotation, would result in identical shear strain rate, shear stress, power required per unit volume, and frequency of passage of any small volume element through regions between rotor tips and mixing chamber walls. Guber[59] assumed that a constant linear scale factor is used for all dimensions, and obtained a relationship between power requirements, frequencies of rotation, scale factor, and degrees of filling, i.e. ratio of actual charge to maximum possible charge. A factor that tends to complicate all scaling-up calculations is that the surface area of cooling channels tends to vary with the square, whereas total energy increases with the cube of the linear scale factor. Funt[24,60] concluded that the requirement for constant maximum shear stress is incompatible with the criterion of identical temperature/time profile. In cases where quality of mix is controlled by break-down of particles, he suggested that internal mixers should be geometrically similar, and should be operated at identical rotor speed for the same time, but that the initial temperature should be higher and the cooling less the smaller the machine. Where mix quality is controlled by total strain, Funt suggested the same approach, except that initial temperatures should be the same whatever the size of mixer. In practice, it is often possible to establish criteria for scaling-up from a particular laboratory internal mixer to a particular production machine on an empirical basis.

4.3.7 *Brabender Plasti-Corder*

Several workers have studied compounding processes by using the Brabender Plastograph or Plasti-Corder[53] (Fig. 4.16), which is rather like a very small internal mixer which has interchangeable rotors, and in which the mixing chamber is jacketed for operation generally at constant temperature. The rotors are coupled to a torque meter that records

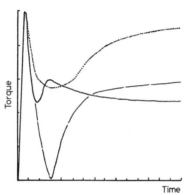

FIG. 4.16. Typical Brabender Plasti-Corder torque vs time curves for three different lubricants in PVC.

throughout the mixing cycle. With plasticised PVC, the curves obtained are similar to those obtained by Tughan[55,56] in a laboratory internal mixer, except that after gelation torque attains a constant equilibrium value when temperature is maintained constant throughout. Omiccioli–Zanella[61] also found a relatively small additional power peak, prior to the major gellification peak, which was attributed to plasticiser absorption into individual polymer particles. Other authors have reported similar results.[62] Mazzur[63] used the Plasti-Corder to examine the plasticiser absorption stage of the compounding process, and in particular to compare the absorption behaviour of different plasticisers. Uno[64] analysed the mechanisms involved in compounding PVC and showed how the Plasti-Corder could be used to evaluate alternative components in both plasticised and unplasticised PVC. Other workers[53,65] have used the instrument to analyse the compounding of unplasticised PVC, and in particular the effects of lubricants,[66-68] impact modifiers[69] and fillers.[70] The Brabender Plastograph or Plasti-Corder has also been extensively used to investigate compounding of rubbers,[71-73] in particular, to assess the effects on rheological behaviour, and ease of mixing of different varieties of reinforcing pigments,[73-75] plasticisers, process oils and other ingredients.[74,76] Some of these studies[72,73] have included direct comparisons with compounding in plant-scale internal mixers and also include correlations with Mooney Plastometer measurements.[71,73,74]

Dispersion of carbon black into powdered rubber compounds, and its effects on physical properties, has also been investigated using the Plasti-Corder.[77] In general, the Brabender Plastograph or Plasti-Corder tends to be used as an empirical guide to processing behaviour, and in the present context particularly to the effects of formulation changes on compounding in internal mixers. It can yield useful data on gelation and viscous behaviour, and on scorching and long-term stability. By comparing thin pressed specimens[76] produced under controlled conditions in a Plasti-Corder, it is possible to make comparative visual assessments of dispersibility of additives, having different optical characteristics to the matrix of compounded material, and thus this procedure can be used to assess degree of admixture.

4.3.8 Operating Procedures

Procedures for operating internal mixers depend on the nature of the polymer and additives, and have often been established as a result of production experience over many years. With thermoplastics it is common practice to pre-blend the polymer with all the additives. Although it is not unknown for some additives, that are minor in the quantitative sense, to be added to the polymer directly in the internal mixer chamber, there are often sound technical reasons for blending the whole of the composition before it experiences the intensive shearing in the internal mixer. Thus, the more thoroughly heat stabilisers are distributed throughout the composition before it encounters high temperatures, the more effective will they be. Moreover, the internal mixer cycle time may have to be extended in relation to uneven distribution of an additive at the start of the cycle. So, in general, it is to be expected that the more thorough the pre-blending, the shorter the minimum cycle time in the internal mixer. Of course, in addition to technical aspects of a particular operation, the cost of improving pre-blending has to be balanced against cost savings due to reduced compounding cycle times. However, with many compositions, e.g. plasticised PVC, pre-blending of some kind is necessary anyway, and in many cases there seems little point in deferring addition of any additives to the compounding stage.

Thermosetting plastic compositions, such as phenolic and amino formaldehyde moulding materials, will usually have been blended, e.g. by ball-milling, and in view of their reactive nature and the inherent limitation on compounding temperatures and cycle times, it seems good practice to blend these materials as thoroughly as possible before submission to compounding. It is conceivable that with a composition that requires a cross-linking agent or hardener to produce the thermosetting reactions, e.g. moulding materials based on novolak resins, it might be possible to add the cross-linking agent to the other ingredients after these have been compounded in the internal mixer, but it is doubtful if dispersion could be sufficiently rapid to reach a high level before curing has advanced to a point where discharge becomes necessary.

Techniques with rubbers tend to be somewhat different, largely because the internal mixer is also commonly being used as a masticator to modify molecular structure.[78] It has been suggested that, in the course of production of rubber vulcanisates, the mixing step introduces more variance than all the other steps together, but notwithstanding the fact that this is known, few studies of the subject have been made.[79]

Powdered rubbers can be pre-blended and compounded in much the same way as plastic compositions, although they may also be processed by techniques that are more usual for rubbers in bale form. Indeed, advantages claimed for powdered over bale rubbers are quite considerable savings in compounding cycle times and energy consumption, and consequent reduction in discharge, or 'dump', temperatures.[15] Rubbers in bale form are either first chopped into fairly large pieces, or charged directly to the mixing chamber as whole bales. Some attention to the shape and size of pieces may be necessary because some forms tend to lodge in the throat of the charging shaft or chute.[78] Unlike the usual procedures with plastics, it is common to charge the different components of a rubber compound at different times during the compounding cycle. This is partly due to the requirement for mastication with natural rubber, at least, unless it has been previously masticated by two-roll milling, and partly because of the need to avoid premature curing or scorching (as premature curing is generally known in rubber processing circles). The normal procedure with natural rubbers or synthetic rubbers that need mastication, if one can reasonably speak of a normal procedure in this context, is to masticate the rubber alone for the required period, then to add softener and antioxidant, and in successive stages proportions of powdered ingredients such as fillers, but not including curing ingredients,[80] which are added after dropping the charge onto a two-roll mill. The terms 'upside down' mixing and 'modified upside down' mixing are applied somewhat confusedly to various alternative procedures. Thus, in highly filled rubber compounds a proportion of the filler, say 30–50%, may be charged to the mixing chamber first, followed immediately by the rubber.[81,82] Once the composition has gelled or made-up the remainder of the filler and other ingredients excluding curing agents are added in the normal way. Alternatively, the rubber and all the compounding ingredients may be added to the internal mixer at the beginning of the mixing cycle, thus reducing mixing time but possibly resulting in inferior dispersion.[12] It appears that the proportion and nature of the filler are major factors determining the optimum procedure, mainly because large proportions of filler added to the rubber at an early stage may interfere with the gelation or making-up process.

With all materials, of course, long runs of successive batches of the same composition are preferred to short runs or single batches because of the disproportionate amount of cleaning time required for the latter, and because with long runs it is generally easier to establish settled conditions. It is good practice to heat the rotors and mixing chamber walls to an appropriate temperature before commencing a run, though with some compositions the frictional heat developed is sufficient to attain and maintain unaided the temperatures required, and in such cases the first few batches of a run are sometimes used to heat up the mixer. This does not seem to be good practice, since it must produce batch to batch variations in the early part of a sequence of batches, particularly if compounding cycles are operated on a time basis. With rubbers, for example, if the time cycle is established for commencing with a cold mixer, batches tend to scorch as the mixer becomes hot, whereas if the cycle is based on operation with a hot mixer early batches tend to be incompletely mixed.[78,83]

With the discharge door closed and ram raised, the rotors are set in motion, and there should normally be no need to stop them during a run of successive batches. The components are then charged to the mixing chamber through the vertical entry shaft or chute, according to the procedural sequence selected. The size of a batch obviously depends on the volumetric capacity of the machine, taking into account that there is usually some lee-way in respect of the lowest position the ram can assume during compounding. Batch size also depends on the nature of the components, not merely on the ultimate density of the composition but also, possibly, on the packing properties of solid particles of polymer and filler, and whether it is desired to submit the composition to high or low ram pressure. For example, if one is considering compounding a given formulation from one or other of two PVC resins of different packing density, but otherwise essentially identical properties, the batch size can be higher for the resin of higher packing density than the other. Provided processing is carried out properly, the products from the two different resins should be essentially identical in density as well as other properties. Although with the resin of lower packing density it would presumably be possible to raise the ram after gelation, and add more material to bring the charge up to the same size as that possible with the resin of higher packing density, such a procedure would generally be avoided because it would increase the overall cycle time and so outweigh the gain in batch size, and is also likely to introduce an element of inhomogeneity.

In general, the relationship between batch size, size of machine and nature of the material is given[84] by the simple expression

$$Q = V \times S \times F$$

where Q = batch size (kg), V = volume of mixing chamber (litres or $m^3 \times 10^{-3}$), S = specific gravity of the composition, and F = 'fill factor' or 'loading factor'.[85]

Fill or loading factor is a function of the nature of the polymer and other components of the composition, e.g. its hardness, the amount of mastication, if any, required, pressure on the ram, rotor speed and the geometry of the rotors, and has been estimated to vary between 0·65 and 0·9 for rubbers.[84] While the relationship may be useful as a broad guide, and possibly for more accurate calculations when considering different sized mixers of the same manufacturing range, published data are not sufficiently precise for it to be used for accurate calculations of batch sizes or throughput. By its very nature, published information on batch sizes of different materials is indicative, rather than specific, to individual formulations, but when in some cases a simple calculation indicates a batch volume larger than the volume of the mixing chamber, doubt is cast on the accuracy of any of the published figures. Nevertheless, a comparison of batch sizes for different materials should be instructive, although the published data varies with size of mixer in an irregular fashion. Table 4.2 lists some approximate relative batch sizes and fill factors estimated from the technical literature.

TABLE 4.2

APPROXIMATE RELATIVE BATCH SIZES AND FILL FACTORS

Material	Specific gravity	Density (kg/m^3)	Relative batch size	Fill factor
Polyethylene	1·0	1000	1·0	0·9
Polyethylene master-batch	1·02	1020	1·1	0·89
Polyethylene master-batch	1·05	1050	1·15	0·91
Polystyrene/SBR	1·05	1050	1·15–1·23	0·91–0·95
Rubber stock	1·1	1100	1·2	0·91
Rubber tread stock	1·15	1150	1·29	0·91
'Easy-processing' rubber stock	1·4	1400	1·86	1·0
Unplasticised PVC	1·4	1400	1·45–1·7	0·86–0·98
Plasticised PVC (25% filler)	1·4–1·45	1400–1450	1·65–1·97	0·96–1·0
Soft PVC flooring (55% filler)	1·7	1700	2·08	0·99
Soft PVC flooring	1·9	1900	2·67	0·99
Vinyl/asbestos floor tile	1·9	1900	2·55–2·7	0·99–1·0

It is singularly unfortunate that it is not possible to produce more precise data of general applicability, because quite small variations in batch size and cycle time can produce very significant changes in overall production rate.

Having charged the whole or the first part of a batch to the mixing chamber, depending on the procedure being adopted, the ram is lowered and the selected pressure applied to it. Over the past 20 years or so, there has been a tendency to use increased thrusts on the ram.[64,82,86] Increase in ram pressure is but one aspect of means to increase power input in order to increase mixing rates, and so reduce cycle times;[86] the other important factors being increase in rotor speed and changing the charging sequence. Up to a certain point, increasing ram pressure reduces voids in the composition, increases the speed of engagement of the material with the rotors, and increases contact between the components of the composition, and thus gives more rapid absorption.[82] With rubbers, the better contact of the components reduces any tendency to 'crumb' and improves reproducibility. A seven- or eight-fold increase from a low value has produced a 30% increase in output for some rubbers.[82] Even larger increases have been found[86] when increase in ram pressure has been associated with increase in rotor speed, but a law of diminishing returns operates, and these kinds of improvement presuppose starting from, what would probably be regarded nowadays, as an inferior technical base, at least for modern machinery. With plasticised PVC, although cycle times may be reduced by increasing rotor speed, increased ram pressure has been reported[86] as having relatively little effect.

Sometimes the ram will be raised and lowered a few times at the beginning of the cycle, to drop any material that has lodged on top of the ram into the mixing chamber, but care is necessary to ensure that this is not done too late in the cycle for the material added late to be properly incorporated. If material still remains on the ram or the sides of the charging chute, there is the danger that on raising the ram at the end of a cycle some will fall into the mass of compounded material, to appear later as undispersed matter. It is good practice, in the design of the charging chute and ram, to include some means for clearing residual material, and for the same reasons it is also desirable to formulate, as far as possible, so that the materials charged to the mixer are free-flowing.

As indicated previously, with rubber compositions, the ram may be raised a few times during the mixing cycle in order to add different components in sequence, but with thermoplastics, such as PVC, it is more common to charge all the components to the mixing chamber at the commencement of the cycle and to leave the ram down throughout. In the latter case, in the absence of forced cooling, the temperature rises steadily, as described previously (Section 4.3.5), and it is common practice to programme the mixer to discharge when some preselected temperature is reached. The maximum temperature attained is of particular importance in the compounding of PVC, since it has a profound influence on subsequent melt flow behaviour.[10,87-89] Of course, with any polymer, and particularly with halogen-containing polymers like PVC, there is always the risk of excessive degradation if temperatures are allowed to reach too high values for too long. With properly stabilised formulations this is rarely a problem, since compounding cycles are usually quite short, e.g. of the order of 1–5 min. Where the cycle has to be extended to ensure adequate mixing of difficulty dispersible components, cooling may be necessary. This has the effect not only of reducing the risk of excessive degradation, but also of keeping the viscosity relatively low, so that the shearing action is maintained at a higher intensity than would otherwise be the case. With rubber compounds, plasticity requirements usually dictate that the temperature range from about 90 to 105 °C[12,90] should be avoided, and cold mastication, i.e. below about 90 °C will necessitate cooling throughout the cycle. With hot mastication, i.e. above 115 °C, the compounded material is usually discharged when a predetermined temperature, usually just below 150 °C, is reached. In this case, any cooling that might be deemed necessary requires rather careful control. The practice of discharging a batch, allowing it to cool, and then recompounding in order to achieve higher melt viscosity and shearing, that has been used in compounding some rubber stocks, seems inherently inefficient and should be avoided if at all possible. It has been suggested[91] that varying the speed of the rotors is a good means of controlling temperature, but drive arrangements are likely to be relatively expensive, and moreover, reducing speed to stop temperature rise will presumably increase cycle time.

As indicated previously (Section 4.3.4) controllers based on power consumption vs time integration are now available. In view of the temperature sensitivity of most polymeric compositions, it might be best to use a controller of this type to trigger discharge, while using a temperature sensor in a thermostat system, for example controlling the valves of the cooling system. Perhaps better is to have heat-exchange medium circulating continuously, and to use the temperature sensor to control the temperature of the medium. This would probably be regarded as too expensive for temperatures above 100 °C, though systems are available for rubber compounding using water as the heat-exchange medium.

At the completion of the compounding cycle, the discharge door is opened and the compounded mass ejected as shapeless lump or lumps. There does not seem to be any uniformity in timing the raising of the ram. Raising the ram before or at the same time as the discharge door is opened, gives a shorter overall cycle time than delaying till the compound has been ejected, but may lead to contamination by uncompounded material from the ram and chute if steps are not taken to prevent it.

4.3.9 Handling Internal Mixer Discharge

The shapelessness and dimensions of the discharged mass from an internal mixer render it necessary to interpose at least one more intermediate processing stage before final shaping. Commonly, with rubbers and some thermosetting plastics, addition of curing or cross-linking agents may be deferred to this stage. At one time, the only possibility was to drop the discharged material directly, or via a conveyor belt, onto a two-roll mill adjusted to an appropriate nip setting and temperature, but extruder-slabbers or strainer-slabbers that will accept the whole of the compounded charge from an internal mixer and convert it to sheeting, have been available for over 20 years.[92] If no further components are to be added to the composition, as is usually the case with plastics, a single two-roll mill suffices and the main requirement is that it shall be large enough not only to accept the complete charge from the internal mixer, but also to hold a buffer stock of material so as to maintain a continuous hide or crepe between batches, while strip or separate portions are removed at one edge. If the objective is to produce granular compound for subsequent processing, it is convenient to remove a strip continuously at one edge. Most compounded granules produced in this way are in the form of approximate cubes of around 3 mm or 1/8 in side, so the nip of the mill is adjusted to yield a hide or crepe of appropriate thickness. The nip itself will be slightly smaller than the thickness of the hide, the actual difference depending on the elasticity of the compounded material. The width of the strip obviously has to be sufficiently small to feed into the granulating machine, 80–300 mm being typical. After leaving the mill, the strip may be cooled by passing through a water-bath, after which treatment it needs to be dried by streams of air, or 'air-knives', above and below the strip, before it passes to the granulator (Chapter 6, Section 6.2.4). From the granulator, the granules are delivered to a conveniently sized and located hopper or silo, whence they may be subsequently packed for dispatch or conveyed to 'in-house' machines for processing.

Where the compounded material is to be calendered, the cooling and granulating are omitted, and hot strips or pieces of hide are transferred directly to the feed nip of the calender, passing on the way a metal detector, set to stop the calender if metal contamination is detected in the compound. Sometimes the compounded material is destined for lamination in a press. In such cases the strip cutter is omitted and whole widths of hide are removed at about 0·2 mm thick, using a doctor knife.

Where further components have to be added, as is frequently the case with rubber compounds, the two-roll mill performs a vital mixing function as well as sheeting. This may help to disperse not only the additional components, such as curing agents, but may also help to improve dispersion of difficulty dispersible components, such as some carbon black master-batches, that were incorporated in the internal mixer.[78] In view of this need to use the mill for dispersion purposes, a second two-roll mill may be advantageous. Procedures for calendering rubbers directly after the milling are essentially the same as for plastics, but rubbers may also be extruded directly by conveying hot strip from the mill to the extruder hopper.[90]

An extruder-slabber or strainer-slabber is essentially a large diameter (e.g. 200–350 mm), short length extruder with a very large throated hopper that will accept a whole charge from an internal mixer and extrude it in the normal way, with the possible assistance of a ram to force the composition into the feed zone flights of the screw. Usually the slabber is fitted with a tube die, with a die-face slitting cutter that splits the extruded tube so that it can be opened out between rollers, and then cooled and granulated in the same manner as strip from a mill, or used as slab stock. Alternatively, they may be multi-holed and fitted with a die-face cutter to produce pellets directly. This is suitable for many varieties of rubber stocks, but is liable to result in overheating if the processed material has high melt viscosity.

Originally, batch compounding was a rather labour intensive activity, requiring operatives for weighing raw materials, blending, charging premix to the internal mixer, operating the internal mixer, operating the two-roll mill, controlling the granulation, and removing granulated compound, as many as seven operatives in all, but nowadays automation has advanced to the point where the whole procedure can be controlled by one person in a central control room. Most, if not all, of the disadvantages of batch processes as compared with continuous processes consequently cease to be apparent.

REFERENCES

1. SPENCER, R. S. and WILEY, R. M., *J. Colloid Sci.*, **6**, 133 p. no. (1951).
2. MCKELVEY, J. M. *Polymer Processing*, Wiley, New York (1962).
3. TADMOR, Z. and GOGOS, C. G., *Principles of Polymer Processing*, Wiley, New York (1979).
4. TOKITA, N. and WHITE, J. L., *J. Appl. Polym. Sci.*, **10**, 1011 (1966).
5. WOLF, R., *India Rubber Man*, Caxton, Caldwell, Idaho (1939).
6. HANCOCK, T. *Origin and Progress of the Caoutchouc or India Rubber Manufacture in England*, Longman, Brown, London (1857).
7. PEARSON, H. C., *Rubber Machinery*, India Rubber World, New York (1915).
8. KILLEFER, D. J., *Banbury the Master Mixer: A Biography of Farnley H. Banbury*, Palmerston, New York (1962).

9. CUDWORTH, J., *Farrel Bridge–Engineers to the Rubber and Plastic Processing Industries*, Farrel Bridge Ltd, Rochdale (1976).
10. MATTHEWS, G., *Vinyl and Allied Polymers; Vol. 2, Vinyl Chloride and Vinyl Acetate Polymers*, Plastics Institute Monograph, Iliffe, London (1972).
11. WHITEHOUSE, A. A. K., PRITCHETT, E. G. K. and BARNETT, G., *Phenolic Resins*, Plastics Institute Monograph, Iliffe, London (1967).
12. CRAIG, A. S., *Dictionary of Rubber Technology*, Newnes-Butterworth, London (1969).
13. LE BRAS, J., *Rubber, Fundamentals of its Science and Technology*, Chemical Publishing Co., New York (1957).
14. LE BRAS, J., *Introduction to Rubber*, Maclaren, London (1965).
15. EVANS, C. W., *Powdered and Particulate Rubber Technology*, Applied Science Publishers, London (1978).
16. GASKELL, R. E., *J. Appl. Mechanics*, **17**, 334 (1950).
17. BERGEN, J. T. and SCOTT, G. W., *J. Appl. Mechanics*, **18**, 101 (1951).
18. BERGEN, J. T. *Processing of Thermoplastic Materials*, Chapter 7, Bernhardt, E. C. (Ed.), Van Nostrand Reinhold, New York (1959).
19. PEARSON, J. R. A., *J. Fluid Mech.*, **7**, 481 (1960).
20. WHITE, J. L. and TOKITA, N., *J. Appl. Polym. Sci.*, **9**, 1929 (1965).
21. TOKITA, N. and WHITE, J. L., *J. Appl. Polym. Sci.*, **10**, 1011 (1966).
22. WHITE, J. L. and TOKITA, N., *J. Appl. Polym. Sci.*, **12**, 1589 (1968).
23. WHITE, J. L., *Rubb. Chem. Tech.*, **42**, 257 (1969).
24. FUNT, J. M., *Mixing of Rubbers*, RAPRA, Shrewsbury (1977).
25. BRICHTA, A. M., *Plastics Rubber Processing*, **2**(2), 49 (1977).
26. BRICHTA, A. M., *Plastics Rubber Processing*, **2**(2), 53 (1977).
27. JOHNSON, P. S., *Rubber World*, **180**(1), 47 (1979).
28. UNITED STATES RUBBER COMPANY, British Patent 847 588 (1960); US Patent 2976565 (1960).
29. CARTER BROS. (ROCHDALE) LTD, *Stock Blending Unit*, trade pamphlet, (1979).
30. BANBURY, F. H., US Patent 1 200 070 (1916).
31. WILSON, K. M., *Plast. Rubb. Wkly*, 12 October, 39, 41 (1979).
32. WALTHER, H. D., US Patent 3 005 229 (1958).
33. CLARK, W. A., US Patent 3 041 659 (1959).
34. ELLWOOD, H., *Developments in the Mixing of Rubber and Plastics*, David Bridge & Co. Ltd, Rochdale (1964).
35. MATTHEWS, G. A. R., *Advances in PVC Compounding and Processing*, Chapter 5, Kaufman, M. (Ed.), Maclaren, London (1962).
36. ENNULAT, H. and HURLER, M., *Kunststoffe*, **49**, 18 (1959).
37. KRAUSS-MAFFEI AKTIENGESELLSCHAFT, British Patent 882 204 (1961).
38. FARREL BRIDGE LTD, Rochdale, *Banbury Mixers*, Technical Bulletin 215B (1970).
39. WHITAKER, P., *J.I.R.I.*, **4**(4), 153 (1970).
40. PEUKERT, H., *Maschinen fur die Kunststoffverarbeitung*, ECON-Verlag, Dusseldorf (1959).
41. STERBACEK, Z. and TAUSK, P., *Mixing in the Chemical Industry*, translated by Mayer, K., Bourne, J. R. (Ed.), Pergamon, Oxford (1965).
42. PALMGREN, H., *Eur. Rubb. J.*, **156**, 30, 70 (1974).

43. FRANCIS SHAW & CO. LTD, Manchester, *The Mark 2 Intermix*, trade pamphlet (1977).
44. WERNER & PFLEIDERER MASCHINENFABRIK, Stuttgart, *Hochleistungs-Innenmischer mit Vorderwand-Entleerung*, technical literature (1977).
45. ELLWOOD, H., *Eur. Rubb. J.*, **159**(1/2), 17 (1977).
46. MOHR, W. D., Mixing and Dispersing, *Processing of Thermoplastic Materials*, Chapter 3, Bernhardt, E. K. (Ed.), Van Nostrand Reinhold, New York (1959).
47. BEBRIS, K. D., VASILEV, R., VERESOTSKAYA, A. and NOVIKOV, M. I., *Soviet Rubb. Tech.*, **18**(11), 25 (1959).
48. EDMONDSON, H. M. *IRI Conference on Recent Developments in Rubber Compounding*, Institution of the Rubber Industry, London (1969).
49. DANIEL, T. J. and WAKE, W. C., *Trans. I.R.I.*, **33**, 135 (1957); **34**, 79 (1958).
50. PERIBERG, S. E., *Rubber World*, **150**(2), 27 (1964).
51. STAROV, I. M., SUSHCHENKO, A. A., ARISTOV, L. G. and ARTEMEV, B. N., *Soviet Rubb. Tech.*, **20**(1), 8 (1961).
52. BOLEN, W. R. and COLWELL, R. E., *S.P.E.J.*, **14**, 24 (1958).
53. BRABENDER OHG, DUISBERG, Application bulletins concerning tests on plastic materials as well as general testing with Brabender measuring and control instruments (1978).
54. BERGEN, H. S. and DARBY, J. R., *Ind. Engng. Chem. ind. Edn.*, **43**(10), 2404 (1951).
55. HAMMOND, R., *Trans. J. Plast. Inst.*, **26**, 49 (1958).
56. DYER, B. S., *Trans. J. Plast. Inst.*, **27**, 84 (1959).
57. BARGELLINI, F., *Mat. Plastiche*, **28**(4), 372 (1962).
58. ANON, *Rubber J.*, **148**(11), 65 (1966); **151**(10), 48 (1969).
59. GUBER, F. B., *Soviet Rubb. Tech.*, **25**(9), 23 (1967).
60. FUNT, J. M., *Rubbercon '77*, Intl. Rubb. Conf. Brighton, PRI, London, pp. 27.1–27.8 (1977).
61. OMICCIOLI–ZANELLA, *Materie Plast.*, **29**, 6409 (1963).
62. TOUCHETTE,N.W.,SEPPALA,H.J.and DARBY,J.R.,*Plast.Tech.*,**10**(7),33(1964).
63. MAZZUR, R. P., *S.P.E. Ann. Tech. Conf. 1967*, *S.P.E. Tech. Papers*, **13**, 117 (1967).
64. UNO, T., *Japan Plastics Age*, February, 51 (1968).
65. JONES, D. R. and HAWKES, J. C., *Trans. J. Plast. Inst.*, **35**, 120, 773 (1967).
66. HARTITZ,J.E.,*S.P.E. Ann. Tech. Conf.1973*,*S.P.E. Tech. Papers*,**19**,362 (1973).
67. DETWEILER, D. M. and PURVIS, M. T., *S.P.E. Ann. Tech. Conf. 1973*, *S.P.E. Tech. Papers*, **19**, 647 (1973).
68. SHAH, P. L., *S.P.E. Ann Tech. Conf. 1975*, *S.P.E. Tech. Papers*, **21**, 43 (1975).
69. MALPASS, V. E., *S.P.E. Ann. Tech. Conf. 1969*,*S.P.E. Tech. Papers*,**15**,55(1969).
70. COOK, P. J., *S.P.E. Ann. Tech. Conf. 1974*,*S.P.E. Tech. Papers*, **20**, 526 (1974).
71. CLAXTON, W. E. and CONANT, F. S., *Rubber Age*, **93**(2), 80 (1965).
72. STUDEBAKER, M. L. and BEATTY, J. R., *Rubber Age*, **108**(5), 21; **108**(6), 21 (1976).
73. HOLCOMB, K. L. and STUDEBAKER, M. L. *The Use of the Brabender Plasti-Corder to Study the Mixing Operation*, Phillips Petroleum Co., Stow, Ohio, Published as Information Bulletin No. 485, Brabender OHG, Duisberg (1976).

74. ONUFER, R. J., BLAKE, W. T. and SCHMITZ, A. O., Boston Rubber Group Meeting, March. Published as Information Bulletin No. 196, Brabender OHG, Duisberg (1964).
75. SCHRAMM, G., Ann. Meeting Swedish Inst. Rubb. Tech., June. Published as Information Bulletin No. 319, Brabender OHG, Duisberg (1967).
76. KERN, N. V., PALMER, J. W. and KRON, R. B., Rubber Age, 100(1), 66 (1968).
77. WOODS, M. E., and KROSKY, R. P., Rubber Age, 106(11), 41 (1974).
78. CROWTHER, B. G. and EDMONDSON, H. M., Rubber Technology and Manufacture, Chapter 8, Blow, C. M. (Ed.), Newnes-Butterworth, London (1977).
79. BOONSTRA, B. B., Rubber Technology and Manufacture, Chapter 7, Blow, C. M. (Ed.), Newnes-Butterworth, London (1977).
80. PENN, W. S., Synthetic Rubber Technology, Maclaren, London (1960).
81. BRITISH GEON LTD, London, Breon Nitrile Rubbers (1964).
82. CROWTHER, B. G. and MORRELL, S. H., Progress of Rubber Technology, 36, 37 (1972).
83. EVANS, C. W., Rubber Age, 101(9), 61 (1969).
84. ELLWOOD, H., IRI 2nd Ann. Nat. Conf., Blackpool, Institution of the Rubber Industry, London, pp. 25–30 (1974).
85. MURRAY, R. M. and THOMPSON, D. C., The Neoprenes, E. I. Du Pont de Nemours, Wilmington (1964).
86. ELLWOOD, H., Plast. Rubb. News, March, 45 (1979).
87. BURKE, G. H. and PORTINGELL, G. C., Brit. Plastics, 36(5), 737 (1963)
88. DOWRICK, D. J., Plastics, 30, 328 (1965).
89. KHANNA, S. K. and POLLITT, W. F. D., J. Appl. Polym. Sci., 9, 1767 (1965).
90. CRAIG, A. S., Rubber Technology, Oliver & Boyd, Edinburgh (1963).
91. PERLBERG, S. E., Rubber World, 150(2), 27 (1964).
92. BROWN, J., Rubb. Plast. Age, 37(6), 400 (1956).

CHAPTER 5

Continuous Compounding Equipment

5.1 GENERAL CONSIDERATIONS

Compounding in internal mixers, as described in the preceding chapter, tends to be expensive at relatively low rates of production. For most materials, an annual production of around seven million kg is desirable, three million kg might be acceptable, but the capital and running costs of anything below one million kg are likely to be prohibitive. The normal internal mixer is a batch compounding machine, and it is widely, though not necessarily always justifiably, believed, that continuous processing is preferable because it is cheaper with respect to labour costs and better for uniformity of quality.[1] Whatever the justification, a considerable effort has been expended in developing continuous compounding machines over the past 40 years, and today a considerable variety of different designs is available. Most of these designs are derived from the principle of the screw extruder. The main function of a simple single-screw extruder is to transport, soften, compact and compress material, and to force it through a forming die, and although some mixing is achieved, this is generally insufficient for most multi-component polymer compositions that have not previously been compounded. So the most obvious differences in design of continuous compounding machines of the extruder type, are those features that have been introduced with the objective of obtaining greatly increased mixing action. While this development of continuous compounding machines has been going on, parallel developments in extruder design have also been proceeding, and nowadays it is often impossible to categorise machines as specifically one or the other. Fortunately, this does not generally create any problems, except when trying to classify machines for the purpose of writing a book such as this. The early development of extruders has been reviewed.[2-5]

The earliest machines were designed for extrusion of rubbers, which were delivered hot direct from compounding on two-roll mills, and were generally of only 3–4:1 length:diameter ratio. Perhaps the most obvious change in extruder design, since their adoption for plastics processing, has been a steady increase in length:diameter ratio from 8:1 in the early Francis Shaw PVC extruder of 1937,[5] to around 15:1 by the 1950s, and to 30:1 and more in the last decade or so. Other things being equal, one consequence of increasing length:diameter ratio is to increase dwell time and so to increase mixing, but the mixing action of even the longest single-screw extruders is inadequate for all but the simplest of polymer mixing operations, if the screw is of the usual simple continuous thread design. As McKelvey,[6] and Tadmor and co-workers,[7] following Mohr et al.,[8] have shown, total strain in a single-screw extruder depends markedly on the initial position of a particle within the screw channel. Their calculations indicate that the total strain associated with positions towards the centre of the channel, may amount to as little as one-third of that associated with positions adjacent the barrel or screw surfaces.

Compared with a single-screw extruder, a twin-screw machine adds the possibility of increased mixing by virtue of shearing in the regions between the surfaces of the two screws, and many modern twin-screw extruders might equally well be regarded as continuous compounders. A small number of compounding machines use more than two screws or rotating members, and there are even machines that depart from the screw principle altogether, though few of the latter have been available for sufficiently long to have been widely accepted for general compounding purposes.

Several reviews of continuous compounding equipment have been published,[9-15] but most of these survey only a limited proportion of the machines available and tend to be biased towards a particular form of machine, or towards the compounding of a specific polymer. One of the earliest machines intended for continuous compounding was that designed by Longo and Angelis, and shown at the Milan Fair in the mid 1950s.[16] This was specifically intended for PVC. Polymer and additives were charged to a heated batch blender that discharged into a hopper, from which a screw conveyor carried premix to the bottom of a vertical heated screw blender. From the top of the screw blender, the material was discharged into the nip at one end of a heated two-roll mill, and the crepe that formed was removed as strip at the far end and fed directly to the feed end of an extruder that could produce profiles, or to a granulator to produce pellets. The Pastorello combined mixer and extruder, which appeared some time later,[17] is really a condensation of the same concept, omitting the two-roll mill. Mixing in extruders depends on the detailed material flow patterns, largely occurs by laminar shearing, and can be assessed in terms of mean total shear deformation or strain and residence time distribution.[1, 13, 18, 19] For this reason, as implied previously, the most obvious differences between any extruder-compounder and a conventional extruder are the design features aimed at increasing total shear and maintaining its uniformity. Other important requirements that are particularly desirable, though not limited to continuous compounding machines include:

(i) smooth delivery of feed stock, even when the latter is a powder blend that is not free-flowing,
(ii) avoidance of regions of over-heating,
(iii) adaptability to different formulations, and
(iv) efficient venting arrangements.

5.2 GENERAL ASPECTS OF EXTRUDER COMPOUNDING

5.2.1 Feeding Arrangements

The feed stock for continuous compounding is usually a blend of polymer and the additives required by the formulation to be processed, although the concept of separate feeding to a continuous conveying, compounding rotor was introduced over 20 years ago.[20] When the blend is made up predominantly of granules or pellets of polymer and perhaps master-batch, smooth feeding is not usually a problem and simple gravity operated hoppers may be adequate. Dry-blends of suspension polymers may also feed satisfactorily by gravity, provided the particle size is relatively large, i.e. having an average diameter not much less than $100\,\mu$m, and provided any liquid or sticky additives have been completely absorbed within the polymer particle structure during the blending process. Blends made from polymers of smaller particle size, or containing unabsorbed soft or liquid additives, will generally not feed smoothly from a gravity operated hopper, and require some means of assistance if consistent delivery is to be achieved (Fig. 5.1). The severity of the problem depends on the flow behaviour of the blend, on the shape of the hopper and particularly the dimensions of the throat and exit port, and

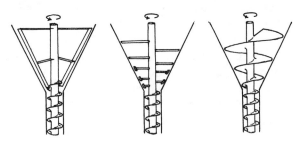

FIG. 5.1. Screw feeding devices.

also on the design of the screw or other design in the region to which feed stock is delivered from the hopper. The simplest form of device to aid feeding consists of a rotating stirrer that sweeps the walls of the hopper and also agitates blend in the region of the exit. Properly designed, such a device can at least prevent bridging in the lower regions of the hopper, but by itself may not be sufficient to ensure smooth feeding with all types of blend.

Particularly with fine particle or damp blends, some form of positive or forced feeding may be necessary. Perhaps the simplest form this can take, though not simple in terms of engineering, is a hopper with a ram that forces the blend into the feed section of the compounding screw. More satisfactory because the necessity of retracting the ram periodically is avoided, is the provision of a rotating agitator and a screw, or more properly an auger, at the bottom cylindrical section of the hopper.[15, 19, 22] Alternatively, the auger may extend upwards into the hopper with a conical shape corresponding to the inside form of the hopper.[21, 24] With arrangements of this type, the hopper may be sealed and fitted with vacuum equipment so that some drying and de-gassing of the material can be carried out. Another form of controlled feed device has a separate single- or twin-screw extruder, conveying ungelled blend to the compounding unit, either directly[25, 26] or in a so-called 'cascade' arrangement.[23] Where poor flow and bridging in the hopper do not present any problem, grooves or notches in the feed section of the barrel can greatly increase feed rate.[12, 23, 24]

Certainly, feeding arrangements are of prime importance if a uniformly satisfactory product is to be manufactured, not only in a compounding process but also in extrusion generally, and it is significant that interest in this aspect of polymer processing has increased in recent years.[23, 24]

5.2.2 Temperature Control

Over-heating is something to be avoided in any polymer processing, but its significance in any specific case obviously depends on the thermal stability of the composition and particularly the polymer to be processed. Good control of external heating is clearly a prerequisite, but since extruder compounding depends on laminar shearing, generation of heat by shear is likely to be more intense than in a simple extruder, and careful design is necessary to ensure that this does not tax the material stability beyond its limits. Also, although dwell time in regions of high shear must be sufficiently long for the required degree of mixing to be achieved, this must be related to the capabilities of the composition, and the design must be such that, as near as possible, all parts of the composition receive the same treatment. The rheological properties of the melt are also significant, because they affect the pattern of flow paths, and the back-pressure arising from interaction between screw pumping action and flow restriction by the head and die. What might be a satisfactory screw and die combination for one composition, may be disastrous for another of higher relative melt viscosity and perhaps lower stability. One final point that should not need stating but which, in spite of its importance, is sometimes overlooked, is that regions of stagnation must be avoided at all costs.

5.2.3 Adaptability

The need, or otherwise, for a compounding machine to be adaptable to different formulations obviously depends on the pattern of production. Ideally, any one machine should operate continuously on a single composition, for then both size and design can be matched closely to optimum requirements. A single-screw extruder may fairly simply be provided with alternative screws, interchangeable according to the nature of the material to be processed. Another approach is to constitute the screw by a number of interchangeable screw and kneader sections of different configurations, carried on a shaft driven as in a conventional extruder.[27, 28]

5.2.4 *Venting*

Venting, i.e. application of vacuum to a port in the barrel or even the screw, in order to remove volatiles and reduce air pressure, has been a possibility for many years,[9,10,29,30] but after a long period of somewhat limited use, it is only relatively recently that the practice is being adopted much more widely. For removal of water, or other substances that are volatile at melt temperatures, an opening in the barrel may be sufficient without using vacuum. For venting to be possible the material must pass through a region of low pressure, and this will usually necessitate a decompression zone following a zone or zones where compression and gelation have occurred. This can be accomplished by dividing the screw into two or more sections in tandem,[10,13] or by using more than one screw in a cascade arrangement.[22,23,31,32]

5.2.5 *Mixing in Extruders*

Perhaps the simplest form of continuous compounding machine to visualise is one in which melts to be mixed are pumped through a rotating hollow barrel. Mixing in a machine of this design has been analysed, and experiments with black and white polystyrene in a laboratory model yielded results in good accord with theory.[33] Such a machine might be suitable for compounding different polymers or polymer with master-batch, but would require some previous compounding operation if it was to deal with more complicated systems. The theory of mixing in screw extruders has received a good deal of attention.[8,18,19,34–40] As indicated previously, the general conclusion seems to be that the conventional single-screw extruder is a poor mixing device because of the way that total shear depends on position within the screw channel.[6–8,39] Erwin[40] extended the analysis to single screws with mixing sections, and suggested that dramatic improvements in mixing can be made without greatly increased work, by having mixing sections that act by orienting interfaces in the melt to more favourable alignment for mixing by subsequent shearing. With the conventional simple screw form the total shear and hence the mixing increases with

(i) increasing screw length,
(ii) increasing or decreasing the helix angle from the optimum for output,

(iii) diminishing channel depth,

(iv) increase in clearance between screw land and barrel,

(v) increase in back-pressure using screen packs, dies with longer land parallels, or restrictor valves, and

(vi) increase in melt viscosity obtained, for example, by judicious use of screw cooling.[12,13]

The importance of melt viscosity draws attention to the significance of formulation in relation to compounding behaviour, in addition to its well-recognised significance in relation to product properties. However, formulation variations may affect not only melt viscosity but also melting and gelation behaviour, which may be even more important.[41] For a particular polymer, selection of additives, particularly lubricants and fillers, may have a profound effect on gelation and hence compounding behaviour.[12,42,43]

5.3 SINGLE-SCREW COMPOUNDING MACHINES

5.3.1 Two-section Screws

Perhaps the simplest, if not the most economic, way to achieve satisfactory mixing with a simple extruder that is not capable of fully compounding some particular composition, is to feed a blend of the composition to the extruder, using a small rod or lace die, to granulate the extrudate and later re-feed it to the extruder, repeating the process for as many times as are necessary. This procedure has occasionally been used as a stop-gap, but it can hardly be recommended for continuous production in normal circumstances. However, to some extent the principle of the two-section screw, effectively two screws in tandem, is not far removed from this idea, and cascade systems using two extruders in succession perhaps seem more obviously based on the same idea, although the basic reason for the introduction of cascade systems is somewhat different. Screws divided into two or more sections, each of which is effectively a single extruder screw, have been available for over 20 years[10] but appear recently to have become more popular. The screw sections of these extruder-compounders (Fig. 5.2) follow normal screw design practice but are separated by zones of no compression, achieved, for example, by means of an intermediate threadless section, or by a rapid change in compression by increased flight depth and/or pitch. In

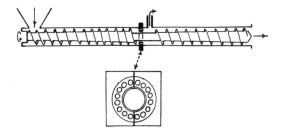

FIG. 5.2. Two-section extruder-compounder with intermediate breaker-plate.

an early machine of this type, the Andouart 'gellifying' machine, a second breaker-plate was interposed through the barrel to locate around the threadless part of the screw.[10] This produces increased back-pressure and hence increased shearing in the first section of the screw. In modern machines with generally rather higher length:diameter ratios, an intermediate breaker-plate is not normally included.[30] Provided the reduction in compression on passing from the first screw section is sufficiently great, volatile materials including water vaporise and cause the melt to froth, so that a vent may be provided in the barrel at this point and the volatiles can be removed,[30] or allowed to escape before the melt is recompressed in the second section of the screw. For successful operation, the second screw section must remove melt faster than the first section supplies it, and to ensure that this is possible with different materials, a throttle valve may be provided at the end of each screw section.[30] For the first section this may involve providing a melt channel, outside the normal barrel, that passes from a point towards the end of the first screw section to the take-up region of the second screw section, the throttle acting on this by-pass channel.[30] Machines of this type are used for compounding polyolefins, plasticised PVC, unplasticised PVC based on low molecular-weight copolymer, polystyrene and acrylic. They can often be used for direct extrusion of finished product from dry-blend, for example in the production of PVC insulated electric cables.

5.3.2 Smear-heads

Putting two screws in tandem, i.e. as a single screw divided into two sections, tends to make the overall length rather high. It is obvious, for example, that arranging two screws of 15:1 length:diameter ratio in tandem produces a screw having length:diameter ratio of at least 30:1, which, though quite common nowadays, would at one time have been regarded as difficult to engineer. Another concept was to add to the tip of the screw a relatively short section designed to give intensive shearing. In its simplest form this consists of a smooth, flightless smear-head with only a small clearance from the inside barrel surface[9,44] (Fig. 5.3). A

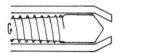 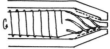

FIG. 5.3. Types of smear-head.

variety of designs has developed from this simple concept. The Gordon 'Plasticator'[45] is based on a somewhat similar principle, but the shearing section tapers down within the narrowing channel of the barrel which has a larger angle of taper than the screw-head. This conical head on the screw is formed with spiral flutes, while the inside of the barrel-head is fluted internally with straight grooves. The flutes are round-topped and round-bottomed, and material passing through them is alternately squeezed and stretched. The clearance between screw-head and barrel-head can be adjusted by longitudinal movement of the screw. This machine was specifically designed for mixing and mastication of rubber stocks, which are usually extruded as tube which is slit to form continuous strip. A Gordon Plasticator, with a 508 mm diameter screw and a 520 kW motor, can masticate something in the region of 3000–4000 kg/h of preheated smoked sheet rubber, equivalent to the output of a 2100 mm high speed two-roll mill operating on a batch of 125–135 kg and a cycle time of 30 min, i.e. a throughput of 250–275 kg/h.[45]

Not dissimilar is the Barmag 'dynamic mixer 3DM'[46,47] which comprises a rotor constructed of profiled discs attached to the extrusion screw, and thus forming a radially grooved rotor, rotating within a radially grooved barrel or stator. The grooves are off-set against each other and partially overlap, so that material passes successively from grooves in the rotor to grooves in the stator and *vice versa*. In some cases, additives may be introduced at the point of entry to the mixing zone. Another variation on the smear-head is to have a number of annular studs or 'slotted discs' instead of a helix around the final section of the screw. Yet another design has the threads interrupted by gaps, and has a number of studs within the flights.[47,48]

A somewhat different arrangement, which is nevertheless based on essentially the same principle, has a separate rotor following the extruder screw and driven from the opposite side.[49] This rotor may be plain or fluted, tapered or regular, to match the contours of the channel inside the associated region of the barrel or stator.

5.3.3 *Helix Angle*

Changing the configuration of the helical shape of an extruder screw introduces several possibilities. As mentioned in Section 5.2, one way of increasing mixing in a simple screw extruder is to change the helix angle from the optimum for output. Although not immediately obvious, the 'Rotomill' compounding machine,[20,49] appears to be based on this principle (Fig. 5.4). The original machine had a fluted tapered rotor

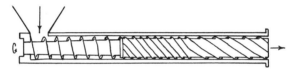

FIG. 5.4. Zones with increased helix angle (Rotomill principle).

revolving in a smooth tapered stator. The flutes were at 70° to the axis, but it was stated that 45–60° should be sufficient. Polymer was introduced at one hopper and dry pigments were added at a second downstream of the first. In a larger version there were three sections: a conventional screw at the hopper end, followed by two consecutive fluted sections of different helix angle, each with its own hopper. A final screw section might follow the second fluted section. These machines are reputed to be satisfactory for rubber tread stocks and for PVC plasticisation. The idea of using fluted sections has been used in a number of other arrangements, and the angle between the channels and the screw axis may have almost any value between zero and a right-angle.[3,39,48,50–52]

5.3.4 *Obstructions and Barriers*

Once having accepted the possibility of departing from the simple configuration of the conventional screw section, there is no reason why special mixing sections should not be located at one or more positions along the screw, rather than at the tip as with smear-heads, and there has been an increasing tendency to follow this concept. Thus, mixing screws may be found with studded sections, like those referred to earlier, following the feed zone and leading to a metering zone[53] (Fig. 5.5).

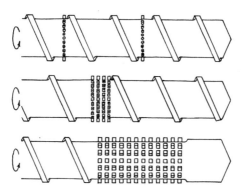

FIG. 5.5. Screws with studs or 'pins'.

Another arrangement is to interpose around the middle section of the screw, a number of circular cams eccentric to the screw axis so that their outermost surfaces move closely to the barrel wall, and each cam being oriented at a small angle, say, 30° to the next (Fig. 5.6). A less dramatic

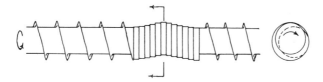

FIG. 5.6. Screw with eccentric discs or circular cams.

change from the screw principle, but having a somewhat similar function to the studded arrangement, is to slot the flight channel walls at intervals,[39, 54] thus effectively causing repeated division and recombination of the flow streams. The so-called 'isobaric back track' or 'gateway' screw has rearward facing gateways cut into the barrel walls over a short section to force material backwards, and so increase residence time.[55] This appears to be achieved by overlapping the ends of the barrel walls at the slots (Fig. 5.7). In the Japanese DIS element, the channel walls are in short sections providing a complex system of spiral passages that are interconnected by channels drilled in the screw.[48] To

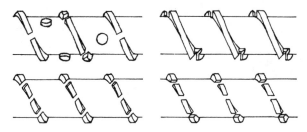

FIG. 5.7. Slotted screws.

the extent that the lands of most of the mixing elements discussed in this and the preceding two paragraphs have rather small clearances with respect to the internal barrel surface, they operate on a barrier principle. Material is subjected to intensive shearing, melt is forced through the narrow gaps between the lands of the barrier and the barrel wall, leading to break-down of agglomerates and solid particles, so acting as a filter preventing forward conveyance of solid and allowing passage of melt only.[48]

This barrier principle operates in conventional rapid-compression extruder screws, such as those commonly used for extrusion of nylons, and several other designs of screw. The Maddock mixing section,[47, 51, 53, 56-59] usually located near the end of a long metering section, has flow channels parallel to the screw axis separated by ridges having small clearances (0·38–0·64 mm) with respect to the barrel (Fig. 5.8). The channels are in two sets, one continuing up-stream to the

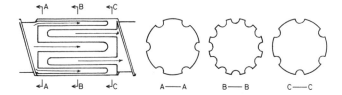

FIG. 5.8. Maddock barrier principle.

metering section but stopping a short distance before the end of the mixing section, and the other set commencing a short distance down-stream of the metering section and continuing to the delivery end of the mixing section. The two types of groove alternate around the periphery of the screw core. In order to pass on, material has to transfer from the inlet to the outlet grooves over the intervening ridges, the latter thus acting as barriers or dams to unmelted polymer. Where the resultant shear is excessive and liable to cause degradation, the shearing effect can be reduced by tapering the inlet channels by gradual reduction in depth.[59] The barrier principle is also the basis of twin-channel screws such as the Maillefer,[3,48,53,58,60] the HPM 'double wave' screws[46,58,59-62] and the 'Barr-2' screw[63] (Fig. 5.9). The former has two spiral channels,

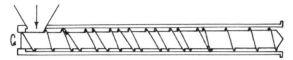

FIG. 5.9. Maillefer two-channel screw.

one starting normally at the feed point and tapering off in width and depth, eventually petering out a few turns before the screw tip, and the other tapering down backwards from the metering zone to peter out just before the feed point is reached. Material is plasticised in the first channel and has to flow over the flight lands to enter the second channel and thence to the metering zone. In a more recent development two or three twin-channel sections are located in series on a single screw. The principle of the wave screw is that the root of screw channel has a succession of humps, so that material flowing down it is repeatedly compressed and decompressed. In a double wave system this principle is used in what is essentially a twin-channel screw. The Barr-2 screw is described as having a 'barrier flight' introduced into the feed section channel,[63] but it is really a twin-channel screw operating on the barrier principle (Fig. 5.10).

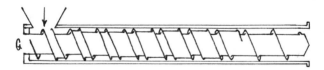

FIG. 5.10. The Barr-2 two-channel screw.

In the feed section the main channel is the solids feeding channel. Running behind it in relation to the screw tip is a narrower melt channel. Proceeding down-stream towards the screw tip each channel retains its original width, but while the feed channel is progressively reduced in depth the melt channel increases in depth, until the two channels merge at the end of the melting section. Transfer of material to the melt channel has to take place over the screw lands, so the barrier principle operates in similar fashion to the Maillefer screw described previously.

5.3.5 *Channelled Barrels*

The 'Transfermix'[13-15,39,64-67] (Fig. 5.11) also employs two sets of channels, in accordance with a so-called 'enforced order', 'convergence–divergence' principle, but the screw or rotor has what is in effect a single channel, and the other channel is in the barrel or stator. The channels in

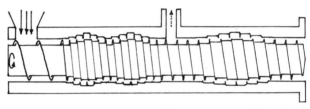

FIG. 5.11. Enforced order, convergence–divergence potential principle (Transfermix).

the barrel spiral in the opposite sense to those in the screw, and the depths of both sets of channels successively increase and decrease out of step with each other. Thus, the screw flight height decreases where the depth of the barrel channel increases. As a consequence of these configurations, the material flow path alternates between screw channel and barrel channel as the material passes from the feed region to the delivery region. Material starts to follow a vortex flow path in the rotor channel as soon as it reaches the barrel and, being immediately transferred to the barrel channel, starts to melt as a result of heat from external heaters. The dimensions of the vortices successively diminish and increase, transfer from one channel to the other occurring by 'unpeeling' the outside layer of a vortex into the receiving channel.[13] For normal rubber compounding four transfer stages are sufficient. Outputs of rubber stock vary from around 270 kg/h for an 80 mm diameter machine to around 16 000 kg/h for a 530 mm diameter machine. Mixing of highly filled stocks is said to be inadequate in one pass,[65] but in addition to normal rubber stocks the Transfermix is said to be suitable for processing colour concentrates and carbon black master-batches, direct mixing of low concentrations of pigments into resin, compounding of resins with low proportions of talc, asbestos, glass, etc., resin/resin compounding, compounding resins with plasticisers, and low shear compounding of sensitive materials such as cross-linkable polyethylene and precharged foamable pellets.[13]

The Ikegai 'SX' extruders also use channelled barrels in the so-called 'plasticating' zone, where special spiral grooving in both screw and barrel produces high shear.[68] An abrupt increase in barrel and screw diameter at the entrance region of the zone induces radial flow into the barrel grooves, and a steady reduction in diameter transfers material back into the grooves between the screw flights. This design is claimed to increase output and decrease power consumption compared with more traditional designs.

5.3.6 Screws with Kneaders

Another means of achieving the shearing required for thorough compounding is to interpose between conventional screw sections one or more kneading zones, each comprising a number of cam-like members off-set in relation to each other. These cam-like kneaders may be eccentrically arranged circular discs, lozenge-shaped, i.e. roughly like an ellipse, or like equilateral triangles with convex curved sides and apices, as in the Werner and Pfleiderer ESK machines,[69] which are based on a similar principle to the well-known twin-screw ZSK machines[10,28,70] (Fig. 5.12). The kneading members are relatively thin, so that a kneading

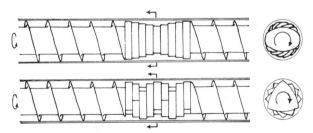

FIG. 5.12. Screws with lozenge-shaped and triangular kneaders.

zone may comprise several kneading members with their apices disposed in progressively different positions around the outside circumference of the maximum screw diameter. Material is conveyed forward by the conventional screw sections. The action of each kneader is to force material between it and the barrel in the direction of rotation with a rolling, kneading motion. Some material, of course, passes into the space swept by the next kneader, and so on until the sheared material passes into the succeeding screw section, and thence to any further kneading and extrusion zones and ultimately to the discharge point. A feature of the ESK and ZSK machines, that seems to be becoming adopted more generally, is to have a variety of kneader and screw sections of different dimensions that can be interchanged to suit different compounding requirements. This is achieved by having a circular shaft with a key-way to carry and hold the various elements, replacing the conventional solid screw. The ESK machine is claimed to be suitable for compounding polyethylene, polypropylene and polystyrene. Throughputs for these machines range from 400–700 kg/h for polyethylene or polystyrene and 350–550 kg/h for polypropylene, with an 83 mm diameter screw powered by a 150 kW motor, to 4200–7500 kg/h polyethylene or polystyrene and 3600–5400 kg/h polypropylene, with a 340 mm screw powered by a 1650 kW motor. These figures indicate energy inputs in the region of 0·013–0·028 MJ/kg, considerably lower than the values suggested for internal mixing of rubber (Chapter 4, Section 4.3.4).

In the machines just described, the shearing action involves deformations of material due to changing configurations of the regions it occupies at different angular positions of the screw. A similar mechanism operates in the Mitsubishi 'high mix' HM extruder, which comprises a screw of polygonal cross-section rotating within a barrel of hexagonal cross-section. As a consequence of this design, 'packets' of material are deformed alternately between triangular and rectangular shaped sections. In addition, there is repeated interchange of contact of material between screw and barrel, thus leading to uniform melt temperature.[68]

5.3.7 *Shear Cone Units*

A rather more apparent departure from conventional screw geometry appears in the Wacker system 'Plastificator', also manufactured by Werner and Pfleiderer.[1,3,10,25,26,71] This machine is intended specifically for the compounding and pelletising of plasticised PVC compositions, and although it has been used for harder materials its use for these is certainly not widespread. The major part of the compounding in this machine is accomplished in what is appropriately described[71] as a 'shear cone' unit (Fig. 5.13). This comprises a conical rotor increasing in diameter in the direction of material flow rotating within, and in close proximity to, a conical fixed housing or stator. The conical rotor may be

FIG. 5.13. Shear cone compounding screw.

regarded as a 'ribbed cone', or as a smooth cone carrying fillets inclined at a small angle to the overall direction of flow. Integral with the conical rotor is a short screw section, that receives blended material from a twin-screw conveying unit and passes it to the shear cone region. Clearance between conical rotor and stator can be varied by axial adjustment of the whole rotor unit, so that shearing intensity can be varied. In operation, both stator and rotor are pre-heated to a temperature appropriate for the composition to be processed, and the clearance is adjusted to a fairly low value. Initially, feeding blended material at a relatively slow rate, once compounded material is emerging from the delivery point, the clearance and feed-rate can be increased together until the optimum settings for output and quality are attained. Once the machine is in operation, the frictional heat generated in the shear cone is usually sufficient to maintain the necessary processing temperatures, and the external heating can be switched off. The behaviour of material in the shear cone has been likened to two-roll milling, without having a rolling bank that is partially cooling.[25] The rolling material becomes elongated and forms circular bands around the rotor, resembling milling rolling banks but without the cooling. On reaching the base of the cone, the shear forces cause these circular bands to leave the gap between rotor and stator, where a separating device causes them to emerge through an appropriate opening in the latter in a form similar to 'chipolata sausages'. Subsequent handling depends on the particular model of machine. In early production machines, the compounded material was passed directly through a die-face cutting pelletiser, to produce pellets of somewhat variable shape and size.[26] A more satisfactory arrangement is to feed the sausages of compounded material directly to a conventional screw extruder with die-face cutting for more regular pellets. The screw may be integral and co-axial with the shear cone,[1,10,26] or a separate extruder aligned in any desired orientation may be used.[71] Outputs of plasticised PVC with Plastificators range from 150–350 kg/h for a machine with a 30 kW main drive, to 450–800 kg/h for a larger machine with 55 kW main drive.

5.3.8 *Barrels with Internal Projections*

Another general principle that has been used in various different ways to increase shear mixing, is to provide projections of one kind or another on the inside surface of the barrel, to interact within channels between slotted annular discs on the rotating member or through slots in the normal screw thread. One such device[72] comprises comb-like members having teeth engaging annular grooves in the rotor. To cope with materials of different melt viscosities, it is necessary to have interchangeable comb-like members of different dimensions. An alternative arrangement[73] is to provide separate 'knives' whose orientations to the channels between the discs can be varied by adjustments from the outside of the barrel. The 'pin' extruder[74, 75] has rows of radial pins projecting through the barrel into the region swept by slots in the screw. As an example,[75] a 150 mm extruder with a length:diameter ratio of 16:1 is fitted with 12 mm diameter pins in eight longitudinal rows of ten pins each, the rows being disposed at equal angles, i.e. 45° around the central screw axis (Fig. 5.14). Each pair of annular sets of pins are 0·8 D apart, and the pins

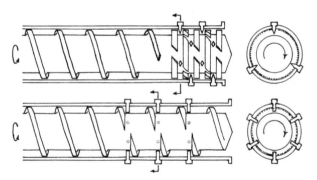

FIG. 5.14. Barrels with internal studs, lugs, pins or knives.

clear the screw root by 1 mm. This machine has been used satisfactorily to compound pigmented natural rubber, difficult carbon black filled natural rubber, and black filled SBR stocks. Experiments with plasticised PVC[38] suggest that satisfactory compounding can be achieved with either of the two arrangements just described.

The List system Buss Ko-kneader[1, 3, 9, 10, 14, 15, 21, 22, 67] (Fig. 5.15) is another compounding machine that has a slotted screw and related studs, lugs or teeth on the inside barrel surface, though it pre-dates the

FIG. 5.15. Buss 'Ko-kneader' with barrel open.

pinned cylinder extruder by nearly 25 years.[21] In the Ko-kneader, the teeth or studs and the corresponding slots in the screw extend through essentially the complete length of the screw, and, in addition to the normal rotational movement, the screw has a reciprocatory motion, during which the slots pass over the mixing teeth (Fig. 5.16). Production

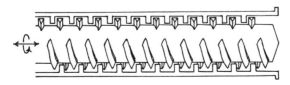

FIG. 5.16. Reciprocating slotted screw in barrel with internal teeth or pins (List system Ko-kneader).

models of the machine usually have three axial rows of fairly wide slots cut at 120° to each other, and extending over the whole length of the screw, so that the screw may be regarded as comprising three rows of kneading elements.[67] As a consequence of the combined rotational and reciprocating motions, each element traces out a figure-of-eight path for each rotation, and practically all the barrel surface is traversed by the screw elements. The fixed kneading teeth on the barrel are located in those areas that are not so traversed. Each fixed kneading tooth, and pair of screw kneading elements associated with it, for the time being act like a mill in imposing shear forces on the material in the space between them. As a consequence, material is subjected to continuous and pulsating shearing as it passes through the machine, but the discharge is also pulsating. It is possible to granulate the extrudate by fitting a multi-hole lace die and arranging a die-face cutter to rotate at a rate integrated with the reciprocating motion, but it is generally more satisfactory to use a cascade arrangement, transferring the extrudate directly to a conventional extruder fitted with a suitable granulation or pelleting arrangement. Alternatively, the screw-head may be fitted with a fluted rotor with small clearance within a die-head, fitted with a cutting ring to produce granules direct. Another means of dealing with the pulsation is to provide the screw with a smooth cylindrical extension that rotates in a wider chamber arranged eccentrically, so that there is only a narrow gap between the rotating cylinder at the entry side of a discharge opening in the lower chamber wall, and practically no gap on the other side[76] (Fig. 5.17). The action of this additional unit is, therefore, not unlike that of a single-roll mill (Chapter 3, Section 3.15).

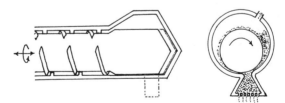

FIG. 5.17. Torpedo and head for handling pulsating discharge.

Ko-kneaders are available in a range of sizes, and with various different screw and kneading teeth configurations to meet varying compounding needs. Because the intense shearing action occurs along its whole length, the screw of a ko-kneader is short relative to other machines of the same diameter.[77] This in itself gives some mechanical advantages,[78] but the combination of rotational and reciprocatory motion does require rather special attention to design of the bearings. Because of the particular geometry, the capacity of larger Ko-kneaders scaled-up on a direct linear basis increases with the cube of the diameter,[77] whereas for other types of compounding extruder the capacity increases by the power of only 1·4–2.[79] Shear rate, residence time and power input per unit mass remain constant at constant speed for the same material.[77] Ko-kneaders have been used for a long time for the compounding of poly-ethylene and PVC, polystyrene and impact polystyrenes, and even thermosetting phenolics and aminoplasts,[21] but now machines are offered for almost all thermoplastics including polypropylene, ABS, SAN, polyacetal and cellulose acetate, some thermosetting compositions including glass-reinforced polyester moulding compounds,[80] synthetic and powdered rubbers, and even powder coatings based on epoxy, polyester, acrylic or alkyd-melamine resins. Depending on the material, the composition may be fed as pre-blend or as separate ingredients to the feed point, or additives may be introduced at points down the barrel. The latter procedure is particularly advantageous where additives are reactive or fragile, e.g. glass fibres in unsaturated polyesters.[80,81] The pattern of gelation and mixing of PVC in a Ko-kneader has been studied in some detail,[79] and energy balances have been calculated for some glass fibre-reinforced polyester compositions.[80]

Because of the variations in machine characteristics and the range of types and grades of materials processed in these compounding machines, it is not possible to give precise figures for output and power consumption, but the following may be taken as a guide. The smallest production machine available appears to be a 46 mm diameter model. With a 15 kW drive unit this has an output of 40 kg/h of UPVC and around 75 kg/h of plasticised PVC, presumably depending on the formulation. A diameter of 100 mm seems to be the most generally used at the smaller end of the range. Powered with a 50 kW drive unit, this should produce up to 120 kg/h of polypropylene, UPVC or cellulose acetate compound, up to 150 kg/h of low or high density polyethylenes, plasticised PVC, general purpose or impact polystyrene, or ABS, and up to 200 kg/h of polyurethane or synthetic rubber stock. Increasing the power of the drive unit to 70 kW raises the output of UPVC to 400 kg/h and of plasticised PVC to 750 kg/h. At the other end of the range. a 300 mm diameter model with a 380 kW drive unit should compound up to 1800 kg/h of polypropylene or cellulose acetate, up to 2000 kg/h of

UPVC, general purpose or impact polystyrene, or ABS, up to 2500 kg/h of polyethylene, polyurethane or synthetic rubber and up to 3300 kg/h of plasticised PVC. Outputs up to 3200 kg/h of UPVC have been claimed.[81]

5.3.9 *Recent Developments*

The late 1970s were remarkable for the number of new extruder and compounder designs that appeared. Two of these that may be regarded as single-screw compounders have yet to be mentioned. Of these, the Scientific Process and Research 'Supermixer' has a superficial resemblance to the Maillefer and Barr-2 machines described previously (Section 5.3.4). However, while the screw of this machine does indeed have twin-channels that do act on a kind of barrier principle, one channel is fed with resin and the other with additives, the barrier being between solid resin and additives rather than solid resin and melt. As usual, melt transfers across the lands from the trailing or 'wiping' side of the resin channel toward the leading side, so that the additives enter the melt film at the beginning of the flight profile, with high-shear mixing occurring in the spaces between screw land and barrel, along the whole length of the screw[82] (Fig. 5.18). The second machine has what is called a

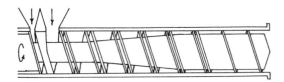

FIG. 5.18. Separate polymer and additives channels.

'bidirectional screw' or 'solids draining screw'. This comprises a conventional rotating screw that has a circular cylindrical hollow from partway within the melting zone up to the delivery end. The inside surface of the screw acts as the barrel wall for a stationary screw or stator within the hollow, threaded so that rotation of the main screw conveys material backwards towards the feed zone. The main screw has two ports into the stator channel, one at the forward end being an entry point for unmelted material, and the other being a transfer port from the stator channel to the melting zone channel of the main screw (Fig. 5.19).

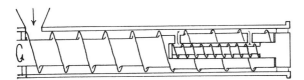

FIG. 5.19. Bidirectional screw.

5.4 TWIN-SCREW COMPOUNDING MACHINES

5.4.1 Twin-screw Extruders

The term twin-screw can occasionally be misleading because, although 'twins' do not have to be identical or indeed very much alike, the term does conjure up the idea that two screws that are identical or mirror images of each other are implied, and this is not necessarily always the case. With twin-screw extruders, there is the possibility of increasing shear straining of the material by virtue of interactions between the two screws. The degree to which this occurs will depend on the shapes of the flights, the degree to which they intermesh, and the relative directions of rotation of the screws.[3, 10] Conventional twin-screw extruders are frequently employed as compounding machines. Twin-screw machines are claimed to be superior to single-screw machines because they can provide

   (i) shorter residence times,
   (ii) improved melt temperature control,
   (iii) high, controlled shear rates,
   (iv) positive pumping action,
   (v) reduced melt slippage, and
   (vi) self-wiping action.[14, 15]

Even with conventional simple screw threads, a number of possible arrangements exists. Thus, the screws may be counter-rotating or co-rotating and they may be non-intermeshing (tangential) or completely or partially intermeshing.[3] In the latter case, various dispositions of the spaces between the screws are possible.

A number of more or less detailed studies of melting and mixing in twin-screw extruders have been made,[83-87] but they are of necessity limited to one or two specific regular configurations, and in view of the large effect that can result from relatively small changes, for example in clearances, generalisations of any real accuracy have not so far been possible. Likewise, comparisons between different types of twin-screw machines, and to some extent between twin-screw and single-screw machines, tend to be based on somewhat subjective judgments. Besides, it will frequently be the case that the relative merits of two particular machines vary with the particular materials being processed. Nevertheless, some broad principles of comparison between the four possible dispositions of two associated screws are apparently widely accepted. Some of these are based on fairly obvious visualisation of material behaviour, some no doubt are based on practical experience, while some others appear to be possibly unsupported claims in support of one particular machine over another. Thus, co-rotating screws are claimed to offer better control of shear and better control of mixing than counter-rotating screws,[14] though why this should be so is not immediately obvious. A claim that the former suffer less wear of barrel and screws[14] might be explained by the fact that co-rotating screws tend to have much less material pressure between the screws, tending to force the latter towards the barrel wall. On the other hand, it might be expected that material pressure between screws and barrel would tend to force the screws towards each other, leading to increased screw wear unless relatively large clearances are used. Closely intermeshing co-rotating screws also tend to be self-cleaning.[15,67] Counter-rotating screws require greater clearances between them since their mode of action is rather like a two-roll mill, passing material through the nip between them,[13] whereas with co-rotating screws material is transferred from screw to screw in a mainly tangential path.[67] Consequently, counter-rotating screws do not have efficient self-cleaning action. A more positive pumping action and pressure development is provided by counter-rotating screws,[14] and if they are intermeshing mixing, shear and transport can be determined by the clearances.[15] Non-meshing counter-rotating screws can produce larger outputs, and operate with relatively more interchange of material between the two screws than the other types. This arrangement tends to be preferred where fibrous fillers are included in the composition being processed. In general, the closer the clearances and intermeshing the more rapid the build-up of pressure. The narrower the lands and the larger the clearances between the screws, the greater the longitudinal mixing.[15] A number of useful reviews of machines available on the market have appeared[14,67,88,89] from time to time, and the prospective purchaser is strongly recommended to study the most recent of these before taking any further steps.

5.4.2 *Tapered Screws*

One of the major problems in designing a twin-screw machine where the screws are both driven from the feed end, is that the radial space available for bearings is strictly limited, and early machines were prone to failure of bearings, even though loading was controlled by limited feeding of material. One of the major advances over the past 15 years or so has been the development of greatly improved bearing arrangements within this spatial limitation. One way of at least alleviating the problem is to have conical screws tapered down towards the delivery end, so that their axes become increasingly separated rearwards, thus providing increased space for bearings. This arrangement also provides a simple means of achieving positive compression as particulate material gels and loses bulk volume.[3] An early embodiment of this concept has one of the screws extending for only the first 25–30% of the total screw length, from whence there is only one non-tapered screw.[3] This machine may, therefore, be regarded as being transitional from single- to twin-screw. More recently, twin screws tapering throughout their total length seem to have become more popular[58,90] (Fig. 5.20).

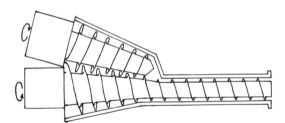

FIG. 5.20. Tapered screws in feed zone.

5.4.3 *Compounding Extruders*

Most modern twin-screw extruders have screws whose configuration departs more or less from that of simple single start and constant pitch. Thus, the screws may have two or more zones differing in pitch, root diameter and outside diameter. The zones might be separated by sections of progressively decreased pitch and number of starts or channels or by 'baffle elements', comprising essentially grooved fluted discs with small clearance in relation to the barrel wall.[91] A somewhat similar arrangement has changes from single to multiple starts in a series of zones, with a central zone where radial compression by reduced channel depth produces fairly rapid gelation and homogenisation. In another design, the screws are cut 'square', and compression is obtained by progressively decreasing the distance between the thrust and trailing edges of the threads. Other arrangements use concepts similar to those used in some single-screw compounding machines. Thus, kneading may be increased by having grooves in the thread lands, or by plain, slotted or 'gashed' discs located mid-way along or towards the forwards end of the screw. It has been suggested that slow pressure rises in the head of an extruder tend to give inhomogeneity, particularly with counter-rotating screws, and to remedy this, screws have been designed with rapidly increasing compression near the delivery end, achieved by decreasing channel depth and overall screw diameter.[92]

All extruders, and twin-screw extruders in particular, have some mixing or compounding action. Whether in any particular case a machine is called an extruder, a compounding extruder, an extruder-compounder, or a continuous compounding machine, is perhaps merely a matter of semantics. Certainly, if a machine will accept simple blended material or even separate components and convert them in one pass to finished extruded product, it is fulfilling all the functions required in a compounding machine. But, of course, a particular machine may be capable of doing this with some compositions and not others. Are we then to call such a machine a compounder on some occasions and an extruder on others?

5.4.4 Twin-screw Compounding Machines

Turning to consideration of machines that are generally regarded as continuous compounding machines rather than extruders, it may be noted that some of the devices used with single-screw machines are also applicable to machines with two or more screws, but the presence of two screws offers more possibilities. Since the most obvious deficiency in compounding action of a simple extruder arises from too short residence times in relation to intensity of shearing, the immediately obvious differences between compounding screws and simple extrusion screws are features designed to increase one or both of these. One simple way of achieving this[3,9,60,93] is to have some of the threads or flights reversed (Fig. 5.21) in relation to the main forwards-driving threads, thus obviously tending to give some degree of back-flow, but also, since this will tend to produce regions of increased pressure, increased shearing. With

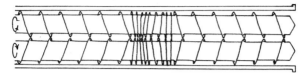

FIG. 5.21. Screw zones with reversed threads.

the proper balance of thread designs, decompression regions are created down-stream of the reversed flight sections, and venting points can be introduced. In some machines of this type exceptionally high proportions of volatiles can be removed by venting. Allusion has already been made to the similarity between the action of a pair of counter-rotating screws and that of a two-roll mill (Fig. 5.22). A number of continuous com-

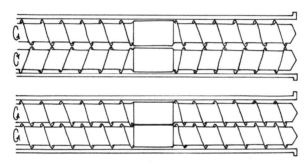

FIG. 5.22. Twin-screw extruders with two-roll mill sections.

pounding machines achieve the required increase in compounding action by introducing a zone which is essentially a two-roll mill, i.e. the threads are replaced by smooth cylinders with a fairly small clearance between them.[10] It is said that these machines even produce rolling banks of material, similar to those produced in conventional two-roll milling. Here again volatile extraction vents can be located at the down-stream end of the mill section. Sometimes, with machines of this type, the two screws are separated at the forward end into what are effectively two single-screw extruders. Another arrangement is for one of the screws to stop short of the other, with all material transferring to the longer screw. Machines of this type are offered for compounding and extrusion of a wide variety of polymeric compositions, including polyolefins, polystyrene, PVC, nylon, polycarbonate, rubbers, polyesters and polyurethanes, especially those including fillers and resinous additives or liquid additives such as plasticisers and oils. Typical outputs range from around 225 kg/h for a 50 mm nominal screw diameter with 75 kW drive, to around 1800 kg/h for a 115 mm screw diameter with 600 kW drive, depending on composition. Thus, for example, the output for unplasticised PVC might be only 50% of that for a plasticised PVC.

5.4.5 Internal Mixer Zones

A somewhat similar idea to the foregoing is to introduce a section with rotors shaped like those of an internal mixer[3, 9, 10, 66, 94] (Fig. 5.23). This was introduced by Joseph Eck as the 'Mixtruder' as long ago as 1952,[94] and has been developed at various times in the intervening period. In the

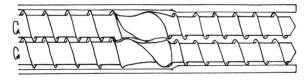

FIG. 5.23. Twin-screw extruder with internal mixer section.

Mixtruder the screws are co-rotating and are divided into four zones. First, there is the feeding zone where the screws intermesh closely to provide a strong forward conveyance of material to the second zone, which is where the intermixer rotors are formed. The third zone comprises a conical annulus and the screws may be plain or threaded in this region. In some models the clearance in this conical annulus can be varied by longitudinal axial adjustment.[95] The final zone consists of two separate screws that are effectively two single-screw extruders, transporting material to the die-head for granulation by die-face cutting. Earlier models had smooth outlet shafts rather than screws, and material was ejected directly to a second low compression extruder in a cascade arrangement.[94] Mixtruder type machines have been recommended for compounding polyolefins, polystyrene, cellulose acetate, and both plasticised and unplasticised PVC, but there seems to be no reason why this type of machine should not be suitable for any composition where fairly intensive compounding is necessary. Typical outputs of plasticised PVC are 70 kg/h for 90 mm diameter screws with a drive power of 14 kW, and up to 1200 kg/h for a diameter of 300 mm and drive power of 180 kW.[95] With the larger machine, outputs in the region of 500 kg/h of unplasticised PVC and 1000 kg/h of low or high density polyethylene can be expected.[95]

5.4.6 Continuous Internal Mixer

Just as one might consider designing a continuous compounding machine by modifying the extruder principle to include elements calculated to give more intensive mixing, one might consider modifying a batch compounding machine by adding an extruder function to it. Superficially at least, the result is scarcely distinguishable from the principles just discussed. Be that as it may, the 'Farrel Continuous Mixer' ('FCM')[1,13-15,39,65-67,96-99] is based on the concept of adapting an internal mixer to continuous instead of intermittent operation (Fig. 5.24).

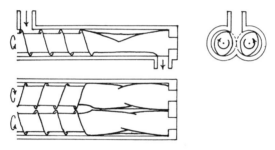

FIG. 5.24. Continuous internal mixer.

In this machine, individual components of the composition are metered at controlled rates into screw sections at the feed end of two rotors. These screws convey the material into the main compounding region which is designed very like an internal mixer. Here the composition is kneaded and rolled in much the same way as in a batch internal mixer. Compounded material leaves the compounding region to be discharged at the far end to the feed entry. In the original design,[99] discharge was through an orifice of adjustable gap size, and material emerged in shapeless lumps which could be fed direct to a calender, but which required further treatment if the product was designed to be feed stock to an extruder or moulding machine. More recently,[14,100] the discharge orifice has been replaced by a screw extruder. The rotors are always run 'starved' or incompletely filled and the throughput is controlled by material feed-rate. Other directly controlled variables are rotor speed and back-pressure. The last of these is determined by material properties, temperature, rotor speed and either orifice opening or discharge extrusion screw speed, depending on which discharge arrangement is fitted.[98] Relationships between stock discharge temperature and power input to production rate, orifice opening and rotor speed have been examined in some detail.[98,101] As might be expected, stock discharge temperature increases with increasing rotor speed and falls with increased discharge orifice opening, but is relatively insensitive to production rate variation. Total power input increases with production rate, rotor speed, and decreasing orifice opening. Also, as might be expected, power input per unit mass of material increases with increasing rotor speed but falls with increasing production rate or increasing orifice opening, but in each case the change tends to become relatively small at some particular value of the independent variable. Because of the controllable variables with the FCM, it appears to be an extremely versatile machine for compounding a very wide range of compositions, including filled and unfilled, plasticised and unplasticised, thermoplastics and rubber compounds and master-batches. It can also be used for devolatilisation of polyolefins, such as polypropylene and polystyrene, and dewatering and drying materials, such as synthetic rubber crumb.[101] The machine is not self-cleaning, but successive batches produce only a small proportion of contaminated material, and the design is such that disassembly for cleaning is relatively easy. FCM machines are available in a range of sizes, indicated by variation of the net volume of the mixing chamber from $0.000\,344\,m^3$ (0.344 litres) to $0.1244\,m^3$ (124.4 litres). While production rate for any one material increases with machine size, it does not do so in proportion thereto but generally to a somewhat lesser extent. The maximum drive power, however, is approximately proportional to production capacity, but by varying production rate, in order to achieve a required quality, the work input per unit mass of material may be varied quite widely in the same machine. Thus, for polyethylene a three-fold increase in throughput may result in a drop in work input from $0.5\,kJ/kg$ to $0.16\,kJ/kg$. As an indication of the relative production rates achievable with different materials, a machine with a mixing chamber of $0.031\,m^3$ net volume and a maximum drive power of $882\,kW$ should give typical production rates in kg/h of 3300 for master-batch compounding, 4000 for colour compounding and 5000 for homogenisation of polyethylene; 3750 for UPVC and 5000 for plasticised PVC compounding; and 5000 for rubber stock compounding. Production rates up to around $16\,000\,kg/h$ are possible with larger machines.

5.4.7 *Screws with Kneaders*

Among the means of achieving thorough compounding with a single-screw machine, mentioned in Section 5.3, is the interposition between conventional screw sections of one or more kneading zones, each comprising a number of cam-like members off-set in relation to each other. Such devices can also be employed in twin-screw machines, with the added possibility that the cam-like kneaders on one screw can be located in favourable positions with respect to the kneaders on the other screw, for example, so that close wiping of one by the other in each pair occurs. As with single-screw machines these kneaders may, for example, be eccentrically mounted circular discs, lozenge-shaped, or like equilateral triangles with convex sides (Fig. 5.25). The Ikegai PCM twin-screw

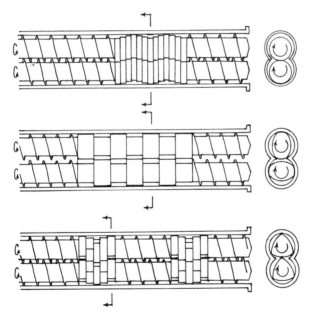

FIG. 5.25. Eccentric circular, lozenge-shaped and triangular kneaders.

extruder[102] is of the first of these types, the Baker Perkins MPC series[103-105] and the Werner and Pfleiderer ZPS series are examples of the second type, and the Werner and Pfleiderer, Erdmenger system,[3,10,13-15,27,28,106] ZSK machines are of the latter type (Fig. 5.26). With the ZSK machines another innovation was introduced, in that the

FIG. 5.26. Werner and Pfleiderer ZSK 83/700—assembling the screw sections.

kneading discs and screw sections of various forms are provided in relatively short lengths that are slid and keyed onto two shafts that replace the usual screws. Thus, almost any combination of kneaders and screw sections can be set up, in order to meet the requirements of different compounding operations. Though it may be true that the best production procedure requires that a compounding machine should operate as continuously as possible on the same material, and should not, therefore, require changing, the system offers other advantages. For one thing, it is obviously much cheaper to replace a small section that is excessively worn than to replace a whole screw. Secondly, the rather complicated screw and kneader configurations that are used in modern compounding machines are expensive to produce in one piece, and provided a sufficient number of the smaller units are required it should be possible to cut manufacturing costs considerably. Be that as it may, several manufacturers have adopted this modular or block system not only for screw sections and kneaders, but also for the barrel.[15,81,102,107,108] The machines using cam-like kneaders presently available all use co-rotating screws or rotors, and the modes of action of the kneaders are similar, although the intensity of shearing action will depend on precise shapes, dimensions and clearances, and on the relative longitudinal disposition of kneading elements. In all cases, whatever their angular alignment, there is always only a small clearance between the closest surfaces of any pair of coacting kneaders, i.e. one on each rotor.

Thus, with eccentric circular discs, the eccentricities are arranged in the same direction for each pair of discs and there is a continual wiping relationship between the closest surfaces of the discs. With lozenge-shaped kneaders, the short tip at the extremity of one kneader moves in close relationship to the longer curved side of its partner, until two tips come together and the co-relationship is exchanged. The dynamic relationship between pairs of curved triangular kneaders is somewhat similar, with the apex of one triangle wiping along the side of its partner, but there are six interchanges of role per revolution rather than four, as is the case with lozenge-shaped kneaders and, other things being equal, this design appears to produce more intensive shearing than the latter. Considering any pair of coacting kneaders there are separate spaces, defined by the inside barrel surface and the surfaces of the kneaders, that material can occupy. During a single revolution, spaces defined by eccentric disc kneaders are constantly changing shape and size, and the number of spaces varies in effect from one to three. A pair of lozenge-shaped kneaders define three spaces and a pair of triangular kneaders five spaces, and although they are changing position and producing a rolling shearing action during a rotation, only one space in the former case and two spaces in the latter case are changing shape. In all cases, material is compressed and stretched, rolled and kneaded, with intensity that depends on the speed of rotation and the precise geometry, and tends to be transferred from one kneader to its partner as it leaves a space defined by the barrel wall and both kneaders (Fig. 5.27). All this is, of course, a simplification of the dynamics of material behaviour in kneader zones, because there will normally be two rows of successive kneader elements rather than a single pair, and longitudinal transfer of material takes place as well as the circumferential movements around the inside of the barrel. Successive kneaders are off-set in relation to each other, and their precise relationship can be important. Thus, with circular discs the angles of their eccentricities is varied progressively along the major axis of the rotor. The resultant overall shape is not unlike the spiral of a simple extruder screw of relatively large pitch, and from this point of view, the principle of action of this type of kneader system is not far removed from the concept of achieving mixing by increasing the helix angle used in other continuous compounding machines (Sections 5.2.5 and 5.3.3). One practical difference is that the lands of kneaders are usually much longer than those of helicoidal type screws. It is clear that the direction of the spiral defined by a set of successive kneaders in relation to the configuration of the screw sections

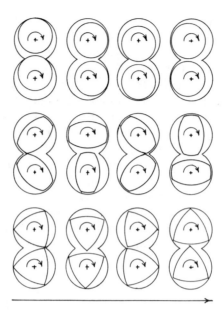

FIG. 5.27. Coactions of various kneading discs.

is important. If the dispositions of successive kneading discs define channels spiralling in the same sense as the screws, forward progression of material is impeded less than if the channels spiral in the opposite sense, i.e. with reversed flights. In the latter case, higher pressures, and consequently more intensive shearing, will occur than in the former case.[102] The same principle applies to machines with lozenge-shaped or triangular kneaders. However, with the former, the individual kneaders are usually relatively thick and successive pairs commonly have their major axes at right-angles to each other. Consequently, the reversed flight effect does not really operate. Spiral channels are not so obviously present when triangular kneaders are used, but strictly speaking, a succession of these kneaders progressively oriented at increasing angular positions to the first produces a section of three flights or channels. In practice, this type of kneader is usually installed so that the spiral is in the same sense as the extruder sections.

As a consequence of the flexibility of configuration of types of design discussed in the preceding paragraph, compounding machines of these designs are very versatile, and can be used for the compounding of a wide variety of compositions. Lozenge-shaped kneaders provide a large volumetric capacity for material, and therefore tend to provide less intensive shearing than triangular kneaders, and for this reason are particularly useful for shear sensitive materials such as glass-reinforced plastics.[104] While die-face cutting to produce pellets is used with these machines, with some compositions restriction of a lace die produces excessive back-pressure and shearing, and other means are then necessary to convert the compounded material to an appropriate form. This matter is considered in the next section. Machines with eccentric circular disc kneaders have been used to compound such difficult materials as epoxy, polyester and acrylic coating powders. With these materials, an 87 mm diameter machine with 75 kW drive is claimed to yield 300–500 kg/h.[102] A fair amount of information is available to exemplify the rates of production of different materials with machines with lozenge-shaped or triangular kneaders, but the ranges of values are so wide, and the precise nature of individual materials rarely delineated, so that detailed reproduction of such data would be of little if any value. The prospective user is recommended to provide as full details as possible of his requirements to the manufacturers, with the request that they propose the most appropriate design of machine. It is highly desirable that full-scale trials be carried out before a final decision to install a particular machine is made; but, of course, this applies to almost any production plant where major capital expenditure is involved. In general terms, these types of compounding machines are used for compounding, including incorporation of fillers, impact modifiers, colourants and plasticisers, production of master-batch, with simultaneous devolatilisation of polyolefins, styrene polymers, copolymers and terpolymers, polycarbonate, nylons, saturated polyesters, polyacetals, cellulosics, PTFE, polysulphones, phenolics, aminos and PVC. There are some reservations with respect to the last-named of these, not because PVC cannot be compounded in these types of machines, but because if the arrangement is one that gives relatively intensive shearing, the machine may have to be run at an uneconomically low rate in order to avoid over-heating or development of excessive pressures.

Consequently, selection of the precise configuration of kneaders and screws requires careful consideration. The problem is not a severe one if the composition has an appreciable proportion of plasticiser, e.g. 50 phr or above, but with unplasticised PVC it may be necessary to use a relatively open die so that back-pressure can be kept to a minimum, and to convert the compounded material to pellets or granules in another stage by a cascade arrangement. As a very rough guide to the capacities of the machines, at the small end of the range, a machine with a nominal screw diameter of 50–60 mm would be likely to have maximum drive power of around 30 kW and be capable of producing anything between 70 and 300 kg/h, depending on the material. With a screw diameter of 120–130 mm, the maximum drive power may be anything between 110 and 360 kW, and production rate from 450 to 3500 kg/h. At the time of writing, the largest machine of the type available appears to be one with nominal screw diameter of 300 mm, maximum drive power of 2050 kW, giving production rates up to 12 000 kg/h for polyethylenes. It should perhaps be noted that the throughput can be increased markedly, if the compounding machine is being operated in conjunction with a polymerisation plant from which it receives polymer in melt form.

Two other developments of the types of machine discussed in the preceding paragraphs, merit brief mention. The first of these is concerned with extruder-compounders for gramophone record compound. These machines are required to deliver softened compound in the form of discrete 'dollies' intermittently with the charging sequence of one or more record presses. For this reason, it is more convenient to extrude vertically rather than in the conventional horizontal direction. The extrusion may be downwards or upwards, according to which is most convenient in relation to the associated equipment. In either case, screw feeding is usually desirable because of the tendency for blends of record formulations to exhibit rather poor flow behaviour. The compounding unit itself may have one or two screws, and these are usually of the screw plus kneader type, similar to the arrangements of the general purpose compounders previously discussed. Usually, adjustable controls are included, by means of which the screws can be automatically stopped and started to deliver dollies of compound of the correct weight, and at the proper times for automatic transfer to press or presses.

The principle of the second development[109] was introduced in a range of extruder compounders of the kneading disc type, but is really of much wider applicability. In a sense, this principle may be regarded as arranging two identical twin-screw machines in direct opposition and joining the opposing screws in pairs (Fig. 5.28). Material feed is divided into two equal streams, one being conducted to the feed port of each of the compounding extruders. Compounded melt from the two units meets at the junction and is delivered through an appropriate cross-head. Considering this arrangement as one of twin-screws delivering compound to their central region, it can be seen that each screw is carried in bearings at both ends, thus reducing considerably the problem present in

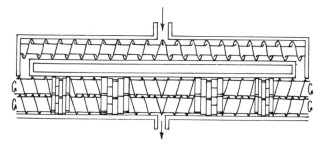

FIG. 5.28. Dual feed twin-screw kneading disc compounder.

all twin-screw, and indeed single-screw machines, arising from departure of the tip of a screw from its true axial alignment with the centre at the driven end, due to its freedom from mechanical restraint. Also, each screw can be driven by a separate drive unit, one at each end of the machine, thus also easing some of the problems of thrust bearing arrangement. It might be expected that the throughput of a machine of this type would be double that of a more conventional kneader-compounder of similar screw design and diameter, but published data suggest that the increase tends to be rather more than double.

5.5 MISCELLANEOUS CONTINUOUS COMPOUNDING MACHINERY

Considered in this section are a number of compounding machines that cannot strictly be called single-screw or twin-screw, and also some aspects of compounding installations that have more general implications.

5.5.1 Multi-screw Machines

Increase in screw diameter, in order to achieve greater output from one machine, tends to lead to high circumferential speeds with consequent excessive shearing and wear. An alternative means of increasing output when increasing barrel size is to increase the number of screws. One form of extruder with three screws has a main central screw and two smaller co-rotating subsidiary screws, one on either side.[110] A machine with a 220 mm diameter central screw and 110 mm diameter subsidiary screws, is stated to be equivalent to two twin-screw machines with 110 mm diameter screws. Throughputs of 800–900 kg/h are claimed with polyolefins, polystyrene, plasticised and unplasticised PVC, ABS and acrylic, with higher rates obtainable with the use of a pre-heater and a special processing section.

Some kneading-disc machines are available with four screws or rotors. These are usually arranged in a U-shaped arrangement with two screws at the bottom each coacting with the other and one of the other two screws which latter form the sides of the U. To some extent, therefore, this arrangement amounts to two twin-screw machines interacting along one longitudinal strip.

5.5.2 Planetary Gears

A more balanced arrangement is offered by so-called planetary roller or planetary gear extruders[1,3,71,89,111-113] (Fig. 5.29). In these machines, after a fairly conventional single-screw feeding section, the overall dia-

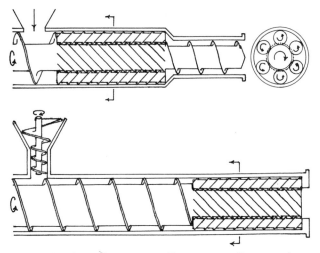

FIG. 5.29. Planetary gear or roller compounding extruders.

meter of the main screw is reduced and is then shaped by helically gearing rather than a single extrusion thread, though the main difference geometrically is in increased pitch and greatly increased number of starts. Typically, the helix angle is 45°. Arranged around the main screw are a number (typically 6–12) of helicoidal screws or gears, meshing with the central screw and with corresponding gear channels around the inside of the barrel. As the gears mesh, gelled material is rolled to a thin sheet and is extruded as strands which can be cut at the head of the machine. Alternatively, the materials can be fed to a second extruder in cascade arrangement. Another form of the machine has the central screw extended and formed into a metering zone beyond the planetary gear section.[111] Machines of this type are claimed to have a number of advantages over other machines performing the same operation, namely smaller space requirements, short residence times at relatively low temperatures and low power requirements. Somewhat surprising, in view of the heat sensitivity of the material, these machines seem to be particularly suited to the processing of unplasticised PVC dry-blend for feeding to a calender, a pipe extruder, an extrusion blow-moulding machine, or a pelletising extruder, or even for direct extrusion. The reason for the capability of these machines to handle unplasticised PVC is apparently due to the high surface area of the helical threads, approximately three times that of a single screw of similar diameter, thus facilitating heat exchange which, with relatively short residence times, minimises degradation.[112] Outputs naturally vary with formulation, including molecular weight of polymer. Typically, a 70 mm diameter machine with drive motor power of 7·5 kW can process 60–100 kg/h of plasticised and 40–80 kg/h of unplasticised PVC. At the other extreme, a 290 mm diameter machine with 400 kW drive power has a capacity of up to 4000 kg/h of plasticised and 2200–3300 kg/h of unplasticised PVC, the latter depending on post-compounding requirements. Total energy input is stated to be between 0·05 and 0·12 kW h/kg (0·18 and 0·43 MJ/kg).

A similar, but much earlier, device than the preceding is the planetary gear mixing head.[3,9] With this device, a conventional single screw terminates in a pinion that drives a number of gears that also mesh with the outer gear ring on the inside of the barrel. The gears are cut longitudinally straight so that they cut across the flow-stream of material leaving the screw helix, and submit the material to intense shearing in similar fashion to the action of a planetary roller or planetary gear extruder. The planetary gear mixing head was shown to be particularly efficacious, compared with a conventional extruder, at dispersing carbon black in polyethylene.[9]

The 'bi-helicoidal gear extruder'[3,114] dispenses with the screw principle altogether (Fig. 5.30). With this device, feed stock is charged to the nip of a pair of helicoidal gears with horizontal axes, counter-rotating upwards from the nip. Material picked up by the gears is carried round within the

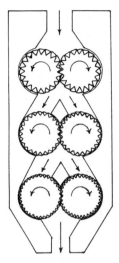

FIG. 5.30. Bi-helicoidal gear extruder.

inner curved surface of a close fitting chamber, where it is sheared intensely and discharged to the upper surfaces of a second pair of gears, below and parallel to the first pair and having a smaller pitch so as to provide compression. From thence the material passes to a third set of gears with still smaller pitch, and thence to discharge. Machines of this type do not appear to have had widespread adoption since their inception some 20 years ago, at least for compounding plastics or rubbers.

5.5.3 *Roll-mill Extruders*

A continuous compounding machine that seems to add the extrusion principle to roll milling, rather than the other way round, is the Shaw 'Mixer–Extruder Double R'[66] (Fig. 5.31). This comprises a grooved, threaded, working roll with a smooth working roll against it in line horizontally. Above the working roll there is a feed roll, also threaded, and the whole is enclosed in a working chamber. The working roll is extended in one direction to form a single-screw extruder with a tapered tip, conducting compounded material to a die forming strip or some other convenient section. Another proposal for a continuous compounding machine based on roll milling employs one or more rollers rotating eccentrically within a hollow cylinder, shaped to follow the swept volume

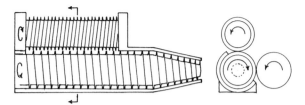

FIG. 5.31. Francis Shaw Mixer-Extruder Double R.

of the roll or rolls fairly closely. Feed stock is introduced at one end, and compounded material is discharged at the other, apparently transported as a result of the eccentricity. Yet another arrangement[115] has a single smooth cylindrical roller, rotating within a chamber on the inside of which are fixed wedge-shaped elements, so shaped and located that each forms a wedged-shaped nip where material is sheared and smeared through the gap. Feeding is at one side of the chamber, i.e. towards a curved surface of the roller, and discharge is at the opposite side.

5.5.4 Disc Extruders

During the past 20 years or so, a number of screw-less extruders, mainly variants on the disc extruder concept, have been introduced,[3,116-123] and some of these seem eminently suited to compounding.[117,121-123] The Rettig mixing, kneading and homogenising machine[117] comprises a disc, preferably with a spiral channel on each side, rotating within a housing chamber with only small clearances (Fig. 5.32). Material to be

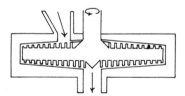

FIG. 5.32. Rettig spiral-channelled disc mixing machine.

mixed is introduced through a port in the housing to a region near the centre on one side of the disc, passes outwards to the periphery, enters the space on the other side of the disc, and then moves towards the axis, eventually to be extruded outwards in the axial direction. Additives such as stabilisers, lubricants, colourants, and fillers, can be introduced into the melt through ports around the periphery of the working chamber where maximum peripheral speed and minimum pressure exist, and volatiles can be removed through vents likewise located around the periphery.

The Diskpack Polymer Processor, introduced by Farrel in 1979, can be used as a melt pump, for devolatilisation, for extrusion of profiles, and, what is particularly germane to the present discussion, for compounding (Fig. 5.33). The Diskpack is most easily visualised as a unit

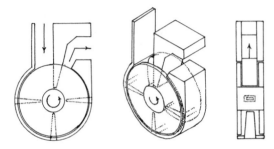

FIG. 5.33. Farrel Diskpack mixing unit.

based construction in which any particular installation will include one or more units in series, and/or in parallel, depending on the requirements of the particular materials and processing operation involved. Each unit comprises two or more circular discs attached to a rotating shaft, running within a close fitting barrel. A pair of discs may be parallel or have the clearance between them increasing radially, the latter being the optimum profile for pumping.[122] A feed port and a discharge port are located in the barrel wall and are separated by a channel block. Barrel, discs and shaft are all temperature-controlled. The operation of a pair of discs may be likened to that of two parallel plates moving jointly, with velocity proportional to distance from the centre and speed of rotation. Flow equations for such a configuration have been derived.[122] Laminar mixing is estimated to be greater than for a conventional screw extruder of equal gap dimensions and surface velocities, mean strain being some 80% higher for the Diskpack principle. It has been shown that with parallel discs, in addition to the double circulatory flow pattern at any given radial location, perpendicular circulatory patterns also occur, leading to randomisation of inhomogeneities throughout the processing chamber. Dispersive mixing can be increased by interposing fixed blocks between the pair of discs, and/or by allowing polymer melt to recycle over the channel block.

Using a number of these units will obviously increase throughput in proportion, whereas connecting two or more units in series increases the mixing capability of the complete installation. The number of units to be used in series will depend on the demands of the mixing operation. Typically, for processing polyolefins the installation might consist of ten units in two sets of five each, fed with polymer to the two end units and discharging into a single pump channel for extrusion through a die. Polymer may be fed as melt, powder, pellets or dry-blend, and additives can be metered into intermediate units where appropriate. As an indication of the possibilities of Diskpack installations, a 350 mm diameter machine with a top speed of 150 r.p.m., with drive motor power of 400 kW, has a production capacity of 500–1500 kg/h; and a 950 mm diameter machine with a top speed of 60 r.p.m. and drive motor power of 3300 kW, has a production capacity of 6000–12 000 kg/h.

5.5.5 Cascade Arrangements

References have previously been made to cascade arrangements of two extruders in series or tandem.[23,31,71] At least one manufacturer is supplying an installation with three extruders in tandem, the first being a kneader type compounding machine, the second a gelation regulator, and the third a discharge screw with a die-face cutting pelletiser. Cascade arrangements (Fig. 5.34) are sometimes supplied as single units and sometimes arise as the most convenient location of two separate machines, interrelated to the extent that one accepts the product discharged from the other. Reasons for using cascade arrangements vary. It may be that the extrudate from a compounding machine is not in a convenient form for direct processing in the final shaping operation. This may be because of the intermittent nature of the discharge, as with the Ko-kneader, or it may be that the extrudate has to be produced with inconveniently large cross-sectional area because small orifice dies would cause excessive back pressures, over-heating and degradation. Separation of the compounding extrusion operation into two quite separate stages, also provides a convenient way of interposing a vacuum extraction unit for devolatilisation, a feature that is becoming increasingly desirable with increasing concern for the possible hazards of residual monomers and other substances. From a different point of view, cascade arrangements

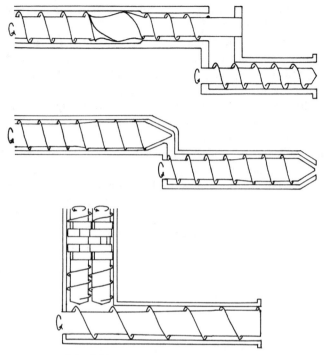

FIG. 5.34. Some cascade arrangements.

may be used in attempts to produce integrated units that can accept basic raw materials and convert them to finished product in one overall operation.[10] A further attraction arises from the fact that, in general, the greater the length of an extruder screw the better the control of temperature and shear, and the smoother and gentler are the changes in these, but of course the greater become the mechanical problems, and a cascade system of two extruders is a convenient way of achieving increased screw length in a relatively simple way mechanically.[124]

One disadvantage of single-unit intensive continuous compounding machines, such as the ZSK type, is that with high viscosity, heat-sensitive materials, like unplasticised PVC, throughputs have to be kept rather low if a conventional multi-hole lace die is used. Otherwise, back-pressure from the die is likely to reach such a high level that excessive degradation will occur, and even if it does not, the subsequent extrusion behaviour of the compound may be impaired as a result of the excessively high temperatures reached by the melt.[125-128] It is not unknown for the pressure in the head of the machine to reach such a high value that cracking of the die plate occurs. By permitting the use of a die with large orifices and hence of low restriction to flow, and following the compounding unit with a mild, low-shearing extruder, some sort of cascade arrangement can alleviate this problem. The Werner and Pfleiderer 'Kombiplast',[1,71,129] comprises essentially a short ZSK twin-screw compounding machine (length:diameter = 15:1), co-rotating at relatively high rate (300 r.p.m.) and shear. On leaving the screws, the material enters a slow running (21 r.p.m.) short (length:diameter = 6:1) single-screw extruder fitted with a pelletising strand die and die-face cutter.[71] Though designed specifically for unplasticised PVC, this machine is also suitable for plasticised PVC, including compositions containing heat-sensitive additives such as chemical blowing agents. Devolatilisation can be carried out at the transition between the two extruders. As an indication of production rates, at the small end of the available range, a machine with 15 kW drive to the twin-screw section and 10 kW to the single-screw section would be expected to compound around 165 kg/h of unplasticised and 280 kg/h of plasticised PVC. At the other end of the range, a machine with 240 kW drive to the twin-screw section and 72 kW to the single-screw section should process around 2500 kg/h of unplasticised and 4400 kg/h of plasticised PVC.[71] The Baker Perkins MPC continuous compounders, based on lozenge-shaped kneaders, also use a single-screw second-stage system.[104] In the Kaufman 'Super 2 Extruder' the discharge of the first screw is fed positively to the second screw through a connecting channel, and a vent is located slightly down-stream of a grooved disc 'melt stream divider' towards the rear end of the second screw.[130] In this machine the axes of the two extruders are at approximately 15° to each other, thus rendering the independent drive arrangements more convenient to arrange.

Other cascade arrangements may be based on single-screw and other types of compounding machines,[1,3,9,10,14,15,21-29,31,67,71,113] and usually there is a distinct separation between the two stages, though the transfer region is usually completely enclosed and supplied with vacuum extraction. At least one manufacturer offers a 'two-phase compounding' unit which is essentially a cascade arrangement in which a single-screw compounding extruder is positioned vertically, transporting material downwards to the second stage metering extruder. In this particular machine, the compounding screw has mixing pins on the inside of the barrel in the first stage and kneading elements in the main compounding stage. A combination of 350 and 400-mm sections is stated to have a capacity of 16 000 kg/h of low density polyethylene of melt flow index of two.[32] This arrangement is not unlike the replacement of the conventional hopper on an extruder by a screw-operated hopper, in which a short screw forces material downwards through a barrel where it is heated and fused before entry into the barrel of the main processing machine.[131]

In addition to the advantages already mentioned, two-stage cascade and other similar systems are said to offer better control of shear and temperature than single continuous compounding machines. One particular field of application where a cascade type arrangement seems to be particularly advantageous is in compounding glass-filled plastics,[105] where excessive shear is liable to fragment the fibres and so result in loss of at least some of the advantage offered by glass filler. In order to keep damage of the glass fibres to a minimum they may be introduced into the compounding extruder at a point relatively close to the die.[104,132] This, of course, requires a screw/kneader arrangement that gives a decompression zone of zero material pressure at the appropriate region.

5.5.6 Integrated Compounding Extrusion

The ultimate development[10] in the direct line of what is basically the cascade principle, has been the introduction in 1977 of the Farrel Bridge 'MVX' integrated mixing, venting and extrusion machine[14,15,67,89,133-135] (Fig. 5.35). This comprises

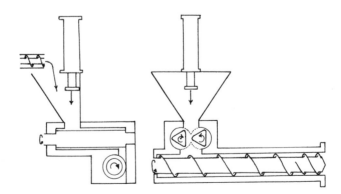

FIG. 5.35. Farrel Bridge MVX integrated mixing, venting and extrusion equipment.

(i) a feed hopper, with a reciprocating compacting ram, into which a blend of the components can be metered by conventional screw conveyor, mounted at one end of

(ii) a specially designed continuous mixer/compounder which discharges at its other end directly into

(iii) an independently controlled single-screw extruder.

The mixer comprises two counter-rotating, three-bladed or 'delta' rotors that are triangular in shape and without any helical twist. This latter feature is said to eliminate preferential forward transport of highly viscous material through softer material, thus ensuring uniform residence time and energy input. The mixing chamber is run at only 60–80% capacity, and volatiles can escape up the feed pocket and through a reciprocating vent pocket in the top of the chamber. Venting also occurs in the transfer passage between mixer and extruder. The extruder can be run in reverse so that it can be used to return unmixed material during start-up. Output rate is controlled by the speed of the extruder screw, and variation of this, together with variation of rotor speed and pressure on the compacting ram, can be used to adapt the intensity of mixing to the requirements of any particular composition being processed. As might be expected, specific work input to the material increases with increase in rotor speed and over a limited range with ram pressure, and decreases with increase in throughput. The MVX has been evaluated for the processing of powdered rubber compositions based on neoprene and natural rubber,[135] but is said to be also suitable for polyolefins, including filled polypropylene, plasticised and unplasticised PVC, polystyrene, ABS and thermoplastic rubbers.

5.5.7 Venting

Now that the early problems associated with venting arrangements on extruders have been largely overcome, one or more venting or evacuation points on continuous compounding machines are commonplace. Likewise, it is becoming quite normal to provide the facility of introducing additives at one or more points along the machine in advance of the main hopper.[14,15,136] This can be advantageous with heat-sensitive additives but, as a general rule, it seems to reduce the probability of achieving thorough dispersion and distribution of additives, and it raises the question as to whether or not some of the processing occurring at earlier stages is really necessary. However, at least with polymer/elastomer compounds, there seems to be a specific energy saving, represented by a fall in power consumption from 0·18 to 0·1 kW/kg. This is apparently accounted for by a corresponding decrease in heat loss to temperature control medium in the barrel.[136] There may also sometimes be advantages to be gained by way of alleviating feeding problems arising from poor flow behaviour of pre-blended feed stock.

5.5.8 Split Barrels

Another facility that is coming to be more widely provided in recent years, although introduced at least 30 years ago,[21] is the split barrel hinged along one longitudinal line, so that its two halves can be swivelled away for more simple cleaning. The recent introduction of modular barrel sections presumably also aids cleaning, as well as offering advantages of versatility in design and relatively cheap replacement.

5.5.9 Motionless Mixers

Before closing this chapter, mention must be made of another development in mixing equipment that has taken place within the past decade, though in truth the principles on which it is based are almost as old as polymer melt processing itself. This is concerned with so-called motionless mixers,[7,36,37,137-140] which, at least superficially, appear to be elaborations of the torpedoes long used in injection moulding machines and extruders, to smear out melt for better heat transfer and mixing. As the name implies, motionless mixers achieve mixing without any moving parts, but operate by rearrangement of melt flow and 'shuffling' of the fluid streams, so that interfacial area is greatly increased as melts flow through them.[7,37] They usually comprise one or more units of more or less complex shape, fixed within a tubular channel placed just before the die or nozzle of an extruder or injection moulding machine. A variety of different designs is available, the simplest being reasonably amenable to theoretical treatment,[36,37,138,140] but others being so complex as to render theoretical analysis difficult and tedious. Probably the simplest motionless mixer to visualise is the Kenics[7,36,37,137,138] static mixer or 'Thermogenizer' (Fig. 5.36). This consists of a number of short right- and left-hand helical elements joined together in alternating sequence. These

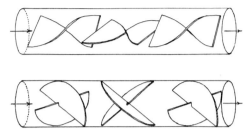

FIG. 5.36. Kenics and Ross 'LPD' static or motionless mixers.

elements are shaped more like short lengths of thick twisted metal strip than a helical extruder screw, in that there is no central root as in the latter. Typically, the length of each element is about one and a half times the diameter, and the elements are joined so that the leading edge of any one is at right-angles to the trailing edge of the next one along.[138] Material flowing through this type of motionless mixer experiences flow division and radial mixing resulting in 'average plug flow' characteristics.[138] Flow paths and mechanisms of mixing in the Kenics static mixer have been analysed in some detail.[36,37,138]

A somewhat more complicated design is used in the Ross 'Interfacial Surface Generator', or 'ISG' mixer.[7,37,139] This, too, comprises a number of elements in series downstream of an extruder or injection moulding machine screw. Each element consists, in effect, of a circular cylinder through which there are four cylindrical channels. The entrances to the four channels are in a straight line along a diameter of the element, and the exits are also in a diametrical straight line at right-angles to the line of the entrances. The channels are arranged so that the two outside entrances lead to the two inside exits and *vice versa*. The ends of each element are shaped to provide a tetrahedral chamber between the exits of one element and the entrances of the next.[37] The number of striations between two components of a melt passing through one element is increased by a factor of four, so that passage through ten successive elements increases the number of striations by a factor of over a million.[139,140]

The Sulzer melt blender or mixing head[36,139,140] is a motionless or static mixer of rather more complex design than the foregoing. Again, the system is made up of a number of successive elements that can be varied in number to meet different mixing requirements. Each element comprises a number of corrugated plates laminated together, with the corrugations in each plate at right-angles to those in adjacent plates.

Alternate mixing elements are set with their planes of lamination at right-angles to each other.

The Ross 'Low Pressure Unit' (LPD) (Fig. 5.36) is specifically designed to develop lower pressure drops than other types of motionless mixer.[139] Like those, it comprises a cylindrical channel containing elements that act by dividing and diverting streams of flowing melt, but it does so less intensely. Each element consists of two plates each in the form of half an ellipse, the division being along the major axis. The two plates are joined at the centres of their major axes with their plane faces at right-angles and their minor axes in a straight line. The element is positioned in the tubular channel, so that the central axis of the tube bisects the angles between the straight edges of the two plates, so aligning each plane face at an angle of 40° to the overall direction of flow, the plates thus diverting their respective streams in directions at right-angles to each other. Compared with the ISG unit described above an LPD element doubles rather than quadruples the number of striations, so that presumably double the number of units would be required to produce the same intensity of mixing.[139]

There have been some practical as well as theoretical evaluation and comparisons of available motionless mixers.[36,37,141,142] Thus, compared with the Kenics system, the Sulzer system should achieve a similar degree of mixing in a shorter distance but with a higher pressure drop.[36,37]

Motionless or static mixers appear to be particularly useful in obtaining good dispersion of colourants, as a result of which appreciable savings of these additives can be achieved. They also appear to reduce considerably the cross-stream temperature variation normally present at the discharge end of an extruder or injection unit. With appropriate selection of units, motionless mixers are suggested for the compounding of polyolefins, polystyrene acrylics, polyacrylonitrile, nylons, and even PVC and polycarbonate. The Kenics static mixer, in particular, has been evaluated for the production of polymer blends, specifically of polystyrene and high density polyethylene.[142]

5.6 MIXING IN INJECTION MOULDING

Mixing in ram injection moulding machines is non-existent, not merely with respect to composition but also in terms of uniformity of melt temperature. Modern injection moulding machines are usually of the reciprocating screw type, and while, strictly speaking, the mixing function of screw injection moulding machines is not continuous, the design features used to achieve adequate mixing are much more analogous to those of extruder compounders than to those of batch machines. Commonly, an injection screw is divided into feed, transition and metering zones,[59] and the metering zone may include a mixing section such as the Maddock type described earlier[47,51,53,56-59] (Section 5.3.4).

5.7 CONCLUSIONS

At the end of Chapter 3 reference was made to the difficulties of selecting and recommending specific blending equipment arising from the bewildering array available. Readers of this chapter will not need to be told that a similar situation exists when considering continuous compounding, but the variety of new designs has increased considerably in the last few years, and the only apparent hope of a halt lies in the exhaustion of possibilities. There have been some useful reviews of continuous compounding machines and extruders,[9-15,66-68,89,97,108] but they are never all-embracing and rarely pass comparative judgments on competing machines. Also, the techno-commercial situation is constantly changing. The best that can be done is to reiterate the recommendations made in relation to blending equipment (Chapter 3, Section 3.16) and modular continuous compounding machines (Section 5.4.7). Essentially, this consists in first characterising as precisely as possible what materials are to be processed, what quality is acceptable, and the production rate necessary; then thoroughly examining manufacturers' technical literature to reject such equipment as is clearly unsuitable and, if possible, to prepare a short-list of potentially suitable equipment; and finally seeking the advice of equipment manufacturers themselves, preferably in conjunction with full-scale production trials.

REFERENCES

1. HESS, K-M., *PRI Int. Conf. on PVC Processing*, Eng. Royal Holloway College, PRI, London, pp. 13.1–13.10 (1978).
2. ANON, BRETT, H. D., GASPAR, E. and ROWE, G., *Plastics*, **18**, 197, 404, 423, 439 (1953).
3. FISHER, E. G., *Extrusion of Plastics*, Plastics Institute Monograph, Iliffe, London (1958).
4. HOVEY, V. M., *Wire and Wire Products*, **36**, 193 (1961).

5. KAUFMAN, M., *The History of PVC*, Maclaren, London (1969).
6. McKELVEY, J. M., *Polymer Processing*, Wiley, New York (1962).
7. TADMOR, Z. and GOGOS, C. G., *Principles of Polymer Processing*, Wiley Interscience, New York (1979).
8. MOHR, W. D., SAXTON, R. L. and JEPSON, C. H., *Ind. Eng. Chem.*, **49**(11), (1957).
9. GRANT, D., *Rubb. Plast. Age*, **39**, 681 (1958).
10. MATTHEWS, G. A. R., *Advances in PVC Compounding and Processing*, Chapter 5, Kaufman, M. (Ed.), Maclaren, London (1962).
11. PRAT, C., *Revue gen. Caoutch*, **39**(10), 1561 (1962); **40**(5), 737 (1963).
12. MATTHEWS, G., Vinyl and Allied Polymers, *Vol. 2, Vinyl Chloride and Vinyl Acetate Polymers*, Plastics Institute Monograph, Iliffe, London (1972).
13. SCHOENGOOD, A. A., *APEJ*, **29**(2), 21 (1973).
14. MURRAY, T. A., *Plast. Tech.*, **24**(11), 83; **24**(12), 65 (1978).
15. WOOD, R., *Plast. Rubb. Intl.*, **4**(5), 207 (1979); **5**(1), 25 (1980).
16. DE ANGELIS, F., *Materie Plastiche*, **21**(11), 952 (1955).
17. PASTORELLO, I., British Patent 848653 (1960).
18. BIGG, D. and MIDDLEMAN, S., *Ind. Eng. Chem., Fundam.*, **13**(1), 66 (1974).
19. FENNER, R. T., *Plast. Rubb. Intl.*, **3**(1), 27 (1978); **4**(5), 219 (1979).
20. JUVE, A., *Rubb. Plast. Age*, **41**(1), 38 (1960).
21. AESCHBACH, J., *Kunststoffe*, **40**, 185 (1950); **45**, 456 (1955).
22. LIST, H., US Patent 2505125 (1950); BUSS, A. G., Basle, *The Ko-Kneader in the Plastics Industry*, Technical Bulletin (1959).
23. HENSEN, F. and GATHMANN, E., *Conf. on Engineering Design of Plastics Processing Machinery*, Vols. 1 and 2, Univ. of Bradford, Bradford (1974); *Kunststoffe*, **64**, 343 (1974).
24. LOVEGROVE, J. F. A., *Plast. Rubb. Processing*, **4**(1), 125 (1979)
25. VOGT, A., *Kunststoffe*, **44**, 151 (1954).
26. WACKER, A., Ges. für Elektrochem. Ind. GmbH, British Patents 758513 (1956); 863521 (1961).
27. ANON, *Rubb. Plast. Age*, **40**, 1291 (1959).
28. ANON, *Intl. Plast. Eng.* **5**(1), 12 (1965).
29. BERNHARDT, E. C., *SPEJ*, **12**, 40 (1956).
30. GRANT, D., *Trans. Plast. Inst.*, **29**, 82, 130 (1961).
31. HENSEN, F., *PRI Int. Conf. on PVC Processing*, Eng. Royal Holloway College. PRI, London, pp. B1.1–B1.12 (1978); *Plast. Rubb. Wkly*, 29 September, 17 (1978).
32. ANON, *Mod. Plast. Intl.*, **10**(2), 53 (1980).
33. SCHRENK, W. J., CHISHOLM, D. S. and ALFREY, *Mod. Plast.*, **46**(1), 164 (1969).
34. GREGORY, R. B., Paper 7, *Conf. on Practical Rheology in Polymer Processing*, Plast. Institute, London (1969).
35. PINTO, G. and TADMOR, Z., *Polym. Engng. Sci.*, **10**(5), 279 (1970).
36. BIGG, D. M., *Polym. Engng. Sci.*, **15**(9), 684 (1975).
37. MIDDLEMAN, S., *Fundamentals of Polymer Processing*, McGraw-Hill, New York (1977).
38. PREDÖHL, W., *J. Macromol. Sci.-Phys.*, **B14** (3), 419 (1977).
39. FUNT, J. M., *Mixing of Rubbers*, RAPRA, Shrewsbury (1977).

40. ERWIN, L., *Polym. Engng. Sci.*, **18**(7), 572 (1978).
41. HINRICHS, D. R. and LILLELEHT, L. U., *Polym. Engng. Sci.*, **10**(5), 268 (1970).
42. JONES, D. R. and HAWKES, J. C., *Trans. J. Plast. Inst.*, **35**, 120, 773 (1967).
43. GALE, G. M., Paper 5, *Plast. Inst. Nat. Tech. Conf.*, Plast. Institute, London (1970).
44. GRANT, D. and WALKER, W., *Plastics Progress*, Iliffe, London, p. 243 (1951).
45. BROWN, J., *Rubb. Plast. Age*, **37**(6), 400 (1956).
46. BARMAG BARMER MASCHINENFABRIK A. G., Remscheid, Information Service No. 13 (1975).
47. PAHL, M. H., *Dispersives Mischen mit dynamischen Mischern*, Praktische Rheologie der Kunststoffe, VD1-Verlag GmbH, Dusseldorf, pp. 177–96 (1977).
48. BRAUN, K. J. and HELMY, H. A., *Plast. Rubb. Wkly.*, 22 March, 11 (1980).
49. JUVE, A. E., US Patent 2894280 (1959).
50. DULMAGE, F. E. US Patents 2453088 (1948); 2753595 (1956).
51. MADDOCK, B., *SPEJ*, **23**, 23 (1967).
52. TADMOR, Z. and KLEIN, I., *SPE ANTEC meeting*, **31**, 129 (1973).
53. CHUNG, C. I., *Plast. Engng.*, **33**, 34 (1977).
54. MENGES, G. and LEHNEN, J. P., *Kunststofftechnik*, **9**, 128 (1970).
55. ANON, *Plast. Rubb. Wkly.*, 3 March, 22 (1978).
56. MADDOCK, R. H., *Plast. Engng.*, **30**(1), 28 (1974).
57. FRADOS, J. (Ed.), *Plastics Engineering Handbook of the Society of the Plastics Industry Inc.*, 4th Edition, Van Nostrand Reinhold, New York (1976).
58. VON HASSELL, A., *Plast. Tech.*, **26**(2), 80-82A-D (1980).
59. HARTUNG, M., *Plast. Tech.*, **27**(1), 83 (1981).
60. ANON, *Intl. Plast. Engng.*, **4**(1), 1 (1964).
61. KRUDER, G. A. and RIDENOUR, R. E., *Plast. Engng.*, **33**(11), 33 (1971).
62. ANON, *Eur. Plast. News*, **8**(4), 33 (1981).
63. ANON, *Mod. Plast. Intl.*, **7**(11), 59 (1977).
64. PARSHALL, C. M. and SAULINO, A. J., *Rubb. J.*, **149**(6), 66 (1967).
65. CROWTHER, B. G. and MORRELL, S. H., *Progress of Rubber Technology*, **36**, 37 (1972).
66. CROWTHER, B. G. and EMONDSON, H. M., *Rubber Technology and Manufacture*, Chapter 8, Blow, C. M. (Ed.), Newnes-Butterworth, London (1977).
67. SALDEN, D. M., *Melt Compounding and Compounding Machinery*, 1st Major Conf. on Thermoplastic Compounding, PRI, London (1978).
68. ANON, *Mod. Plast. Intl.*, **11**(1), 50 (1981).
69. WERNER & PFLEIDERER, Stuttgart, *ESK Einwellige Knetscheiben-Schneckenpresse zur Aufbereitung thermoplastischer Kunststoffe*, Technical Bulletin.
70. ANON, *Rubb. Plast. Age*, **40**, 1291 (1959).
71. RICE, P. and ADAM, H., *Developments in PVC Production and Processing* — 1, Chapter 5, Whelan, A. and Craft, J. L. (Eds), Applied Science Publishers, London (1977).
72. LEONCE, MARIE HENRI KRAFFE DE LAUBARDE, British Patent 738784 (1955).

188 POLYMER MIXING TECHNOLOGY

73. PLASTIVU, S. A., British Patent 924635 (1963).
74. MENGES, G. and HARMS, E., *Kaut. u. Gummi, Kunststoffe*, **25**, 469 (1962); **27**, 187 (1974).
75. HARMS, E. G., *Elastomerics (Rubber Age)*, **109**(6), 533 (1977); *Eur. Rubb. J.*, **160**(5), 23 (1978).
76. BADISCHE ANILIN-&-SODA-FABRIK A. G., British Patent 930828 (1963).
77. TODD, D. B. and HUNT, J. W., *SPE ANTEC Meeting*, **19**, 577 (1973).
78. FENNER, R. T. and WILLIAMS, J. G., *Polym. Engng. Sci.*, **11**(6), 474 (1971).
79. SQUIRES, P. H. and WOLF, C.F.W., *SPEJ*, **27**(4), 68 (1971).
80. STADE, K. H., *Polym. Engng. Sci.*, **18**(2), 107 (1978).
81. ANON, *Mod. Plast. Intl.*, **9**(6) 14 (1979).
82. ANON, *Plast. Tech.*, **23**(2) 23 (1977).
83. FISHER, E. G. and WHITFIELD, E. C., *Extrusion of Plastics*, Newnes-Butterworths, London (1976).
84. SCHENKEL, G., *Schneckenpressen für Kunststoffe*, Munich (1959).
85. KONSTANTINOV, V. N. and LEVIN, A. N., *Soviet Plastics*, No. 5, 41 (1962).
86. JANSSEN, L. P. M. and SMITH, J. M., Flow and mixing in twin screw extruders and processors in *Polymer Rheology and Plastics Processing*, Brit. Soc. Rheol. and Plast. Rubb. Inst. Conf., pp. 160–9 (1975).
87. SMITH, J. M., JANSSEN, L. P. B. M., DE KONING, W. L. and ABELN, P. P. J., *Polym. Engng. Sci.*, **18**(8), 660 (1978).
88. MACK, W. A., *Plast. Tech.* **21** (2), 45 (1975).
89. ANON, *Plast. Rubb. Wkly*, 3 March, 17; 10 March, 15; 17 March, 21 (1978); 15 March, 13; 22 March, 11; 29 March, 15 (1980).
90. ZIELONKOWSKI, W., *Kunststoffe*, **58**, 394 (1968).
91. ANON, *Plast. Mod. Elast.*, **29**(5), 4951 (1977).
92. SELBACH, H. W., *MM Maschinenmarkt*, **83**, 14 (1977).
93. RIESS, K. and MESKAT, W., *Chem. Ing. Tech.*, **23**(9/10), 205 (1951).
94. JOSEPH ECK and SOHNE, British Patent 738461 (1955).
95. ANON, *Intl. Plast. Engng.*, **2**(5), 218 (1962).
96. ANON, *Plast. Tech.*, **9**(5), 13 (1963).
97. SCHEINER, L. L., *Plast. Tech.*, **13**(6), 39 (1967).
98. ELLWOOD, H., *Developments in the Mixing of Rubber and Plastics* (1964) and *The Mixing of Rubber and Plastics* (1968), David Bridge & Co., Ltd, Rochdale.
99. FARREL CORPORATION, US Patent 3154808 (1962).
100. FARREL BRIDGE LTD, Rochdale, *Farrel Continuous Mixers*, Technical Bulletin 227D (1970).
101. FARREL MACHINERY GROUP, Ansonia, *FCM Continuous Mixer*, Technical Bulletin (1964).
102. MAKAJO, S., NÜNA, T. and HAYASHIZAKI, Y., *Japan Plast.* **10**(4), 15 (1976).
103. LOOMANS, B. A. and BRENNAN, A. K., US Patent 3195868 (1965).
104. TODD, D. B. and BAUMANN, D. K., *Chem. Engng. Progr.*, **73**(1), 65 (1977); *Polym. Engng. Sci.*, **18**(4), 321 (1978).
105. ANON, *Plast. Rubb. Wkly*, 29 June, 12 (1979).
106. ANON, *Eur. Plast. News*, **8**(5), 25 (1981).
107. TENNER, H. *Kunststoffberater*, **21**(6), 278 (1976).
108. TANAKA, S., *Japan Plast. Age*, **11**(3), 27 (1977).

109. WERNER & PFLEIDERER, Stuttgart, Twin Screw Compounder Type ZZK Dual Feed, Technical Bulletin (1970).
110. ANON, *Plast. Rubb. Wkly.*, November, 20 (1979).
111. GEWERKSCHAFT SCHALKER EISENHUTTE, British Patent 902513 (1962).
112. ANON, *Mod. Plast. Intl.*, **7**(7), 18 (1977).
113. ANDERS, D., *Plast. Engng.*, **34**(5), 56 (1978).
114. PASQUETTI, C., British Patent 638364 (1950).
115. FARBENFABRIKEN BAYER AG, British Patent 859959 (1961).
116. MAXWELL, B. and SCALORA, A. J., *Mod. Plast.*, **37**(2), 107 (1959).
117. BADISCHE ANILIN-&-SODA-FABRIK AG, British Patent 891177 (1962).
118. ANON, *Mod. Plast.*, **40**(3), 119 (1962).
119. WESTOVER, R. F. *S.P.E.J.*, **18**(12), 1473 (1962).
120. SCHARGORODSKII, A. M., *Sov. Plast.*, No. 11, 35 (1972).
121. ANON, *Mod. Plast. Intl.*, **9**(6), 43 (1979).
122. TADMOR, Z., HOLD, P. and VALSAMIS, L., *Plast. Engng.*, **35**(11), 20; **35**(12), 34 (1979); *The Diskpack Polymer Processor*, Farrel Connecticut Division (1979).
123. TADMOR, Z., US Patent 4142805 (1979).
124. BURGER, F., HANSLIK, W., HEILMAYR, P. and KERSCHBAUMER, A., *Kunststoffe*, **59**, 134 (1969).
125. BURKE, G. H. and PORTINGELL, G. C., *Br. Plast.*, **36**(5), 254 (1963).
126. DOWRICK, D., *Plastics*, **30**, 328 (1965).
127. KHANNA, S. K. and POLLETT, W. F. D., *J. Appl. Polym. Sci.*, **9**, 1767 (1965).
128. MOORE, D. R., *PRI Int. Conf. on PVC Processing*, Eng. Royal Holloway College. PRI, London, pp. 11.1–11.11 (1978).
129. BECKER, K., *Kunststoffe*, **54**, 23 (1964).
130. PONT-A-MOUSSON, S. A., Paris, SMTP DIVN, *The Kaufman Super 2 Extruder*, Technical Bulletin (1980).
131. REED–PRENTICE CO., British Patent 838319 (1960).
132. WERNER & PFLEIDERER, Stuttgart, *KS-Information Brief Reports*, Nos. 8 (1973) and 25 (1977).
133. FARREL BRIDGE, *Product Development News* (1977).
134. ANON, *Plast Tech.*, **23**(11), 143 (1977).
135. FARREL BRIDGE LTD, Rochdale, *New Developments by Farrel Bridge Ltd— Integrated Mixing Venting and Extrusion Equipment for Particulate Rubber* (1977 and 1978).
136. SKIDMORE, R. H., *New Developments in Machinery Design and Polymer Processing*, Welding Engineers Inc., King of Prussia, Pennsylvania.
137. CHEN, S. J., *S.P.E. ANTEC Meeting*, **19**, 258 (1973).
138. CHEN, S. J. and MACDONALD, A. R., *Chem. Engng.*, **80**(7), 105 (1973).
139. ANON, *Chem. Engng.*, **80**(7), 111 (1973).
140. ANON, *Eur. Plast. News*, **5**(2), 46; **5** (12), 25 (1978).
141. SCHOTT, N. R., WEINSTEIN, B. and LA BOMBARD, D. *Chem. Eng. Prog.*, **71**(1), 54 (1975).
142. HAN, C. D., KIM, Y. W., and CHEN, S. J. *J. Appl. Polym. Sci.*, **19**, 2831 (1975).

CHAPTER 6

The Complete Mixing Installation

6.1 INTRODUCTION

The preceding three chapters have been concerned with those particular items of equipment that contribute specifically to blending and compounding processes, but, of course, other items of equipment are required to make up the total mixing facility. These may be divided into

(i) those required for the handling, including receipt and storage, of raw materials, and their delivery to the mixing equipment,
(ii) intermediate handling equipment,
(iii) equipment required to deal with compounded material, and
(iv) safety equipment.

The purpose of this chapter is to consider briefly items of equipment coming under the above headings, to bring the whole together in a consideration of how a polymer mixing facility should best be planned to meet specific requirements, and finally to consider the all-important matter of costs.

6.2 ANCILLARY PROCESSES AND EQUIPMENT

6.2.1 *Raw Materials Handling*

Much of what is included under this heading is not specific to polymer mixing technology, and, indeed, is not specific to polymer technology in general, and for that reason, if for no other, the discussion is fairly brief.

The nature and not merely the size of individual items of equipment is likely to be influenced by the size of the total operation. Thus, for example, a small business operating a single small compounding line with an annual production of say 500×10^3 kg/a is unlikely to install elaborate storage facilities. Polymer deliveries might be in 25-kg paper or plastic sacks, or in the case of rubbers, 33-kg bales wrapped in film, probably in pallet loads in both cases, liquid additives in metal drums, and smaller quantities of solid additives in cardboard kegs. The materials may be stored in the containers in which they were delivered, and storage arrangements may be of the simplest, perhaps merely a shed to keep out the weather. It is not unknown for incoming basic raw materials to be stored in the open, under the cover of a plastic sheeting. Weighing will be on simple scales of capacities appropriate to the quantities required for blending, conveyance and charging to mixing equipment by hand. Not highly technological one might think, but, of course, it is all a matter of capital and running costs. At the other end of the scale, a plant processing several thousand tonnes a year may have large silos for particulate polymer storage, holding several tons, smaller silos or bins for solid additives, and tanks for liquid components, polymer, fillers and liquids in quantity being delivered by tanker. Even minor components will have their own storage containers permanently installed. Weighing is likely to be automatic and conveying mechanical or pneumatic, and the whole plant might be operated by remote control.[1,2,59] Inevitably, the ubiquitous computer is also to be found playing its usual dominant role in the control and running of some compounding plants.[4]

Between these two extremes, a variety of procedures is to be found. Thus, for example, the 25-kg sack may be replaced by much larger cardboard containers holding up to around 500 kg, or by more substantial mobile metal or plastic bins with capacities as low as 100 kg or as high as 1000 kg. Some of these have chambers for more than one component, and built-in blending arrangements. As the capacity gets higher it becomes exorbitantly expensive to make these bins mobile, and so from 500 kg upwards they are generally static. This, of course, requires arrangements to deliver incoming materials to their locations and means for transporting materials from the discharge ports to weighing and blending equipment. The disadvantages of manual handling and the merits of fixed storage and pneumatic methods of conveyance have been cogently summarised.[3] Large silos are expensive to install, but there is often a reduction in delivery charges to be gained if deliveries by road or rail tanker can be accepted. Thus, it was estimated that the cost of installing a 20-tonne GRP silo could be recovered over 14 deliveries, and this means that such an installation would probably be justified for any material for which the annual consumption was 300 tonnes or more.[3] This was in 1968 and the situation has changed since then, quantitatively if not qualitatively, but the principle still holds since depreciation on a well-designed and constructed silo should be minimal.

One problem with large silos that calls for consideration, is the fact that pressure on material near the bottom increases with the height of the solid bed and may seriously impair flow behaviour, particularly if the solid is at all deficient in this respect anyway or is liable to agglomerate. This is possibly less important if solids are drawn off by a pneumatic line inserted into the bed, but could be serious with bottom discharge using a slide or rotary valve. One means of alleviating the problem is to install a planetary screw auger that draws material towards the central discharge opening, while traversing the whole of the base of the silo by rotation about the centre point.[5] An alternative that has been used for solid additives in smaller bins is to keep the contents in a state of fluidisation.[6] Powdered or granular solids can usually be handled conveniently in silos, but large blocks of material such as bale rubber obviously cannot, and large-scale storage and mechanisation of handling such materials is not so easy to devise. Liquids, on the whole, present no problems as far as containment and transport are concerned, but corrosion and contamination need to be watched carefully.

Some raw materials are particularly prone to pick up water, or may contain other undesirable volatiles. This depends on chemical nature and physical form. It is well known that nylons tend to absorb water to an extent that is often unacceptable in subsequent processing. Nylons have even been called 'hygroscopic', though this term does give an exaggerated picture of their water absorbing behaviour. Even polymers that are usually regarded as water-repellent, such as polyolefins, can take up sufficient water to impair their processing behaviour. In this connection a problem that can sometimes arise, particularly when using polymer packed in sacks stored in a cold environment, is condensation of water from the moist atmosphere of the processing plant on to the cold polymer if the container is opened directly it has been brought in from storage. The solution to this problem is simply to transfer the polymer in sealed containers, and to allow ample time for the contents to reach the temperature of the processing plant before opening. Bales of natural rubber may need similar treatment for a rather different reason, for if they have been stored below 0°C crystallisation may have occurred, and the first step is to thaw the rubber by warming at quite high temperatures, e.g. up to 70°C.

Apart from the possible presence of water that will require removal by volatilisation, some polymers contain undesirable volatile residues from polymerisation processes, unreacted monomer in particular. Water and other volatile contents of polymers and additives have become less of a problem with the widespread adoption of venting and vacuum extraction in melt processing equipment, but it is still often desirable to remove water before subsequent processing. Ideally, of course, it would be better to keep the materials dry from the outset, but this is not always easy and can be expensive since it may involve heating of a large space. Be that as it may, intermediate drying equipment is sometimes desirable. In its simplest form, this can be an airflow oven with stainless steel trays on which the solid can be spread out in thin layers to expose a large surface area to the warm air flow. Protection from contamination from the air, in the form of a synthetic fabric cover, is desirable. More sophisticated arrangements operate on what is essentially the fluidised bed technique, though uniform fluidisation may not necessarily be achieved. Such a system can be combined with a hopper charging directly to a processing machine, such as a continuous compounder. It can also be combined with a blending process if an air or fluidised bed mixing system is used (Chapter 3, Section 3.9). Where re-circulated air flow is employed, it is desirable to pass the air through a desiccating unit before each return to the solids drying chamber. Vacuum drying equipment is also available. This has the attraction that it does not require drying of re-circulating air, and is particularly advantageous where it it necessary to achieve very low levels of concentrations of monomer or other volatiles. Drying by hot air or by vacuum can be continuous. For example, in one form of hot air drier the moist product and dry air are introduced at the bottom of a vertical cylindrical drying chamber, and the material is conveyed upwards in the air stream through a slowly rotating spiral channel, to be discharged as dry product at the top.[7] A good deal of data on the basic principles of drying and the capabilities of different systems is available from equipment suppliers.[8-11]

Conveyance of raw materials, like storage, can range from the simply manual to the sophisticated automated labour-free system. Between the extremes are various mechanical devices such as the familiar fork-lift truck, movable intermediate materials holding bins, bucket elevators, and conveyor belts or vibratory conveyors. For fairly short distances, Archimedean screw conveyors are often convenient, but for longer distances the most commonly employed non-manual methods are pneumatic,[59] of which there are three alternative variants, namely

(i) pressure systems,
(ii) vacuum systems and
(iii) vacuum/pressure systems,[3] which convey particulate solids through appropriate pipe work.

The first of these systems requires air blowers, though existing plant compressed air might be used. It does tend to be expensive to install and also to run, because of its inefficient power usage. Technically, the system is more liable to produce contamination than a vacuum system, and flow and build-up problems can sometimes arise at bends in the flow path. Vacuum systems are more efficient and generally to be preferred for conveyancing rates below 7000 kg/h. At higher rates a vacuum/pressure system, i.e. using a combination of positively generated air flow and vacuum, may be preferable. A comprehensive account of the theory and practice of pneumatic conveyance and bulk storage of polymers has recently been published.[59] Pneumatic and screw conveyors are also available in portable form, suitable for fairly small transference of solids from bulk containers or bins directly into weighing equipment or hoppers. Conveyance of liquid components by pumping through pipes has few problems that are specific to polymer processing, except perhaps from those arising in the handling of highly reactive viscous compositions. Mention should also be made of the recently introduced system of materials conveying by computer-controlled robot-trailers.[12]

There seems to be little point in using continuous weighing or metering to supply raw material for batch blending or compounding. Consequently, these processes normally employ fairly conventional weighing and handling equipment, although this is likely to be highly sophisticated in mechanism and automation. Where possible, the weighing machines should discharge directly by gravity into the mixing machine, but space availability may preclude this so some form of conveyance may be necessary. One simple arrangement is to discharge weighed amounts of each component into open containers, travelling on a conveyor belt below the discharge points. Alternatively, individual conveyor belts or screw conveyors can be used. The accuracy of metering machines for solids or liquids has increased considerably in recent years and they are becoming very much more widely used. For continuous blending they are essential, and in continuous compounding, if the compounding process is able to achieve all the required mixing, preliminary blending may be omitted by installing continuous metering equipment for each component, discharging into the feed point of the continuous compounder. Metering is effected by control of either weight or volume. Weigh feeders operate by sensing the progressive loss in weight of the material container, or by continuous monitoring of weight on a continuous conveyor belt. The former is suitable for liquids or solids, but the latter can only really be used for solids. Another form of meter, the 'impact flow meter',[13] operates by sensing the impact of particles by means of an inclined plate. Measurement is made of the reaction of the plate, which is proportional to mass and square of velocity. Calibration is necessary because some bouncing particles impact the plate more than once. Metering by volume can be by means of a metering pump, an Archimedean screw or screws, or a specially designed volumetric solid flow meter of the 'Flow Star' type[14] (Fig. 6.1)

 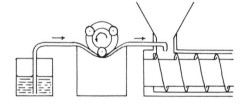

FIG. 6.1. Principle of Flow Star indexible feeder.   FIG. 6.2. Metering liquid colourant by peristaltic pump.

or of the reciprocating piston type.[15] In the Flow Star indexible volumetric feeder, material falling under gravity passes over a 'flow cone' that spreads the flow outwards towards the perimeter of a stationary circular base plate, that has a circular discharge port at its centre. An S- or Z-shaped blade rotating about a vertical axis moves material horizontally inwards to discharge. Flow rate is controlled by the configuration of the cone and blade.[14] In a reciprocating piston flow meter, material from a hopper falls into a horizontal cylinder as the piston retracts and the quantity that has entered the cylinder is discharged by forward movement of the piston, in much the same way as feeding was controlled in early ram injection moulding machines. The flow rate is adjustable by varying the distance of retraction of the piston.[15] For particulate solids metering pumps will normally be of the rotary type, but for liquids any suitable accurate pump can be used.

6.2.2. Liquid Colourants

In recent years the use of so-called 'liquid colourants' has increased in popularity. These are highly concentrated dispersions of colourants in liquid media that are claimed to be advantageous from the points of view of cost, cleanliness, ease of automation and ease of colour changing. They are not suitable for all polymers but can be used for many plastic compositions. These liquid colourants can very conveniently be metered by means of a diaphragm or peristaltic pump (Fig. 6.2), and very simple systems based on these are being used in injection moulding and extrusion, to meter liquid colourants directly into the remainder of the composition near the bottom of the feed hopper.[15] This technique can only be used, of course, with materials that will tolerate the liquid carrier and with which adequate mixing can be achieved in the course of one passage through the machine. Devices are also available to meter pelletised colourant concentrates into a machine hopper. Where the capabilities of the final processing machine and the behaviour of the materials permit, it is becoming increasingly popular to combine metering and simple blending equipment in one unit, particularly in small-scale operations, e.g. feeding an individual injection moulding machine or extruder. Self-contained units for this procedure comprise separate hoppers for individual components, each with its own volumetric metering device discharging into a simple small continuous blender,[16] for example consisting of a horizontal shaft carrying several paddles that lift and agitate the contents in similar fashion to some forms of ribbon blender (Fig. 6.3) (Chapter 3, Section 3.6). Because the components are metered in side by side at controlled rates, and because the quantity in the mixing chamber at any one time is small, the blending operation is quite efficient, and the resultant blend is delivered directly to a holding hopper or directly into the hopper of the injection machine or extruder. These devices are particularly suitable for dry-colouring and blending regrind with virgin polymer.

6.2.3 Breaker Plates

The preceding discussion is mainly concerned with operations leading up to blending and/or compounding. Much of what was said is also applicable to handling of product after a blending or compounding

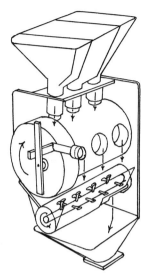

FIG. 6.3. Foscolor 'Mastermeter' meter/blender.

process, but there are a few items specific to the latter that deserve some mention. The first of these concerns continuous compounding equipment itself. In those of the extruder type there will commonly be a breaker plate located in the flow channel, somewhere betwen the die entry and the tip of the screw. Sometimes the breaker plate will carry screen gauzes, whose function is partly to filter-off solid impurities and undispersed particles, and partly to increase back-pressure by restricting melt flow. By their very nature, screens tend to become blocked sooner or later and this can result in marked reduction in throughput and changes in shear conditions over a period. Since the ideal in any compounding operation should be to continue running for as long as possible, blockage of screens, even if it builds up slowly, necessitating shut-down merely for the purpose of cleaning or changing screens can be a serious nuisance. For some time now, mechanical screen changing devices, some at least of which do not require a break in processing continuity, have been available for extrusion, and there seems to be no inherent reason why they should not be more generally applicable to continuous compounding machines. If continuity is not interrupted during screen changing, this operation can be carried out more frequently than would otherwise be the case, thus reducing any variation in quality that might arise from changing processing conditions.[17,18] The 'Cresta' system (Fig. 6.4),

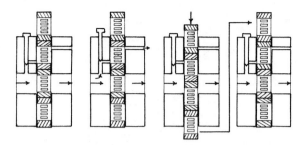

FIG. 6.4. Cresta breaker plate and screen changer.

for example, operates by having four screen blocks in line. While one of the central two is in position in the normal melt flow stream the other is being heated. When it is desired to change screens, a valve in the assembly is opened to allow melt to flow into the second of the central blocks and purge out the air in it. Then a hydraulic ram moves the whole of the assembly, so that the second of the two central screens now becomes aligned in the main melt stream, and the outside screen farthest from it is ejected for cleaning to be replaced at the other end of the assembly.[12] Using four screen blocks in this way, the procedure can be repeated *ad nauseam*. Manually operated screen changers are also available, usually using three screen blocks, the direction of movement for changing reversing at every second change.

6.2.4 *Handling Mixed Product*

The form of products from a mixing process varies with the nature of the composition and the particular process. Simple blending will result in dry, damp or sticky particulate blends or viscous liquids, and although dealing with these forms may not always be simple, there is little more to be said about handling them that is in any way specific to polymer technology. Compounding, as defined in Chapter 1, Section 1.2, produces a melt or shapeless crumb-like material that usually requires some additional manipulation to convert into a form suitable for subsequent processing. That manipulation depends on the nature of the particular compounding process, and on the nature of the process to which the compound is to be submitted subsequently. As we have seen earlier (Chapter 4, Section 4.2) the compound produced by two-roll milling can be handled in a variety of ways. If the product is required for calendering it may be removed from the mill in small quantities and fed direct to the first nip of the calender. Alternatively, the compounded stock can be removed as a strip and fed continuously to the calender, additional material being compounded at a sufficient rate to match the rate of removal. In either case, it is preferable to have an intermediate two-roll mill between the compounding mill and the calender to act as a buffer. Some materials, some forms of unplasticised or vinyl flooring PVC for example, can be removed as complete sheet for subsequent calendering or laminating in a press. Where the subsequent process is extrusion or moulding the treatment will depend on the material. Rubbers are commonly removed as strip for extrusion, but thermoplastics are generally processed from granules or pellets, while thermosetting plastics are most commonly converted to powder prior to moulding. The latter is straight forward in theory, but can be more difficult in practice because of fairly specific powder and flow requirements. Thermoplastics will normally be removed as strip of say 80–500 mm wide, cooled and granulated. At one time, impact granulators with screens having openings of the required granule size were common, but they produce irregularly shaped granules of rather wide size distribution and relatively high proportions of fines. Consequently, they have largely been replaced by 'cube-cutters', 'stair-step' or 'stepped-stair' dicing machines (Fig. 6.5).

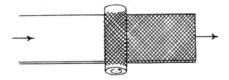

FIG. 6.5. Stepped-stair cube cutting.

A stair-step dicing machine comprises a rotating cylinder carrying knives that cut across the strip, while the latter is fed below but in close proximity to the cylinder. The knives are shaped so that they cut across the strip in a succession of right-angled zig-zagged lines, so that adjacent cuts form squares of side approximately equal to the strip thickness, usually about 3 mm, and the resultant granules are approximately cubic in shape. Another type of dicer that produces cubes does so in two stages, the strip first passing through a series of longitudinally rotating knives that cut the strip into square-sectioned strands, and then passing to a rotary cutter that cuts the strands transversely to produce cubes. A sheet granulator intended mainly for reprocessing sheet but which should be suitable for processing virgin compound in sheet form, produces rectangular granules approximately 3 × 8 mm by a somewhat different mechanism.[18] In this machine, sheet is fed in horizontally in the usual way but is deflected into a vertical direction between two rotary cutters that carry cutting teeth. The cutter points cut the sheet in the transverse direction, while the tooth faces cut in the longitudinal direction.[18] The optimum temperature of the material for cutting depends on the nature of the composition, but for ease of operation and to save space, the strip is usually cooled by passing through an appropriate length of water-bath on its way to the granulator. On leaving the bath, water is removed, preferably by air knives,[12] i.e. continuous blasts of air, one on either side of the strip. It is good practice to include a metal detector before the strip reaches the granulator, preferably arranged to stop granulation and divert the strip until the contamination has been isolated and eliminated (Fig. 6.6).

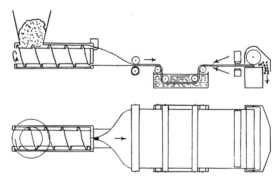

FIG. 6.6. Granulation from an extruder-slabber.

As indicated in Chapter 4, Section 4.3, the discharge from an internal mixer is normally either sheeted on a two-roll mill, and then treated essentially as described in the previous paragraph, or converted to continuous sheet, strip or strand formed by passage through an extruder-slabber. Some materials are liable to over-heat if extruded through multi-hole dies and it is more common to use a tube die on an extruder-slabber, slitting the tube longitudinally as it leaves the die, by means of a knife attached to the die-face, opening the tube to form a wide strip or sheet by passing through pairs of rollers, and then treating the strip in the same way as previously described for strip discharge from a two-roll mill.

The extrudate from an extruder-slabber or a continuous compounding machine may be in the form of many strands or laces (Fig. 6.7). This is accomplished by using a straight-through or cross-head die with a series of small orifices of appropriate size arranged in a horizontal line, or alternatively in a fairly uniform way around the central axis. Handling

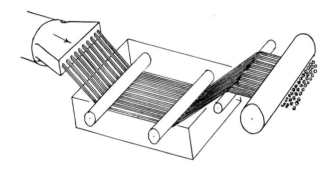

FIG. 6.7. Strand or lace cutting.

the strands is simpler in the former case, but it is easier in the latter case to design a die that will produce strands of essentially the same cross-section from all the orifices, particularly as the number of orifices increases. The extruded strands can be cooled by passing through a water-bath, dried, and granulated in much the same way as strip or sheet. Granules produced in this way are known as spaghetti or lace-cut.[19] In the Scheer SGA pelletising system the strands are extruded vertically downwards into a water-bath, where they are picked up by a forced conveyance arrangement, consisting of two continuous highly elastic belts that carry the strands around the bath and deliver them to feed rolls that carry the strands to a rotary cutter. This system is claimed virtually to eliminate stoppages due to strand breakages.[20] The Automatik USG system also has extruded laces passing downwards, but the strands drop down into grooves in a guide plate that is flooded with water. Thence they are drawn to be cut under water between a bed knife and a rotary cutter.

As an alternative to cutting the strands after they have left the die they may be die-face cut, i.e. cut as they leave the die (Fig. 6.8). This is accomplished by means of a rotary cutter blade that wipes across the face of the die as it rotates. By adjustment of the speed of rotation in relation to extrusion rate, the lengths of the granules or pellets can be

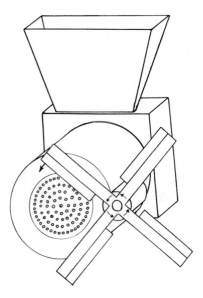

FIG. 6.8. Die-face cutting.

varied. Die-face cutting avoids the problem of handling large numbers of strands, but unlike strand pelletising, the strands are cut while still hot and usually need to be cooled before being allowed to congregate in heaps in containers, otherwise agglomeration may occur. This can be effected in a variety of ways, either 'dry' or 'wet'. The former involves cooling the granules in an air stream, for example in a form of continuous fluidised bed,[21] and subsequently conveying them in a pneumatic vacuum system. There are three slightly different forms of wet cutting.[22] In one, the granules are extruded directly into a circulating water system that carries them away. In the second system, sometimes called 'water-ring pelletising',[22,23] the granules are thrown into a stream of circulating water by the action of the rotating knives, and in the third system the granules are cooled by a water spray. Ideally, when using water cooling, the granules should be separated from the water while they still retain enough heat to evaporate off any that remains on them, but usually some form of drying arrangement will be necessary, for example a centrifugal or cyclone dryer. Choice of method of granulation is usually dependent on the recommendation of the manufacturer of the compounding machine concerned, and perhaps not enough consideration is given to the possible importance of the granulation process in relation to product properties. Where the composition has low melt strength, strand extrusion can be difficult unless the strands are extruded directly into water, as is common in melt-spinning, and die-face cutting may be distinctly advantageous in such cases. It is also desirable to cool, as rapidly as possible, those compositions that are particularly sensitive to oxidative degradation. However, the temperature of the composition at the moment of cutting can be important. If the temperature is too low excessive fines may result, particularly with hard compositions, and localised degradation at the cut face can occur if the state of the composition and the knife are such that the cut is not clean. In all cases care should be taken to ensure that the cutter blades are always sharp.

Little fundamental study of the process of granulation has been published, though experiments with one particular machine suggested that normally used speeds are appreciably removed from the optimum, and that changing to the optimum from standard speed improved output rate and particle size distribution, while at the same time reducing noise.[24] Noise, in fact, has always been a major problem with granulating machines, but considerable advances have been made in overcoming this problem in recent years. One approach is to enclose the noisy parts of the machine in a sound insulating enclosure, but this is bound to be a hindrance, and modifications in machine design[25-27] are much more acceptable if they are sufficiently effective. Some improvement can be achieved by running the cutting rotor at lower speeds than normal, and compensating for the drop in cutting rate by increasing the number of cutting knives on the rotor.[24,26]

An aspect of granulation that has received inadequate attention is the importance of particle size, size distribution and shape on behaviour in subsequent processing. It is generally accepted that fines amongst granules are to be avoided, and that particle size and shape should be as regular as possible, but nothing appears to have been published about the relative merits of cubes, spheres, prisms, and other shapes, or of different sizes of granules, since Kennaway's papers in the mid 1950s.[19] Working with both single- and twin-screw machines, it was shown that the rate of extrusion of polyethylene was highly dependent on granule form. 'Caviare' or die-face cut granules, of 'spheroid' shape, were found to extrude twice as fast as rough cut disintegrated granules. Cylindrical spaghetti or lace-cut granules extruded 90% faster than the disintegrated material, while the rate for cube-cut granules was only slightly below that for the spaghetti cut. There were indications that the extrusion rates were dependent on bulk density and ease of flow of the granules, but the quantitative correlations were poor. It is possible that the optimum will vary depending on the subsequent processing machine, in particular the geometry of hopper, hopper throat, and the feed section of its screw or screws, though as pointed out in Chapter 2, Section 2.4.3, softening and compaction may also vary with different particle shapes and sizes.

If material is being compounded for subsequent calendering, the two processes will normally be carried out simultaneously, the hot, softened compound being fed to the calender without intermediate granulation. Although, as indicated previously, a calender can be fed by discreet small charges removed at regular intervals from a two-roll mill, continuous feeding seems preferable. This suggests that continuous compounding is advantageous, the extrudate therefrom being fed directly to the calender, passing a metal detector on the way. Sensing devices on the calender train can be instrumented to feed back to the controls of the compounding machine, so that the output of the latter can be closely matched to that of the calender at all times.

Where the product of the mixing process is dry-blend or granules for subsequent extrusion or moulding, some form of containment will usually be necessary. It is possible to construct a mixing plant that delivers product directly to extruders or moulding machines, but some form of buffer stock-holding is highly desirable. Containers and handling equipment are essentially the same as those used for incoming solid raw materials. Where the compounded material is manufactured for despatch, packaging in paper or plastic sacks is still common. Plastic or plastic-lined (usually polyethylene) sacks are preferable to paper sacks, because they are less liable to introduce contamination and are less permeable to moisture. While filling and weighing of sacks or bins can be done manually, in a production unit of any size it is preferable to install automatic filling and weighing equipment.[28-30]

6.2.5 Safety Precautions

Turning to the matter of safety, it must be obvious, even to the least observant, that some polymer processing equipment, for example roll mills, presses and Z-blade mixers, are inherently dangerous if safeguards are not provided, but serious hazards are often present with equipment that looks superficially innocuous. The most obvious hazards arise from the possibility of physical injury and burns, but others such as the risk of inhaling toxic gases, fumes or dusts are often present, and the risk of fire and dust explosions is not always absent from some polymer processing plants. Obviously, the type and extent of hazard depend on the nature of the particular plant and the materials being processed, and the advice of the suppliers of both should be sought. It is to be hoped that any processing machinery these days would be supplied with in-built adequate safety arrangements. Of course, the nature of the hazards and the means of minimising them are not peculiar to polymer processing, and nowadays there are several individuals, public bodies and companies with expertise in the provision of safety devices, and these should be consulted where there is the slightest doubt about the extent of the hazard or the efficacy of installed safety measures. It is rarely, if ever, necessary for a physical presence to exist close to parts of machinery that can cause injury, and such parts should be screened to prevent such contact, and so interlocked that the machine will not operate if the guards are removed. Easily operable emergency stops should also be provided at strategic points. Devices of this kind can be very effective in keeping operatives and others away from moving parts, but protection from hot machinery is not so easy to ensure because hot metal can retain its heat for such a long time.

Ideally, nobody should enter, let alone work in, an area where there is a risk that the atmosphere might contain toxic gases, fumes or dust continuously or intermittently, even at very low concentrations, but where such hazards exist thorough ventilation and warning systems must be installed, and any individuals having to enter such an area should only do so wearing adequate protective clothing and breathing apparatus.

6.3 THE TOTAL MIXING FACILITY

The principles to be followed in planning the lay-out for a polymer mixing plant are, obviously, essentially the same as those operating for other types of plant. They may be summarised under a number of broad headings, namely smooth running, conservation of energy, conservation of space, safety, and of course minimum capital and running costs compatible with these. The optimum lay-out in any particular case will depend on the size of the operation, the nature of the particular mixing operations to be carried out, the destination of the product, i.e. to an in-house integrated subsequent processing plant or for transportation within company or to customers, and the location of the plant. The major suppliers of mixing equipment and complete installations have published a considerable amount of information on the subject[31-40] and are usually very willing to plan new plants to meet customers' specific requirements. A good description of the logical approach to selection and lay-out of equipment for polymer compounding was published nearly 20 years ago, in connection with an automated compounding plant for wire insulation material.[31]

The accompanying diagrams are intended to illustrate some of the points discussed in the preceding section, showing their application to possible arrangements for a number of typical polymer processing plants including or devoted completely to mixing. Precise inter-spatial relationships of the different items of equipment obviously depend on particular circumstances.

The first diagram (Fig. 6.9) illustrates an automated handling and

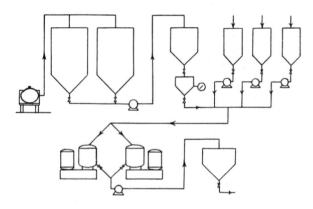

FIG. 6.9. Flow diagram for dry-blend manufacture.

blending plant for the manufacture of dry-blend such as, for example, unplasticised PVC for pipe extrusion.[37] Polymer is delivered by road or rail tanker from which it is conveyed to a bulk storage silo. If consumption is sufficiently high, powdered fillers could be handled in the same way. Likewise, if the plant was to produce plasticised dry-blend, it could well be that consumption would be great enough to justify delivery of plasticiser by tanker and transfer to storage tanks by pumping. Except in very large plants, usages of other additives are likely to be too low for tanker deliveries and these might have to be accepted in bins, drums or sacks to be transferred manually or mechanically to their respective storage containers. In the particular case of unplasticised PVC dry-blends, it is common practice for the stabilisers and lubricants to be supplied together in 'one-pack' systems, and since a formulation of this kind might well include as many as five components an obvious saving in storage, weighing and handling facilities results. Since the dry-blending machine operates batch-wise, intermittent batch-weighing to match blending cycle time can be used, and sequencing of introduction to the blender can be varied. On completion of the blending cycle, discharge to a cooling mixer is effected automatically and transfer to intermediate storage after appropriate cooling is also automatic. Transfer to extruders or injection machines from the intermediate storage can also be auto-mated using sensors in the hoppers. The whole operation can be controlled from a central control point by manual or fully automatic control.

In the internal mixer two-roll mill compounding plant for the manu-facture of granules or pellets illustrated in the second diagram (Fig. 6.10), the system is similar except that blended material is transferred

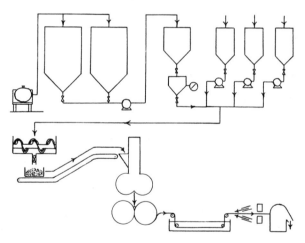

FIG. 6.10. Flow diagram for internal mixer/two-roll mill compounding.

batch-wise from intermediate storage to the internal mixer.[31] By match-ing the rate of removal of compounded strip from the mill to the rate of transfer of compound from the internal mixer, no manual intervention should be necessary during a production run of the same composition.

In a typical rubber compounding plant using internal mixer and extruder-slabber (Fig. 6.11), rubber and small ingredients may be fed by

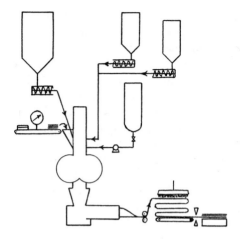

FIG. 6.11. Flow diagram for rubber compounding by internal mixer.

hand on to the feed conveyor, although the rest of the operation is automated.[32-35] Process oils may be metered volumetrically and pumped directly into the mixing chamber, to avoid sticking of damp powder to the ram and hopper.[34] Compound extruded from the slabber is passed through a 'batch-off' machine, cooled in a festoon rack, cut into slab stock and stacked.[33,35] Alternatively, the extruder-slabber could be a pelletising extruder with a die-face cutter using water cooling.[35] Automation and computer control of rubber compounding is similar to that suitable for plastics.[41]

Arising out of the need to ensure uniformity of heat-treatment and shearing, and a minimum of cooling, there is an old adage in calendering of plastics film and sheeting that runs 'little and often', referring to the size and frequency of transfer of portions of compounded material to the calender nip.[42,43] For essentially the same reasons, there is something to be said for using two smaller matched internal mixers rather than one larger one, when preparing feed stock for calendering[35] (Fig. 6.12). Where a two-roll mill is used to receive the discharge from the internal mixers, it is best to use it as a buffer stock-holder, with a second two-roll mill carrying material for delivery to the calender. It seems desirable to run the mills as for the production of granules, with a continuous strip transfer from first mill to second mill, and a second continuous strip from the latter to the calender nip, but it is common practice to transfer compound to the calender in discrete pieces taken periodically from the second mill.

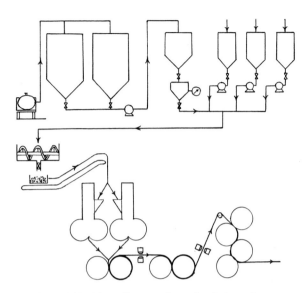

FIG. 6.12. Flow diagram for calendering plant.

From the foregoing paragraph, it seems that there are distinct advantages in using a continuous compounding machine to feed a calender[33,36] (Fig. 6.13), provided the capacity of the former can be varied to meet the varying requirements of the latter.

The final illustration (Fig. 6.14) is of a floor-tile plant. There is quite a variety of different plants and procedures used for the production of

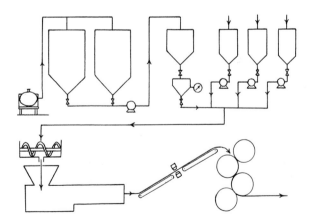

FIG. 6.13. Calendering plant with continuous compounding.

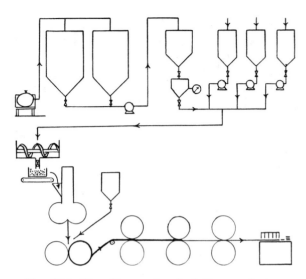

FIG. 6.14. Flow diagram for vinyl tile manufacture.

floor-tiles, and the one illustrated is typical of those used for the manufacture of vinyl/asbestos floor tiles.[35,43] After sheeting the main stock, coloured material for mottling is added, either directly on the mill or as the sheeting passes from the mill to the first two-roll calender. Otherwise the compounding operation is much the same as with other internal mixer/two-roll mill combinations.

6.4 COSTING

Costing procedures for mixing operations do not differ from those used for other manufacturing processes. Any reader requiring instruction in costing should refer to the many books on the subject, of which a few are listed in the references.[43-48] Perhaps anyone in that position would be better advised to give up the idea altogether or to use others' expertise. There would be little point in discussing costing procedures here, if it was not for the fact that when trying to decide what are the best machines and procedures to select for mixing, and indeed whether or not to install mixing plant at all, so often a bewilderingly wide variety of alternatives exist. The situation is even more complicated by changes in commercial climate that are likely to occur. This is particularly a problem in polymer mixing technology, where some firms have large capital investments in plant manufacturing blends and granulated compounds for sale to 'converters' using extrusion or moulding for the manufacture of finished products. Although there will probably always be a place for separate manufacture of blends and compounds, any trend towards in-house mixing tends to stimulate commercial reaction, so that the situation is constantly changing. Hence there are different points of view from which a costing might be required. To the manufacturer of blends or compounds for sale, the choice between plants that will effectively do the same job is difficult enough, particularly when the future market is uncertain, but the converter has also to evaluate these alternatives against the additional possibilities of buying in ready blended or compounded material, as well as deciding between other alternatives in the latter case, such as whether to use master-batch techniques or not. Decisions in this situation are complicated by virtue of a number of intangibles, such as the cost equivalent to transfer of responsibility for quality from an outside supplier to 'within company' or in-house. Critical factors in any costing, that are difficult to estimate accurately in the absence of data from practical experience of the contemplated plant and materials, are production capacity, taking into account down time, and proportions of acceptable and reject quality product, also taking into account the possibility of reworking reject material. These considerations reinforce the suggestions given previously (pp. 86, 169 and 185) to carry out full-scale plant trials on equipment whose purchase is contemplated. These should be based on the compositions it is intended to process, and should provide meaningful indications of likely production and reject rates. If these quantities are known with any accuracy, there should be little difficulty in arriving at reasonable estimates of likely costs and therefore cost comparisons. Of course, the fact that so many alternative possibilities exist and appear to be operated with commercial success suggests that any cost differences are small.

As indicated earlier, the problem is not merely one of comparing plants and procedures that will manufacture the same product, but also of deciding which is the best form of product to use. Thus, for example, a manufacturer using extrusion or moulding needs to decide between using fully compounded granules, dry-blend or natural material plus master-batch as feed stock. It is also necessary to decide between buying in the feed stock ready made or producing it in-house. A calendering operation will almost of necessity require compounding to be carried out directly in conjunction with it. Likewise, rubber compounding and moulding or extrusion tend to be operated side by side, although there has been increasing involvement of specialist compound suppliers in recent years.[49] The complexity of the problem is indicated by the diagram showing major routes for melt processing of polymers (Fig. 1.1, Chapter 1), and that obviously does not include non-melt processing. If the correct choice is to be made, there is rarely any short-cut from the assessment of all possible alternatives by as accurate cost estimates as possible. Fortunately, nowadays the computer can be used to take most of the drudgery and perhaps some of the risk of error from the calculations.

The Society of Plastics Engineers have published an instructive *Compounding Primer*,[50] which includes processing costings and cost comparisons for seven alternative systems for compounding unplasticised and plasticised PVC. Although these are based on US finance, and are no doubt out of date with respect to actual costs today, they could well serve as a basis and guide for cost comparisons of compounding operations generally. These costings take into account investment in capital equipment, building and installation costs, labour costs, services and depreciation, but specifically exclude raw materials costs. If full costing is required, raw materials costs clearly have to be included. For alternative plants with the same production and reject rates, these will be the same provided the rework possibilities are also the same. If the production rates are different, raw materials costs may differ as well because of the possibility of rebates for large volume purchases available at higher production rates. The seven systems, assessed in the Society of Plastics Engineers' *Compounding Primer*, were designed to produce seven different throughputs of unplasticised and plasticised PVCs in a variety of different ratios. Two of the systems were based on blending followed by internal mixer compounding leading to a two-roll sheeting mill, three were based on blending, continuous compounding and milling, and two were based on an intensive, non-fluxing mixer followed by an extruder. It is interesting to note that the costings presented show nearly six-fold variation between the lowest and highest costings, and a near linear inverse log–log relationship between unit cost and annual production over a ten-fold range of the latter from 2·26 to 22·6 million kg/a. In fact the figures are anomalous, in that the fall in unit cost with increasing production rate is rather greater than would be predicted by the simple exponential relationship, that might be expected if production rate was varied with a particular single plant. A rather less comprehensive comparison of colour compounding at two levels of production,[51] also shows a pronounced reduction with increase in production (2·4:1 for a five-fold increase from 7 million to 36 million kg/a). Even if these figures are true for the whole range of mixing operations, their effects are, of course, less dramatic than they appear since processing costs are only a part, and hopefully only a small part, of total unit costs. Different compositions vary considerably in raw materials costs, and these and labour costs are changing all the time, but processing cost is likely to amount to a relatively small proportion of the total cost, for example typically around 5% of material cost for a small-scale continuous compounding unit.

A cost comparison of automatic as against manually operated compounding several years ago[51,52] showed distinct advantages for the former and these are probably greater nowadays. Similar comparisons have also been made between different types of compounding machine.[53] Published costings become out-dated fairly rapidly, so that the actual figures quoted are rarely valid for any length of time. Nevertheless, they are worth studying for the guidance they give with respect to the factors to be taken into account, and for the indications they give of the relative orders of magnitude of effects of different items. As the representative of one leading machinery manufacturer has pointed out,[54] 'equipment has all too often been selected on the basis of original cost without considering installation or long-term operating costs' and 'value analysis requires consideration of future operating costs, including raw material and direct labour costs, utilities, maintenance, salaries of line supervisors, and other overheads. Operating cost savings achieved by using an efficient compounding line rather than inefficient alternatives are the daily dividends which effectively pay back initial capital costs faster'. Depending on the degrees of sophistication, competitive machines can differ in energy consumption by as much as three-fold. An important factor, that is difficult to predict with any accuracy, is reliability, though some guidance can be obtained from past experience.[54] Indeed, it has been claimed[54] that initial cost of equipment can be less significant than efficiency, ease of maintenance, and factors from other parts of the production line, in affecting product cost. It is probably best to under-estimate annual production when estimating costs for a proposed production unit, and to regard any production over the target as a bonus. Other costs that are liable to be overlooked, particularly when a converter who is purchasing ready compounded materials considers installing in-house mixing plant, are capital installation and running costs for test facilities for incoming raw materials. Also, as mentioned previously, there are intangibles from the change in situation from that where one supplier can be held responsible for inferior quality of compound to one where, not only are there likely to be several suppliers of the different components, but in addition the company itself has to carry responsibility for the mixing process itself. In spite of these and other considerations,[55] in-house blending and compounding seems to be increasing, particularly where the mixing required is relatively simple.[16,54,56-58] For PVC, an annual usage of 400 to 450 tonnes has been suggested as the level above which substantial cost advantages can often be gained, by establishing in-house compounding facilities.[38,53] Thus, in the USA in mid-1977, Adam[53] reported that PVC resin was costing between 20 and 30 cents/lb, and that the cost of compounding was as high as 10 cents/lb, so that a processor using 1 000 000 lb/a of resin was spending 100 000 dollars on compounding. A compounding plant with a throughput of 500 lb/h operated on the basis of one shift per five-day week, can produce compound for a processing cost of 6·7 cents/lb, and a plant with a throughput of 2000 lb/h operated on the same basis, can produce compound for a processing cost of 3·2 cents/lb.

6.4.1 *Costing Example*

Although, because of the present inflationary financial situation, it is not possible to present actual costings that can be used directly, it might be instructive to consider a hypothetical case in order to illustrate the factors that need to be taken into account, and to indicate one method of calculation in estimating the cost of producing compounded material. It should not be necessary to stress that the actual sums of money used in this illustration are nominal, and in some cases have been selected to keep the arithmetic simple, although it is hoped that they are at least not far removed from the correct orders of magnitude in relation to each other.

Having decided what product or range of products is required, it is necessary to decide the quantity to be produced. In this exercise it is assumed that a single composition is to be processed. Although this may be unrealistic, the approach if several compositions are envisaged is only somewhat more complicated but does not involve any different principles. For the purposes of calculation, it is assumed that the requirement is to be 3 000 000 kg/a.

Next, the number of working hours per annum has to be estimated. This obviously depends on the working arrangements, that is whether the plant operates, for example, on a basis of continuous shifts, two shifts, or just day work, but is also affected by stoppages whatsoever their cause. These are conveniently considered under three headings, namely, planned shutdown periods, unplanned shutdown periods, and shutdowns due to extraneous disturbances.[54] The first of these are mainly for maintenance and tend to fall into two groups, depending on the lengths of time involved, i.e. greater or less than 10 h.[54] Estimating the time to be allowed for planned shutdowns of mixing plant is no different to estimating for other machinery, but as usual requires some knowledge of the maintenance needs of the various items of equipment, which will generally be indicated in instruction manuals. Unplanned shutdowns arise from operational errors, premature wear or failure of components and instrumentation, contamination, and electrical disturbances. Extraneous disturbances include failures of power supplies and other services, non-delivery of raw materials and operating hazards. Studies of plants, at a number of companies over a period of five years,[54] showed that downtime for planned maintenance amounted to about 0·4% of total time for the first year, increased to 1·7–2% for the next three years, and then jumped to 4·5% for the fifth year, mainly as a result of five-year complete overhauls. For the same period, unplanned shutdowns accounted for between 0·5 and 1·1% of total time, while shutdowns due to extraneous disturbances accounted for 0·28% of total time. If these figures are typical, they indicate that over a period of several years planned maintenance accounts for considerably more downtime than other causes, amounting to 2·06% compared with 0·76% and 0·28%, respectively, for the other two causes. If the plant is operated on a continuous shift basis, all downtime has to be deducted from total time, but if other shift systems are operative, it might be possible to arrange for at least planned maintenance to be carried out outside of nominal production working hours, thus appreciably reducing interference from shutdowns. A continuous shift system, operating five days a week for 50 weeks a year, corresponds to a total time of 6000 h/a. Taking this to be the case, and accepting the previously suggested values for shutdowns amounting to 3·1% of total time, gives a total production time of $6000 \times 0.969 = 5814$ h/a. Therefore, the production rate while working has to be $3\,000\,000/5814$ kg/h $\cong 520$ kg/h. This determines the size, or the sizes and number of units, of equipment. Since this is a compounding operation, the most appropriate equipment would probably be a continuous compounding machine of appropriate capacity with a matching blending machine, but associated items such as storage bins, handling equipment and weighing machines also need to be included in the costing. Suppose the cost of these comes to £80 000, to which must be added costs of installation, say £20 000, building or part of a building (even if already existing), say £20 000, and heating, lighting and furnishings, including test facilities, say £10 000. From these figures, a total capital cost is calculated, which in this example comes to £130 000.

The capital cost is charged to production cost in two ways, namely depreciation and return on capital. There are various ways of calculating these, and each individual company is likely to have its own procedure for calculation. Because of possible obsolescence, machinery is usually regarded as depreciating more rapidly than buildings and may, therefore, be separated from other capital costs for this calculation. Thus, the equipment might be written off at a fixed rate over five years while buildings are written off over ten years, say, and this depreciation can then be calculated as a charge per unit of product. Using this procedure in the present calculation, the total depreciation per year $= £ (100 000/5 + 30 000/10) = £23 000$, which is equivalent to $£23 000/3 000 000 = £0.0077$/kg or $£7.67/1000$ kg.

In addition to investment in the plant, capital is also involved in purchasing raw materials to cover production before payments are received from customers, and this should be included in the capital cost in calculating the required return on capital. This, obviously, depends on the particular raw materials involved, but depending on circumstances one month's supply of raw materials, for example, might be taken as a basis for this charge. Thus, taking raw materials costs as £0.5/kg, one month's supply would cost $£0.5 \times 3 000 000/12 = £125 000$, which added to the plant capital gives a total capital of £255 000, on which a return has to be calculated. If the expected return on capital is 15%/a, say, this amounts to $£255 000 \times 0.15 = £38 250$, which spread over one year's production represents a charge of $£38 250/3 000 000 = £0.0128$/kg, or $£12.75/1000$ kg.

Even with a modern highly automated plant, some labour and supervision will be required, but for this exercise it is assumed that, since the plant is quite a small one, only a low level of automation is to be included, and that the plant will require the full-time services of an operator and a labourer to handle raw materials and product. In addition, some supervision will be allocated. If the factory situation permits, this could be the part-time services (say 20%) of a foreman. Depending on the local and general company situation maintenance labour, management and quality control might be charged as overheads, but for present purposes maintenance is costed at 10% each of the wages of an electrician and fitter, and 5% each of the salaries of a plant manager, a plant engineer and a quality controller. The total annual labour/management charge may then be calculated as follows:

Shift	£	£
20% of a foreman at	6 000 =	1 200
1 operator at	4 000 =	4 000
1 labourer at	3 000 =	3 000
10% of an electrician at	5 500 =	550
10% of a fitter at	5 500 =	550
Total per shift		9 300
Total per three shifts		27 900

Management		
5% of a plant manager at	8 000 =	400
5% of a plant engineer at	8 000 =	400
5% of a quality controller at	6 000 =	300
Total		1 100

Total labour bill = £ 27 900 + £ 1100
                  = £ 29 000 per annum

This is spread over 3 000 000 kg of product, so the labour charge = £29 000/3 000 000 = £0·0097/kg or £9·67/1000 kg.

In order to calculate the basic conversion or processing cost, some other contributions have to be evaluated. These include material losses, consumable stores (oil, rags, etc.), services (electricity, water), materials and components needed for maintenance and testing, packaging and transport. These may be estimated and added to the labour charge to provide the basic conversion cost, or may also be combined with works overheads, depreciation and return on capital to provide a processing cost. The whole may then be combined with the cost of raw materials to arrive at a manufacturing cost, exemplified as follows:

Basic conversion cost	£/1000 kg
Material loss (2%, say)	10
Consumable stores	2
Services	40
Labour	9·67
Maintenance and testing materials	10
Packaging and transport	4
Total	75·67

Manufacturing cost	£/1000 kg
Raw materials	500
Basic conversion cost	75·67
Works overheads	23·91
Depreciation	7·67
Return on capital	12·75
Total cost	620·00

It is stressed that the preceding is only an outline of one method of several that can be used to estimate processing and total manufacturing costs. The important thing is that, whatever method is used, it must be designed to ensure that all relevant costs are included.

As suggested previously, it is not possible to offer detailed actual costings and cost comparisons of different types of mixing plant because of the great variety available and changing financial situations. Also, there is difficulty in determining true raw material costs, since these are usually related to quantity, often decided by individual contract, and may differ considerably from published figures. Knowing the formulation to be used and the costs of the individual components it is a simple matter to calculate the raw materials cost for the whole composition.[43] Note, however, that if a formulation is to be changed significantly the density of the compounded material may also change. If, as will usually be the case, the compound is destined for a product that sells on a volume basis, account of a density change will have to be taken. As a first approximation, the density of the product may be calculated from the formulation knowing the densities of the individual components,[43] but if there is a change in density as a consequence of compounding it is preferable to check by measurement of the actual material.

6.4.2 *Conclusions*

In spite of the foregoing comments about the difficulty offering precise cost comparisons here, a few broad suggestions can be made. Sometimes the nature of the raw materials will dictate, or at least strongly influence, the type of mixing plants. Thus, natural rubber in bale form cannot easily be charged to a continuous compounder and is not in a convenient form for many blending machines, and consequently its mixing is most commonly carried out in internal mixers or on two-roll mills. Particulate polymers can generally be blended and then compounded in batch or continuous machines. At relatively low levels of production, continuous compounding will generally prove to be cheaper than batch compounding, but as production rate increases it becomes more economical to employ internal mixers, and the choice may then depend more on the pattern of production and flexibility desired. As suggested previously (Chapter 5, Section 5.1), for economic operation of an internal mixer, an annual production of the order of seven million kg is desirable, three million acceptable, but below one million likely to be prohibitive. This depends to some extent on the material. Some 'speciality' compositions may be so much easier to handle and process in an internal mixer than in other equipment, that the expense of a small-scale internal mixing unit may be justified.

Perhaps a more difficult, and more common comparison that is called for, is that of deciding between dry-blend and fully compounded granules as feed stock to converting equipment, such as extruders and moulding machines. The correct decision may well depend on the situation already existing. For example, if a potential project is to start from scratch, i.e. all equipment is to be purchased new, it will generally be cheaper to opt for dry-blending without compounding, provided converting machines that can satisfactorily handle the particular dry-blend compositions are obtainable. Whether this requirement can be met, depends on the nature of the composition and the quality demands for the end-product. Polymers appear to differ in their responses to processing in dry-blend form. Thus, for example, it often appears to be possible to disperse pigments satisfactorily in acrylic polymers, whereas with similar processing of polystyrene streaking tends to result. Of course, using dry-blend as feed stock to the final conversion machine may mean that special attention has to be devoted to the blending equipment and procedure, to ensure that the blending is adequate for the conversion machine to achieve the required result, but the extra cost of sophisticated blending equipment is unlikely to outweigh the cost of a compounding line. However, if the conversion machinery is already installed but is incapable of processing dry-blend to satisfactory end-product, the most economic course of action might be to purchase compounding equipment with relatively unsophisticated blending.

REFERENCES

1. ANON, *Eur. Plast. News.*, **5**(9), 13 (1978).
2. KADYKOWSKI, R., *Plast. Rubb. Wkly.*, 28 September, 45 (1979).
3. COOPER, D. C., *Rubb. Plast. Age*, **14**(12), 1138 (1968).
4. ANON, *Plast Tech.*, **27**(1), 71 (1981).
5. ANON, *Plast. Rubb. Wkly.*, 13 July, 11 (1979).
6. ANON, *Plast. Rubb. Wkly.*, 17 March, 33 (1978).
7. WERNER & PFLEIDERER, Stuttgart, *Spiral-drier, Ruhrchemie System*, Technical Bulletin (1968).
8. JOHANNABER, F., *Bayer Information* 185/78e (1978).
9. WHITLOCK INC., Farmington Hills, *Drying systems*, Technical Bulletin.
10. ANON. *Eur. Plast. News*, **5**(2), 33 (1978).
11. GRACE, K. and SMITH, E. A., *Plast. Rubb. Wkly.*, 20 October, 21 (1978).
12. ANON, *Plast. Rubb. Wkly.*, 7 December, 2 (1979); DIGITRON A. G., Brugg, *Robotrailer System*, Technical Bulletin (1979).
13. KING, G. T., *Eur. Plast. News*, **4**(7), 36 (1977).
14. MERRICK SCALE MFG. CO., Kirby-in-Ashfield, *Flow Star Indexible Volumetric Feeder*, Technical Bulletin (1978).
15. MORPETH, F. J., Paper 5, *PRI Conf. on In-plant Colouring of Thermoplastics*, Bradford. PRI, London (1979).
16. ANON, *Brit. Plast. Rubb.*, January, 33 (1978).
17. CRESTA TECHNOLOGY LTD, Fareham, *Continuous production Screenchanger*, Technical Bulletin (1979).
18. ANON, *Plast Tech.*, **25**(12), 15 (1979).
19. KENNAWAY, A., *Brit. Plastics*, **28**(1), 18 (1955); in *Plastics Progress*, Morgan, P. (Ed.), Iliffe, London, p. 149 (1957).
20. ANON, *Eur. Plast. News*, **7**(12), 38 (1980).
21. ANON, *Plast. Rubb. Wkly.*, 15 March, 22 (1974).
22. ANON, *Eur. Plast. News*, **5**(4), 41 (1978).
23. ANON, *Plast. Rubb. Wkly.*, 19 January, 16 (1980).
24. FENNER, R. T. and KOLAYASHI, M., *Plast. Rubb. Processing*, **2**, 3 (1977).
25. ALEXANDER, R. M., *Plast. Tech.*, **24**(12), 20 (1978).
26. ANON, *Plast. Tech.*, **24**(9), 15, 95 (1978).
27. ANON, *Plast. Engng.*, **34**(8), 42 (1978).
28. GREIF–WERK–ERNST MAHLKUCH GMBH, Lubeck, *Velox Programme of Machines*, Technical Bulletin (1972).
29. WEBSTER GRIFFIN LTD, Tunbridge Wells, *Bonapeller Packer*, Technical Bulletin (1977).

30. REGIS MACHINERY (SUSSEX) LTD, Bognor Regis, *Bag Filling and Weighing with the Accrafil*, Technical Bulletin (1977).
31. BARCLAY, W. H., *Plastics World*, **20**, (1962).
32. ELLWOOD, H., *Developments in the Mixing of Rubber and Plastics*, David Bridge and Co. Ltd, Rochdale (1964).
33. ELLWOOD, H. and JACKSON, D., *Process Engineering in the Rubber and Plastics Industries*, David Bridge Co. Ltd, Rochdale (1968).
34. ELLWOOD, H., *The Mixing of Rubber and Plastics*, David Bridge and Co. Ltd, Rochdale (1968).
35. ANON, *Banbury Mixers*, Technical Bulletin 215B, Farrel Bridge, Rochdale (1970).
36. ANON, *Buss Ko-Kneader in the Calender Line*, Buss A. G., Basle (1971).
37. ANON, *Stock Compounding, Storing, Weighing and Handling Plants*, Rheinstahl A. G., Kassel (1973).
38. RICE, P. and ADAM, H., *Developments in PVC Production and Processing*, Chapter 5, Whelan, A. and Craft, J.L. (Eds.), Applied Science Publishers, London (1977).
39. TIRELLI, A. *Poliplasti*, **243**, 47 (1978).
40. HESS, K-M. *PRI. Int. Conf. on PVC Processing*. Eng. Royal Holloway College. PRI, London, pp. 13.1–13.10 (1978).
41. WATTS, R. M. and STEPHEN, D. S., *Plast. Rubb. Processing*, **4**(3), 101 (1979).
42. ELDEN, R. A. and SWAN, A. D., *Calendering of Plastics*, Iliffe, London (1971).
43. MATTHEWS, G., *Vinyl and Allied Polymers, Vol. 2, Vinyl Chloride and Vinyl Acetate Polymers*, Iliffe, London (1972).
44. PORTERFIELD, J. T. S., *Investment Decisions and Capital Costs*, Prentice-Hall, New Jersey (1965).
45. HAWKINS, C. J. and PEARCE, D. W., *Capital Investment Appraisal*, Macmillan Studies in Economics, Macmillan, Basingstoke (1971).
46. PILCHER, R., *Appraisal and Control of Project Costs*, McGraw-Hill, New York (1973).
47. MOORE, P. G., THOMAS, H., BUNN, D. W. and HAMPTON, J. R., *Case Studies in Decision Analysis*, Penguin, Middlesex (1976).
48. LEVY, H. and SARNAT, M., *Capital Investment and Financial Decisions*, Prentice-Hall, New Jersey (1978).
49. BARRETT, G. F. C., *Compounding of Thermoplastics. An Assessment of the Industry, Conf. Thermoplastic Compounding*, PRI, London (1978).
50. SCHOENGOOD, A. A., *S.P.E.J.*, **29**(2), 21 (1973).
51. MACK, W. A., *Plast. Tech.*, **21**(2), 45 (1975).
52. SCHUTZ, S., *Plast. Rubb. Wkly.*, 25 February, 17 (1972).
53. ADAM, H. J., *Plast. Des. Process*, **17**(5), 56 (1977).
54. SCHULER, E. W., *Plast. Engng.*, **34**(2), 18 (1978).
55. BLUNT, T. S., *Colour Compounding. A Service to Industry, PRI Conf. on Thermoplastic Compounding*, PRI, London (1978).
56. GAUNT, N. M. and CURETON, R. W., *Plast. Rubb. Processing*, **3**(3), 121 (1978).
57. ANON, *Mod. Plast. Intl.*, **8**(10), 14 (1978).
58. ANON, *Plast. Rubb. Wkly.*, 15 June, 16 (1979).

59. BUTTERS, G., CROSS, J., DIXON, G. and TILLOTSON, J. F., *Plastics Pneumatic Conveying and Bulk Storage*, Butters, G. (Ed.), Applied Science Publishers, London (1981).
60. *Conference on Granulation of Thermoplastics*, Baden–Baden, December 1974, VDI–Gesellschaft Kunststoffetechnik, Dusseldorf.

CHAPTER 7

Materials Aspects of Mixing

7.1 GENERAL

The preceding four chapters have been very largely concerned with machinery and operations, but of course mixing is very much a matter of materials. The variety of materials that can be involved in polymer mixing is indicated in Chapter 1, Section 1.3, and effects of the nature of components of a composition on mixing processes are discussed in Chapter 2, Section 2.4. Also, some reference to particular materials was necessary during consideration of mixing equipment and processes. This chapter is intended to deal with a number of aspects of polymer mixing technology concerned with materials, in general or specifically, that have not been treated adequately in previous chapters.

Dependence of mixing on the 'net shear' or 'total strain' that a system experiences has already been discussed[1-5] (Chapter 2, Sections 2.3 and 2.4), and the possibility of relating this to power consumption in internal mixers has been touched upon (Section 4.3), though it has been pointed out[2] that the manner in which work on the system is expended is also important. It has been suggested that, at least for rubber, the specific energy of mixing is independent of machine design or size.[6-8] These considerations lead to the suggestion that specific energy input requirements might serve as guides to the relative ease or difficulty of mixing different materials. Some specific energy inputs for rubbers have been published,[6,8-12] these ranging from 0·1 to 10 MJ/kg. Values for some other polymer systems have also been published in relation to particular compounding machines,[14] but comparisons between data from different sources are likely to be tenuous, because it is not always obvious whether or not the values quoted include energy that does not reach the material, e.g. energy used in overcoming friction in the machine itself, and

223

doubtless different machines vary in efficiency of energy usage. Clearly, the precise nature of the polymer and the composition as a whole has a significant influence on specific energy requirements. For polyolefins, published specific energy inputs for a given level of compounding depend on melt index, i.e. on molecular weight, and on the particular mixing operation. Thus, for colouring low density polyethylene with carbon black or pigment master-batch, specific energy inputs are stated to be from 0·54 to 0·72 MJ/kg for melt indices between 1·5 and 20, and 0·72 to 0·9 MJ/kg for melt indices between 0·2 and 1·5. For high density polyethylenes and polypropylene the comparable values are also 0·72–0·9 MJ/kg. Colouring polystyrene in the same manner apparently requires only 0·36–0·54 MJ/kg. Production of pigment master-batches appears to require twice as much energy, the specific energy inputs for this operation being 1·44–2·16 MJ/kg for low or high density polyethylene, or ABS; 0·9–1·26 MJ/kg for polystyrene; and 1·26–1·62 MJ/kg for polyamides. However, although the published data may serve as a useful guide, they have so far been too imprecise and limited in scope, to permit much to be done by way of formulating useful conclusions about the fundamental requirements of particular mixing operations. Indeed, a superficial inspection suggests that published specific energy inputs are dependent on melt flow properties rather than on requirements of mixing. This must be considered as an over-simplification, since it seems certain that energy requirement for mixing must depend on the ease or otherwise with which particular additives may be dispersed and distributed, and this will depend on the nature of the additives as well as the behaviour of the polymer.

7.2 ADDITIVES

In the first chapter, some 30 types of possible additives to polymers to produce plastics or rubber compositions were identified. For some types of additives, there are hundreds of alternative materials that may be used separately or sometimes in combinations of two, three or even more. Additives differ widely not only in function but also in nature, from more or less viscous liquids, to sticky, waxy or dry powdery solids. Pro-portions of additives also vary widely, from a fraction of a percent of the composition to a larger fraction than that of the polymer itself. Selection of the nature and quantities of additives to be used, i.e. formulation, depends on the nature of the polymer, and requirements of processing and the end-product. It tends to be rather specific to particular polymers or groups of polymers. Thus, for example, the stabilisers, lubricants, and impact modifiers used for PVC are unlikely to be used with polyolefins, and the cross-linking agents used for phenolic and amino resins are not used for vulcanisation of rubbers. Some additives, on the other hand, such as fillers, and particularly colourants, blowing agents and flame retardants, are used more generally.

7.2.1 Fillers

It might be expected that few problems would arise in mixing polymers with relatively large proportions of additives, such as fillers, but this is not entirely true. Generally, the properties of a filled composition, such as appearance and toughness, are better the smaller the particles of the filler, but this is only so if the filler is adequately dispersed. Unfortunately, the finer the particles the more they tend to agglomerate and the more difficult it is to disperse them. Where this is a problem, some alleviation can sometimes be achieved by coating the filler particles with a small proportion of a lubricant,[15-18] but attention to the mixing process is still required if thorough dispersion is to be achieved, and the coating may produce other changes in the processing behaviour of the composition. Another problem associated with fillers is that they tend to absorb liquid additives, and effectively remove a proportion from the system. Some alleviation is offered by the coating just referred to, but it is sometimes desirable to defer addition of fine particle fillers, until after any liquid additives have been thoroughly distributed throughout the polymer.[17] Pigments are also prone to absorb liquid components, but their proportions are generally too low for this to have a significant effect on polymer properties.

7.2.2 Master-batches

Apart from fillers, most solid additives are used in only small proportions in polymeric compositions. This raises problems of dispersion and distribution throughout the polymeric matrix. A popular solution to these problems is the use of master-batch techniques,[19-21] which in some circumstances also carry commercial advantages. As far as polymer technology is concerned, the basic principle of the master-batch technique is that additives are thoroughly blended or compounded into polymer at much higher concentrations than those required in the finished product, and then the master-batches so formed are 'let down' by blending into 'natural' polymer, i.e. polymer not containing the additives. Master-batches may be dry-blends in powder or powder and granule form or fully compounded granules. The master-batch technique may usefully be employed as part of an in-house compounding operation, but many types of master-batch are offered by specialist compounding companies. Where a number of slightly different formulations based on the same polymer are processed, using master-batches can offer financial incentives. Thus, for example, a company that is extruding or moulding a particular polymer composition in a variety of different colours, can make significant savings in stock-holding and storage space by using natural compound with colourant master-batches, rather than separate fully compounded material for each colour. With some additives, particularly carbon black and other 'messy' pigments, an additional advantage of purchasing master-batches is that the problem of dust is transferred to the supplier. Though widely used for colouring, master-batches of other additives such as accelerators, activators, antioxidants and flame retardants, are also available from specialist suppliers. They are also available in most of the common polymers, including polyethylene, polypropylene, polystyrene, PVC and rubbers. Concentrations of additives in master-batches depend on the nature of the particular additives and polymer, but are typically such that two to five parts of master-batch per hundred of natural polymer are required. Thus, a polyolefin carbon black master-batch may contain 40% of the black, but even higher concentrations, e.g. 50% of titanium dioxide in a white master-batch, may be used.

7.2.3 Dispersions

Other techniques for dealing with the problems of incorporating small proportions of powdery additives, are to bind the powder into granules by means of paraffin or other waxes, oils, latex, or hydrocarbon polymers,[20] or to disperse the solid at very high concentration into a liquid medium. Binding into granules is used particularly for rubber chemicals, such as accelerators, activators, antioxidants, some pigments, peptizing agents, and flame retardants.[20]

Dispersions or pastes are also used for rubber chemicals, and are being increasingly used for chemical blowing agents and pigments. Good dispersion and distribution of blowing agents before the expansion process is particularly important, if uniform and maximum expansion are to be obtained, and dispersion into a liquid medium is a convenient way of achieving this, provided the composition can tolerate the liquid, because the dispersion can be achieved effectively in the cold, for example by using a triple-roll mill. Pigment dispersions, in the form of so-called liquid colours or colour concentrates, have received increasing attention during the past decade.[18,22-32] They may be used as aids to dispersion in conventional blending or compounding, and in some circumstances, as mentioned previously (Chapter 6, Section 6.2.2), may be metered directly to conversion machines, e.g. injection moulding machines and extruders. This procedure may be regarded as carrying out the mixing operation in two stages: dispersion in the preparation of the colour concentrate, and distribution in the conversion machines.

7.2.4 Colourants

As far as colouring in general is concerned, the converter has a choice from a number of alternative courses of action. He may purchase fully compounded or blended coloured feed stock; he may purchase fully compounded or blended polymer and coloured master-batches or concentrates to be blended to feed stock; he may compound or blend polymer and additives including colourants in-house; or he may use the services of specialist colour compounders. The case for the latter has been strongly argued,[33,34] but apart from their comparative messiness, it is not obvious that colourants should require any different treatment to most other additives. It is true that defects in colouring of finished product are usually readily seen, but just because this is not so with other additives does not mean that any less care is desirable in ensuring their proper selection and mixing. However, if colourants are to be predispersed before blending or compounding, the quantities used by many companies may be so small as to make the use of specialist colour compounders desirable on that count alone. Undoubtedly, careful selection of colourants is important, just as it is with all other components, and a considerable volume of published guidance is available in respect of selection, methods of incorporation and quality control.[17-50] A comparison between the various possible means of incorporating colourants into polymers[26,29] showed marked differences in cost. Using master-batches was stated to cost only 20–30%, liquid colourant only 20%, and dry colouring only 15%, of the cost of using fully coloured compound. In the same study, the advantages and disadvantages of the different systems were well summarised. From the converter's point of view, handling fully compounded granules is the simplest and cleanest of the various alternatives, and the mixing capability of the converting machine can usually be minimal, but it is relatively expensive. Master-batch techniques are somewhat cheaper as a rule, need only the simplest of blending systems and are clean to use. Where they are technically acceptable, liquid colourants are usually cheaper to use than master-batches but may have adverse effects on properties in some polymeric systems. Dry colouring is cheapest of all the techniques, but often requires particularly thorough blending, and can be somewhat messy with a risk of contamination that may necessitate troublesome cleaning. It is not intended that formulation should be discussed in this book, except in so far as it affects mixing behaviour and selection of mixing equipment and procedures, but plenty of information in respect of specific colourants and specific polymers is available.[47]

7.2.5 Fillers and Reinforcing Agents

Fillers and solid reinforcements are commonly compounded into many polymeric compositions. Often it is not possible to be certain whether the additive is a filler or a reinforcing agent, but this will only worry the over ardent taxonomist. Good dispersion and distribution is vital if the introduction of fillers is not to result in too great a deterioration in properties, and is even more vital if worth-while reinforcement is to be achieved. With particulate solid and rubber reinforcements, the attainment of good dispersion and distribution throughout the polymer matrix is a matter of good mixing equipment and technique. Fibre reinforcements such as glass, however, present a problem in that additionally fibre length needs to be retained as much as possible, and the processing indications for this are opposed to those for good dispersion. Effects of extrusion compounding on fibre length and product strength have been studied in conventional extruders[51,52] and in continuous compounding machines.[53-55] Dispersion of glass fibres is considered to involve filamentisation of fibre bundles and reduction in aspect ratios of the monofilaments, and is thought to occur by bending of monofilaments around others, by turbulence in the polymer melt; and by break-down of the size film between adjacent filaments.[56] It is, therefore, greater the higher the melt viscosity or the shear rate. Continuous compounding machines with screw configurations that give relatively mild shearing, seem to be preferable (Chapter 5, Section 5.4.7), and where possible there seem to be advantages in introducing glass-fibre reinforcement between the hopper and the die of a continuous compounding machine.[53-55,57,58] A typical plant for incorporation of glass fibres into most thermoplastics, including polyethylene, polypropylene, polystyrene, ABS, SAN, nylon 66, polyacetal, polycarbonate, polyphenylene oxide, polysulphone, polybutylene terephthalate or acrylics, comprises a twin-screw compounder with lozenge or lens shaped kneaders of the type described in Chapter 5. Polymer and additives other than the glass are fed into the machine through the hopper, and the glass is metered in at a decompression point some way down the barrel, so that the bundles of fibre glass are said to be folded into the melt, with a rolling action that segregates them without smashing them.[53,55] The compounding machine discharges directly into a transversely located simple extruder with a multi-hole die and die-face cutter, thus offering better process control and the possibility of venting at the entrance to the pelletising extruder.[53,55] Machines with triangular kneaders,[57] and reciprocating screw Ko-Kneaders,[58] may also be used for compounding glass into thermoplastics or thermosetting materials.

7.2.6 Plasticisers

Other additives, whose significance in relation to mixing has been studied in some detail, are plasticisers, lubricants,and processing aids, all mainly in PVC. With plasticisers, most work has been concerned with the variation of absorption and diffusion into polymer particles,[59,60] fusion temperature and rate,[61-64] and energy consumption,[61,64] with chemical nature.[17] Selection of plasticisers, therefore, is mainly a matter of formulation for properties and processing behaviour,[17] and has little influence on choice of mixing equipment, except in so far as they are usually liquid, and therefore attention has to be given to such special items and treatment as additives in that form necessitate. Problems can arise when compounding polymers with relatively inactive plasticisers, such as polyesters, where mixing is slow, requiring extended cycles that may be difficult to achieve in continuous compounding machines, and necessitate extended cycles and therefore cooling to avoid over-heating in internal mixers.

7.2.7 *Lubricants and Processing Aids*

Lubricants and processing aids are selected for their effects on melting and melt processing behaviour, so it would be surprising if they did not also affect compounding. External lubricants are intended to reduce friction between molten polymer and metal, while internal lubricants are supposed to lubricate between polymer molecules, presumably reducing melt viscosity. In both cases shearing and rate of shear mixing must be reduced. However, the fundamentals of behaviour of lubricants during processing are not completely understood. It seems very likely that their behaviour is critically dependent on temperature, and since this is usually non-uniform throughout a compounded mass, it is conceivable that the effects of a lubricant vary with locality. However, although lubricants clearly do affect compounding behaviour, they are mainly selected for their effects in moulding or extrusion, and do not generally determine the type of mixing equipment that is to be selected. They are, moreover, very specific to the particular compositions and even the conversion equipment involved, and more detailed discussion is not appropriate here. Processing aids are sometimes lubricants, or even plasticisers, but others are solid polymers of quite different effect. The precise mode of action of the latter is not fully understood, but they do appear to aid mixing, perhaps by increasing apparent viscosity and hence shear mixing, or perhaps by increasing the flow behaviour index so that shear rate becomes more uniform throughout the melt.

7.3 SPECIFIC POLYMERS

7.3.1 *Polyolefins*

Low density forms of polyethylene are usually supplied as granules that have already been submitted to an homogenising/compounding process, and may have additives such as antioxidants already incorporated. The polymer may be compounded with other additives in internal mixers or continuous compounding machines, or may be dry-blended for conversion by extrusion or moulding. Dry-blending with pigment is aided by the presence of 0·2 to 0·5 % of light oil or plasticiser, and is conveniently carried out in intensive non-fluxing mixers of relatively low impeller speed (Chapter 3, Section 3.5). This also applies to polyolefins in powder form, e.g. high density polyethylene and polypropylene. The advantage of these low intensity mixers, compared with the more common highly intensive type, is that they do not damage delicate pigments such as thiocyanine blues and greens. The dry-blends can be moulded directly, or compounded to granules if the conversion machinery cannot perform adequate mixing on dry-blend. As well as colourants, thermal and light stabilisers for polyolefins are available as dispersions in inert liquid carriers. Economics of polyolefins compounding have been studied, with particular reference to the effects of shutdown periods, and up-stream and down-stream failures,[65] but the conclusions are applicable to the compounding of other polymers and were discussed earlier (Chapter 6, Section 6.4).

7.3.2 Styrene Polymers

Polystyrene can be moulded direct from dry-blends, preferably made with 'medium intensity non-fluxing' mixers, but complete dispersion of pigments in polystyrene is sometimes difficult, and continuous compounding, usually with kneading-type screw machines, is common. In addition to pigments, rubbers are commonly compounded into polystyrene to produce impact-resistant grades. Other common additives are plasticisers or 'flow promoters', liquid or chemical blowing agents, and fire retardants. Removal of residual solvents and styrene monomer is also commonly required during compounding, and for this reason vented machines are preferred. Venting efficiency can be improved by introducing 1-3% of water into the melt, and this technique enables reduction in residual monomer levels, that could only otherwise be achieved by using high vacuum.[66] As with other common polymers, coloured master-batches are available from specialist compounders.

7.3.3 PVC

With the possible exception of rubber, more has been written about the blending and compounding of PVC than of any other polymer,[17,61, 67-80] and much of what is known about the fundamentals of compounding processes comes from studies on PVC. This arises partly from the great variety of formulations that are used, partly from the fact that most of the problems of mixing are encountered with PVC, and partly because two methods of preparing PVC compositions, namely plasticised dry-blending and formation of plastisols, are more or less unique to the polymer. For convenience, mixing of PVC compositions may be considered under several headings, namely, dry-blending unplasticised PVC, dry-blending plasticised PVC, blending PVC pastes, compounding unplasticised PVC and compounding plasticised PVC. Partly because dry-blending machines and procedures became available at the same time as the onset of a rather rapid rise in usage of unplasticised PVC, a high proportion of this material that is extruded is in the form of dry-blend rather than compounded granules.[81] For some not immediately apparent reason, the proportion of dry-blend that is injection moulded is somewhat lower. The normal calendering process demands compounded feed stock, though there is something to be said for forming a dry-blend rather than a simple premix to feed the compounding machine in a calendar line.

Machine design and procedures for dry-blending of PVC,[74,81,82] and the behaviour of materials during dry-blending,[83,84] have received a good deal of attention, as has the processing behaviour of dry-blends once formed.[83-89] For satisfactory processing in conversion machinery, well-mixed dry-blends are essential, and non-fluxing intensive mixers (Chapter 3, Section 3.5) are almost universally used. However, there are some variations in procedure. With an unplasticised composition all the ingredients may be charged at the start and mixing carried out at high rotor speed, until a temperature of 120–140°C is reached, at which point the blend is discharged into a cooling mixer. Alternatively, the cycle might start with a short period of slow rotor speed to improve distributive mixing. Another alternative is to withhold addition of lubricant, until a temperature some 20°C below the maximum is reached, so delaying the reduction in friction due to lubricant, and achieving a higher rate of heating.[74] Cycle time to peak temperature depends on the composition, the machine design, and the procedure for a typical unplasticised PVC dry-blend for pipe production, and is typically between 6 and 12 min (Fig. 7.1). A gramophone record composition based on polymer of lower softening temperature will normally be blended much faster, possibly in a cycle time as short as 1–1·5 min. If the blending process was absolutely identical and reproducible, temperature, power consumption and time would be related to each other in the same way during every cycle, and control could be based on any of the three variables, but slight variations will occur. Nevertheless, each of the variables has been used. On balance, there is something to be said for controlling on the basis of temperature, provided it can be measured

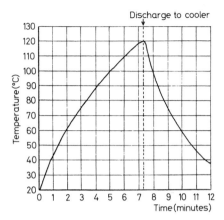

FIG. 7.1. Typical temperature vs time cycle for UPVC dry-blend manufacture with non-fluxing intensive mixer and cooler.

accurately, because it is a measure of the amount of shearing the composition has received, and because the behaviour of some additives, particularly lubricants, may be critically dependent on it. During dry-blending there is increase in bulk density that has a direct bearing on subsequent extrusion behaviour.[74] The increase depends on the temperature rise during blending.

Plasticised dry-blends can be produced from emulsion polymers in non-fluxing intensive mixers, but easy-processing suspension or mass polymers are preferable. With small proportions, it is possible to add the plasticiser with the other ingredients at the start of the blending cycle, but the technique used, more generally, is to defer addition of plasticiser until the temperature of the blend has reached 15–20°C below the discharge temperature. The latter varies over a range of approximately 90–120°C. If the plasticiser is added cold, the blend temperature drops over a period of about a minute, and then rises again as frictional heating outweighs the cooling effect of the plasticiser. Typical cycle times to peak temperature range from 5 to 10 min (Fig. 7.2). Preheating the plasticiser will obviously reduce or avoid the cooling effect, and plasticiser absorption by the polymer particles is more rapid. It has even been suggested that previous simple premixing in a relatively cheap blender can be worthwhile. As mentioned previously, there is a possibility with filled plasticised compositions that some of the plasticiser is effectively removed from the system by being absorbed by filler particles. A similar effect occurs with compositions in which nitrile rubber is used as a

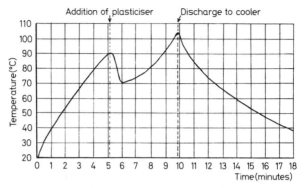

FIG. 7.2. Typical temperature vs time cycle for plasticised PVC dry-blend manufacture with non-fluxing intensive mixer and cooler.

partial replacement for liquid plasticiser. For this reason, deferment of addition of filler or rubber until after all the plasticiser has been absorbed by PVC polymer is generally recommended.

It has been stated[74,90] that throughputs of PVC dry-blends in twin-screw extruders is directly proportional to bulk density. Even if this is not strictly true, there is no doubt that there are advantages in dry-blends of relatively high bulk density. For this reason, and because higher temperatures make removal of moisture, residual monomer and other volatiles more efficient, it might be thought that high discharge temperatures are to be preferred.[74,91] However, higher temperatures require longer cycles and more cooling, and can lead to a risk of excessive degradation. The main problem in blending plasticised PVC, especially when true dry-blends are not being produced, is the tendency for material to stick to the walls and blades or rotors of the equipment. 'Easy-processing' or 'EP' type polymers yield much drier blends than do emulsion or other fine particle resins, and it is partly for this reason that they were given their name.

In the blending of PVC paste resins with plasticisers to produce plastisols or organosols, heating is generally to be avoided, because it may produce excessive increase in viscosity and premature gelation. Depending on the plasticiser, temperatures should generally be kept below 35–38°C.[17] Nevertheless, mixers of the non-fluxing intensive type have been recommended,[93] though almost any type of simple mixer or disperser can be used.[17,92] Depending on the total concentration, a proportion of the plasticiser may be withheld from the initial mixing to ensure that the shear developed is sufficient to break down the resin particles to the required level, and to disperse all the solids adequately. Remaining plasticiser is added after a smooth paste has been formed. Solids such as pigments, lubricants, stabilisers, and fillers are preferably added in the form of previously prepared smooth dispersions in a small proportion of the plasticiser. Planetary mixers seem to be preferred by many manufacturers of pastes, but ribbon blenders, propeller mixers and dispersers, and particularly Z-blade mixers are also commonly employed. Cycle times vary with the intensity of the mixing action and with the particular formulations, and might be anywhere between 15 and 30 min. With this type of mixer, the choice of tool or rotor design depends mainly on the viscosity of the paste. The lower the latter the greater the number of mixing blades that can be used. With these mixers and some models of other types, venting and de-aeration by vacuum can be carried out in the mixing chamber itself, and a separate evacuation vessel is not necessary. It is also claimed that blending pastes under vacuum in a non-fluxing intensive mixer, produces a grinding action that can sometimes obviate any need to triple-roll mill to achieve adequate dispersion. In most cases some cooling through the jacket, depending on the intensity of the mixer and the viscosity of the paste, will be required.

Compounding of PVC is carried out in a variety of different machines. As already mentioned, care in choice of design of machine and operational procedure is particularly necessary with unplasticised PVC, because excessive shearing and overheating are not only liable to cause degradation, but may also produce compound of poor melt flow behaviour.[17,94-97] Even fracture of dies due to high pressures resulting from attempts to avoid high temperatures, is not unknown. Consequently, careful control in temperature in compounding in internal mixers or in continuous compounding machines is necessary. For essentially the same reasons, cascade type arrangements of continuous compounding machines are preferred.

In spite of the apparent complication of an additional component, the compounding of plasticised PVC is on the whole much simpler than that of unplasticised PVC, and all kinds of compounding machines may therefore be used for the material. This is because the presence of plasticiser lowers softening temperatures and reduces melt viscosity at any particular processing temperature, so that even with high molecular weight polymer, there is a much reduced tendency to cause degradation by overheating or to develop excessively high melt pressures. However, subsequent processing may well still be dependent on temperatures reached during compounding, so that careful attention needs to be directed at this operating variable. Possibly, the major problem in compounding plasticised PVC is to obtain complete dispersion of polymer particles.[17,68] As mentioned in Chapter 4, Section 4.3.5, in opaque compositions these are generally masked and are, therefore, unobjectionable, but in transparent products, particularly thin film, undispersed particles show up as defects commonly known as 'fish eyes'. For these reasons, the compounding cycle for a transparent material may have to be longer than that for an opaque but otherwise identical composition. Herein lies a possible advantage of a batch internal mixer over continuous compounding machines, in that it is relatively easy to vary cycle time with the former.

Master-batch techniques are quite common with plasticised PVC processing. For unplasticised PVC dry-blending, and for plasticised PVC, a variety of stabiliser-lubricant one-pack systems, very often custom-designed, are available. They may be in the form of powders, agglomerates, or granules of various shapes such as rods, flakes or beads, whose particle size can be reasonably well matched to that of the PVC resin.

7.3.4 *Other Thermoplastics*

Of other thermoplastics, including acrylics, ABS, polycarbonate, nylons, polyacetal, linear polyesters, polysulphones, and cellulose acetate, all are compunded with colourants and stabilisers in continuous compounding machines, particularly those with kneading sections. Sometimes conventional twin-screw extruders can achieve adequate mixing, and indeed direct conversion from dry-blend is also sometimes possible.

7.3.5 *Rubbers*

So much has been written about the formulation and mixing of rubber compositions, that the uninitiated might be excused for thinking that is all there is to rubber processing. Indeed, perhaps it would be true to say that these are the most important aspects of the manufacture of rubber goods, though this might also be said of many other polymers, particularly PVC, the mixing of which bears at least a superficial resemblance to that of rubbers. A useful review of mixing of rubber compounds by Morrell has been published by the Plastics and Rubber Institute,[98] and Funt's *Mixing of Rubbers*, to which reference has already been made,[99] though essentially a theoretical treatment, contains useful practical indications on mixing, particularly in the matter of scaling-up, and there exists a considerable body of published information, both theoretical and practical, relating specifically to the mixing of rubbers.[12,100–145] Derringer has presented a useful guide to the use of statistical methods to aid rubber technology and mixing in particular.[131] Brydson has reviewed the literature on the mixing of styrene-butadiene rubbers (SBR).[146]

Simple blending of a rubber is scarcely possible unless it is in latex or powdered form (see later). Where blending of rubbers is carried out, equipment and procedures are the same as for other polymers, but compounding, in the sense used throughout this book, involves a number of features that differ from the compounding of other polymers. At the time of writing, most rubbers, both natural and synthetic, are supplied in bale form, the trend being towards a standard 33-kg bale wrapped in plastic film,[98] and the future relationship between bale and powdered rubbers seems uncertain. For this reason, batch compounding in internal mixers and, to a lesser extent, on two-roll mills is much more common than continuous compounding, and where the latter is used it will frequently follow mastication and mixing in of some components in a batch compounding machine. Although whole bales may be charged to internal mixers, some cutting will usually be required, if only because the optimum batch size will rarely correspond to an exact whole number of bales. For this purpose, special bale-cutting guillotines are available, in which the thickness of slice may be varied to suit the requirements of different batches.[147]

Compounding of rubbers on two-roll mills and in internal mixers has already been discussed briefly (Chapter 4, Sections 4.2.5 and 4.3.8), and a number of theoretical and practical studies, aimed at understanding the process and improving its efficiency in manufacturing operations, have been published. Thus, Gehman[101] applied probability theory to the characterisation of mixing fillers into rubber, used the resultant model to estimate modulus enhancement to be expected from increased cross-linking density at the surface of reinforcing particles, and indicated that this model could explain the enhancement obtained with reinforcing fillers when contrasted with inactive fillers. Claxton and Conant[102] attempted to separate the contributions made by thermal degradation and cross-linking reactions during rubber processing, and suggested methods of characterisation that could be used to reprocess out-of specification rubber to bring it to an acceptable state. The Brabender Plastograph has been extensively applied to studies of rubber processability and to predict behaviour.[102-107] Some studies have concentrated attention on the mixing of specific additives, particularly carbon black,[108,109] zinc oxide,[111] and magnesium oxide.[112] On the basis of microscopic examination during mixing, Boonstra and Medalia[108,109] suggested that the primary process in mixing carbon black into rubber is one of penetration by the rubber of voids between carbon aggregates, to form a system comprising concentrated agglomerates held together by rubber matrix. This comprises incorporation[6] (Chapter 1, Section 1.2). These concentrated aggregates become subjected to high shear forces that tend to break them down again, until the required dispersion is attained. It is interesting to note that in the mixing of carbon black into oil-extended SBR, where complete dispersion was obtained in 8 min, maximum tensile strength and elongation at break were attained after only 3 min, by which time dispersion had already reached nearly 97%, and even after only 1·5 min, with dispersion at only 23%, tensile strength and elongation at break had attained over 65% of their maximum values.

The large number of publications devoted to milling of rubbers[113-123] is, presumably, a reflection of the greater importance this process has with rubbers than with other polymers. The usual procedures for compounding rubber compositions on a two-roll mill are different to those commonly used for thermoplastics or thermosetting plastics, in that initially the rubber alone is fed to the nip, and only after a reasonably smooth crepe is formed are the other components added.[118] Depending on the nature of the rubber, this may take between 2 and 10 min, and full mixing may require a total time of 15–45 min.[122] As with the compounding of all polymers on a two-roll mill, it is necessary to have a rolling bank of material in the nip, and to ensure cross-mixing by frequent cutting and folding back of the crepe.[113,115] (Chapter 4, Section 4.2.6). It is to alleviate this problem that stock-blending units were introduced. Colm[117] has suggested ways of improving the design of mills or modifying existing machines to improve efficiency and prolong their usefulness. He states that the term friction ratio has been a misnomer since its conception, and that the idea that friction ratio is associated with increase in power consumption and heat build-up is false, both in theory and in production. On this basis, mills for warming and mastication have been built with even speeds for maximum conversion of available power into useful work. Conversely, high friction ratios and low peripheral speeds for holding and feed operations have permitted reduced cooling water usage or faster cooling, while at the same time reducing power consumption and minimising the heat history of the stock. Colm also suggests that mills feeding calenders or extruders often run at unnecessarily high speeds. Brichta and Welding[119,120,123] have suggested that improved monitoring and control over power input, forces in the nip and feeding, can reduce milling times and contribute to an effective control of mix temperature.

Probably the most common procedure used for compounding rubbers in internal mixers is similar to that used with two-roll mills, namely, first to masticate the rubber for 1 to 2 min and then to introduce the additives.[122] With low rotor speeds, it appears to be usual to operate on a fixed cycle time, whereas a predetermined stock dump temperature or integrated power input are used with high rotor speeds. Presumably, this is because at low rotor speeds, temperature rise, if any, is a relatively insensitive guide to the progress of the operation, and cycle times are relatively long and, therefore, controllable with fair precision. On the other hand, with high rotor speeds, cycle times are relatively short, and temperature and power input become more sensitive guides. After dumping, the compound is further mixed on a two-roll mill or in an extruder-slabber, sheeted and cooled (Chapter 4, Section 4.3.8). Cycle times with low rotor speeds may take from 5 to 10 min or even longer, and an error of 30 s does not appear to be over-important,[118] but with high rotor speeds, and consequently shorter cycle times, timing becomes critical. Output is, of course, increased by increasing rotor speed and power input,[7,124,125] but this may place greater demands on the cooling system, possible necessitating high speed circulation of refrigerated water[125] and requiring special attention to cooling after dumping.[126] Increase in ram pressure from around $110 \, kN/m^3$, typical until the late 1950s, to values of the order of $400-500 \, kN/m^3$, more usual in modern machines, also seems distinctly advantageous in reducing cycle times without losing out on total energy consumption or dispersion.[8,12,100,118,127] As a result of flow visualisation studies of internal mixing, Freakley and Wan Idris[129] identified fill factor as one of the key variables influencing uniformity of mixing, though the optimum value probably depends on the particular design of mixer and may depend on formulation. Another factor that can affect performance of an internal mixer is wear, arising from the fact that internal mixers tend to be used for many years, and periodic checks on dimensions and clearances should be made.[136]

As a general rule, internal mixers are not pre-heated to the required operating temperature when processing rubbers, but reach that temperature after about five consecutive batches.[118] As suggested previously (Chapter 4, Section 4.3.8), this practice seems likely to result in batch to batch variation.[118] Many types of rubber compound, including tyre tread compounds for example, are mixed in steps by what is sometimes called a master-batch technique,[118,122] although the concentration of carbon black or filler is preferably the same as that in the final compound.[118] With synthetic rubbers, carbon black has often been formed into a master-batch at the latex stage, but there seems to be some disagreement as to whether this is advantageous or not.[118,122] To avoid scorch, the curing agents are omitted until the final mixing stage, which may be carried out in an internal mixer, on a mill, or in a continuous compounding machine. However, other variations in the order of adding components to the mixer are practised. Choice of procedure seems usually to be based on empirical assessment of performance, particularly with respect to

  (i) the ease with which the rubber makes-up, i.e. forms a more or less continuous body of polymer (cf. gelation of thermoplastic polymers),
 (ii) efficiency of dispersion of carbon black and other fillers, and
(iii) overall cycle time.

Addition of large proportions of filler tend to break up the rubber, and so it is desirable to disperse the filler in portions at a time. Thus, where the rubber requires mastication in the internal mixer it may first be masticated alone, softener and antioxidant, and then fillers added, curing agents being added finally on a two-roll mill.[148] If the quantity of filler is such as to interfere with the making-up of the rubber, it may be added in two or three portions, allowing each portion to become well dispersed before adding the next. Where the rubber does not require masticating an upside-down procedure may be used.

In the upside-down procedure, filler is placed in the mixer first, followed by the rubber. In modified upside-down procedures, filler and oil followed by 30–50% of the polymer are mixed for up to 2 min, when the remainder of the polymer is added, or alternatively part of the oil is withheld and added in successive stages.[125,132,149] The former procedure is particularly suitable for rubbers with high loadings of coarse carbon blacks and oil, whereas the latter is suitable for high quality compounds using reinforcing carbon blacks and only moderate amounts of oil.[132]

Continuous compounding machines have not been used with rubbers to the extent that they have with some thermoplastics, partly because rubbers are not often in a form that make them appropriate as feed stock to relatively small hoppers, where free flow is a prime desideratum. Apparently, the most common use of continuous compounders with rubbers is down-stream of an internal mixer, thereby increasing the output of the former by 20–30%. The usual extruder-slabber will accept the whole charge from a matched internal mixer, but most other continuous compounding machines require strip or particle feed. Machines of this type that appear to have been used successfully with rubbers, include the Gordon Plasticator,[150] the Transfermix,[98,99,117,125] the Farrel Bridge FCM continuous mixer,[78,98,99,118,125] the Shaw Double R[118] and the Werner and Pfleiderer EVK extruder.[98,99,133,138] This latter is a single-screw mixing extruder, which has a mixing zone with interrupted channels providing high shear and interrupted threads that increase back-mixing.[99]

Powdered rubbers have received a fair amount of publicity over the past decade,[151–154] and powdered nitrile rubbers have been available since the late 1950s,[164] but even today the penetration of the rubber market appears to be well below the figures predicted.[156] As well as nitrile rubbers, acrylonitrile-butadiene, styrene-butadiene, polychloroprene, ethylene-propylene, polyurethane and natural rubbers are also available in powder form.[157,160] Although their physical form renders them amenable to techniques not directly applicable to rubbers in bale forms, powdered rubbers often appear to be used as direct replacement for bales using precisely the same mixing procedures. Clearly, bales cannot be blended in the same ways as powders, and it is indeed claimed that powdered rubbers must be blended in low shear non-fluxing intensive mixers.[157] The order of addition of components is said to affect the physical form of the blend. Thus, to obtain the smallest particle size, it is recommended that carbon black or other fillers be added first with a low rotor speed, the rubber being added after 1 min of mixing, and any liquids being added last, so that the rubber becomes coated with filler and is thus not swollen by the liquids. If the rubber is placed in the mixer first, agglomeration can occur at the blade surface, so producing a coarser blend and possibly poor dispersion of filler. Liquids should be added over a period of time, after which rotor speed is increased before dumping at a temperature of around 80°C.[155,157] Using blends prepared in this way as feed stock to mills can offer appreciable savings in overall mixing times. With internal mixers, the overall mixing time, including the blending, may be longer, but the compounding cycle may be reduced, thus making it possible to increase the output from rather expensive capital equipment. In fact, the whole future of powdered, crumb or pelletised rubbers in relation to bale forms seems to depend on relative costs rather than on technical performance, since with careful attention to procedures the latter are comparable.[153,157,160] There is a suggestion that more attention is necessary to ensure adequate dispersion of carbon black, but this can be assessed reliably by measurements of electrical resistivity.[156] The economics will obviously depend on existing plant and, in particular, whether or not it is operating at or near full production capacity. If desired increase in production can be taken up by existing spare capacity there may not be much point in investing in blending equipment, but if a relatively cheap blender can increase already fully used capacity by up to 50%, there may well be cost savings in doing so. Account has to be taken, of course, of any premium on powdered rubber as compared to bales. A number of examples of cost comparisons have been published,[154,159,161] and it should be a simple matter to adjust these to match prices current at the time of calculation. Provided a continuous compounding machine or an extruder can achieve sufficient mixing, it seems logical to feed powdered rubber blends directly,[98,166] but there may be advantages in first compacting it to a ribbon, and a machine for this purpose has been developed.[98,160]

Before leaving the subject of mixing rubbers, mention should be made of poly-dispersions, which are essentially master-batches (Section 7.2.2) of additives in an elastomeric binder.[168] These are available in the form of small slabs that can be easily broken to pieces of appropriate weights for various mix requirements. They are advantageous, both in achieving dispersion more rapidly in the compounding operation, and thus cost savings, and also in reducing hazards arising from handling neat chemicals. A wide range of rubber chemicals is now available in this form, including sulphur, curing agents, accelerators, anti-oxidants, pigments, blowing agents, and flame retardants.

7.3.6 Thermosetting Plastics

Mixing procedures used for thermosetting plastic compositions vary considerably and depend very much on the nature of the particular materials and of the final processing. Phenolic moulding powders are produced from solid novolaks or resols. After manufacture these resins may be ground to powders in ball mills (Chapter 3, Section 3.3.5), possibly blending with solid additives at the same time. The major proportion of phenolic moulding composition is compounded by two-roll milling (Chapter 4, Section 4.2.6) at temperatures ranging from 70 to 100 °C for the back roll, and 20 to 30 °C hotter for the front roll.[169] When the cure has advanced to the required stage, after anything from 1 to 10 min milling, the sheeted material is quickly removed, cooled, and ground to powder form. If the composition is difficult to gel to a continuous sheet, as is often the case with fillers that are fibrous and bulky, e.g. cotton linters, it may be first premixed briefly in an internal mixer. As happens with any polymeric composition, fibrous fillers tend to be broken down by shearing action during compounding. It is possible to avoid this by omitting a melt compounding operation, and instead blending the additives into a solution of resin in methylated spirit, evaporating off most of the spirit to yield a composition of the desired consistency.[169] More recently, blending of thermosets, particularly phenolics, to produce moulding powders directly in intensive non-fluxing mixers has been described, though very careful control is required in order to achieve suitable flow and cure characteristics.[170] A mixing time of 7·5 min is typical.

Mineral-filled melamine-formaldehyde moulding materials are sometimes compounded on two-roll mills, in much the same way as phenolics, but aminoplants are more commonly processed by a wet method.[171] The filler, usually bleached cellulose pulp, is disintegrated and charged to a sigma-blade mixer (Chapter 3, Section 3.7) into which an appropriate quantity of resin syrup is then metered. The composition is blended for 1–2 h, usually at 40–60°C, and lubricants, plasticisers and possibly catalyst, stabilisers and pigments are then added. The product, in the form of a wet crumb, is discharged, screened, dried, disintegrated, and ball-milled. Pigments and further lubricant, and catalyst and stabiliser, if not already added, are usually introduced at this stage. Finally, the powder may be densified to improve moulding behaviour.[171]

Many thermosetting systems are reactive at room temperatures, once all the components have been blended, and this does impose the problem of achieving adequate blending before cross-linking, or curing, has advanced too far for satisfactory forming (Chapter 2, Sections 2.3.3 and 2.4.1). These materials include unsaturated polyesters, epoxy resins and polyurethanes. Most of these systems involve liquid components, so that they are often amenable to continuous metering, blending in a small volume mixing head, and discharge into moulds or other locations where they cure *in situ*. It is convenient to blend other components into one or other of the major liquid components, so that the system does not become reactive until the final mixing stage. In this way, fillers, pigments, catalysts and accelerators can be thoroughly dispersed in conventional blending equipment such as paddle or sigma-blade mixers, thus limiting the demand on the efficiency of the final mixing process. The intensity of shearing required in this pre-blending operation depends on the nature of the additives. Thus, in unsaturated polyesters, the finer the particle size of the filler the more intense the shearing required to achieve adequate dispersion, so that with a coarse filler a low speed paddle mixer might be used, whereas with fine fillers a high intensity mixer of the disperser or turbine type (Chapter 3, Section 3.4.2) might be desirable.[172] A variety of metering units, mixing heads and control systems is available for highly reactive compositions such as polyurethanes.[173,174] The Farrel medium intensity mixer[175] uses a conical mixing chamber into which liquid and solid components can be metered, and, while particularly designed for mixing glass-fibre reinforced polyester compounds for injection moulding, is said to be suitable for other blending applications, such as DMC, PVC and suspensions of wood or other particulate solids in liquid resins. Solid reactive systems, such as epoxy powder coatings can be blended in simple machines, such as tumble blends and ribbon blenders, but may also be blended in intensive non-fluxing mixers having relatively low rotor speed (Chapter 3, Section 3.5).

7.3.7 *Polymer Blends*

Finally, mention is made of a subject that seems to be receiving increasing attention, namely polymer blends. Entropy changes are always positive for mixing and therefore promote the process, but are so small for two polymers, that they are swamped by other factors.[176] Blending of polymers in powder form presents no special problems, but not all polymers are readily available in powder form, and in any case at some stage compounding in the melt stage is involved. Clearly, the melt behaviour of each polymer is significant, and it might be expected that similar apparent melt viscosity and flow behaviour at compounding temperatures would be desirable. The type of compounding equipment used is likely to be highly significant in determining degree and mode of dispersion.[177-179] Thus, in studies of the blending of particular grades of polystyrene and polypropylene processing in a simple single-screw extender, dispersed the former as long fibrils in a continuous phase of the latter, but the addition of a motionless or static mixer (Chapter 5, Section 5.5.9) broke the discrete phase polystyrene into particles of well-defined shape.[179] With a twin-screw compounding machine of the triangular kneader type (Chapter 5, Section 5.4.7), the mode of dispersion was different though not necessarily better.

REFERENCES

1. SPENCER, R. S. and WILEY, R. M., *J. Colloid Sci.*, **6**, 133 (1951).
2. MOHR, W. D., SAXTON, R. L. and JEPSON, C. H., *Ind. Engng. Chem.*, **49**(11), 1855 (1957).
3. TADMOR, Z. and PINTO, G., *Polym. Engng. Sci.*, **10**(5), 279 (1970).
4. BIGG, D. and MIDDLEMAN, S. *Ind. Eng. Chem. Fundam.*, **13**(1), 66 (1974).
5. TADMOR, Z. and GOGOS, C. G., *Principles of Polymer Processing*, Wiley, New York (1979).
6. PALMGREN, H., *Eur. Rubb. J.*, **156**, 30, 70 (May/June 1974).
7. EDMONDSON, H. M., *IRI Conference on Recent Developments in Rubber Compounding*, Institution of the Rubber Industry, London (1969).
8. BEBRIS, K. D., VASILEV, R., VERESOTSKAYA, A. and NOVIKOV, M. I., *Soviet Rubb. Tech.*, **18**(11), 23 (1959).
9. DANIEL, T. J. and WAKE, W. C., *Trans. I.R.I.*, **33**, 135 (1957); **34**, 79 (1958).
10. STAROV, I. M., SUSHCHENKO, A. A., ARISTOV, L. G. and ARTEMEV, B. N., *Soviet Rubb. Tech.*, **20**(1), 8 (1961).
11. PERIBERG, S. E., *Rubber World*, **150**(2), 27 (1964).
12. WHITAKER, P., *J.I.R.I.*, **4**(4), 153 (1970).
13. WERNER & PFLEIDERER, Stuttgart, *ZSK Variable*, Technical Bulletin (1971).
14. WERNER & PFLEIDERER, Stuttgart, *Twin Screw Compounder Type ZZK Dual Feed*, Technical Bulletin.
15. WHISSON, R. R., *Fillers for Plastics*, Chapter 2, Wake, W. C. (Ed.), Iliffe, London (1971).
16. KING, A., *Plasticisers, Stabilisers, and Fillers*, Chapters 18–20, Ritchie, P. D. (Ed.), Iliffe, London (1972).
17. MATTHEWS, G., *Vinyl and Allied Polymers, Vol. 2, Vinyl Chloride and Vinyl Acetate Polymers*, Iliffe, London (1972).
18. TITOW, W. V., *Developments in PVC Production and Processing–1*, Chapter 4, Whelan, A. and Craft, J. L. (Eds), Applied Science Publishers, London (1977).
19. BRAENDLE, H. A., *Masterbatching Techniques*, IRI/Plast. Inst. Joint Conference, February (1958); *Trans. IRI*, **34**(2), 58 (1958).
20. RHEIN-CHEMIE RHEINAU GMBH, Mannheim, *Product Information on Polymer-Bound Chemical Granules for Modern Compounding*, Technical Report No. 53E (1977).
21. HUBRON, LTD, Manchester, *Plastic Masterbatches*, Technical Booklet (1978).

22. ANON, *Mod. Plast. Intl.,* **3**(2), 41 (1973).
23. MANZIONE, J. and DANKS, S., *Plast. Tech.,* **21**(8), 37 (1975).
24. FREEMOTT, J. H., *Plast. Engng.,* **34**(8), 40 (1978).
25. ANON, *Eur. Plast. News.,* **6**(2), 31 (1979).
26. MORPETH, F. J., Paper 2, *PRI Conf. on In-plant Colouring of Thermoplastics,* Bradford. PRI, London (1979).
27. GAUNT, N. M., Paper 5, *PRI Conf. on In-plant Colouring of Thermoplastics,* Bradford. PRI, London (1979).
28. ANON, *Plast. Rubb. Wkly.,* 15 June, 16 (1979).
29. ANON, *Mod. Plast. Intl.,* **9**(6), 40 (1979).
30. CRODA CHEMICALS LTD, *Crodinject Liquid Colourants for Plastics* (1979).
31. FISHBURN PRINTING INK CO., LTD, *Inmont Liqui-Kolor Colourants for Thermoplastics* (1979).
32. ANON, *Plast. Rubb. Wkly.,* 5 April, 8 (1980).
33. FERGUSON, D., *Polym. Age,* **6**(9), 250–251 (1975).
34. BLUNT, T. S., Paper 2, *PRI Conf. on Thermoplastic Compounding,* London PRI, London (1978).
35. HALL, C. H., *Trans. J. Plast. Inst.,* **23**, 4 (1955).
36. I.C.I. LTD, Manchester, *The Colouring of Plastics* (1960).
37. ESTEVEZ, J. M. J., *J. Soc. Dyers Colour.,* **77**, 300 (1961).
38. MUSGRAVE, C., *J. Soc. Dyers Colour.,* **77**, 638 (1961).
39. MUSGRAVE, C., *Fibres Plast.,* **21** (10), 291 (1962).
40. HIRSEKORN, B., *Gummi. Asbest. Kunststoffe,* **16**, 977 (1962).
41. DeCOSTE, J. B. and HANSEN, R. H., *S.P.E.J.,* **18**(4), 341 (1962).
42. BALLEY, E. J. G., *Trans. J. Plast. Inst.,* **35**, 119, 707 (1967).
43. SCHIFFERS, H. and WICHARDT, G., *Kunststoffe–Rundschau,* **17**(6), 277 (1970).
44. REEVE, T. B., *Plast. Engng.,* **33**(8), 31 (1977).
45. OSMER, D., *Plast. Engng.,* **33**(9), 38 (1977).
46. SORICE, R. G., *Plast. Engng.,* **34**(8), 37 (1978).
47. CATTLE, G., and SCHOFIELD, P. Paper 1, *PRI Conf. on In-plant Colouring of Thermoplastics,* Bradford. PRI, London (1979).
48. BARKER, S. J., BEST, R. P., GRANGE, P. W. and KORNMAYER, H., Papers to *PRI Conf. on In-Plant Colouring of Thermoplastics,* Bradford. PRI, London (1979).
49. ANON, *Plast. Compounding,* May/June, 98 (1979).
50. CLARKE, H. S., *Plast. Engng.,* **36**(1), 38 (1980).
51. MOSKAL, E. A., *Plast. Des. Process.,* **17**(1), 10 (1977).
52. LUNT, J. M. and SHORTALL, J. B., *Plast. Rubb. Processing,* **4**, 108 (1979).
53. TODD, D. B. and BAUMANN, D. K., *Chem. Engng. Progr.,* **73**(1), 65 (1977).
54. STADE, K. H., *Polym. Engng. Sci.,* **18**(2), 107 (1978).
55. TODD, D. B. and BAUMANN, D. K., *Polym. Engng. Sci.,* **18**(4), 321 (1978).
56. JOHNSON, A. E. and LUNT, J. M., *Mod. Plastics,* **53**(7), 58 (1976).
57. WERNER & PFLEIDERER, Stuttgart, *Continuous Production of Glass Fibre Reinforced Thermoplastics;* KS-Information Brief Report No. 8, *Polymer Processing News,* **1**, 2 (1976).
58. BUSS A. G., Basle, *Buss Ko-Kneader Plant for the Continuous Processing of Reinforced or Filled Thermoplastics or Thermosets* (1979).
59. McKINNEY, P. V., *J. Appl. Polym. Sci.,* **11**, 193 (1967).

60. BERGER, F. DRAP, C., and MALAVOI, R., *S.P.E.J.*, **24**(7), 37 (1968).
61. BERGEN, H. S. and DARBY, J. R., *Ind. Engng. Chem.*, **43**(10), 2404 (1951).
62. SCHMIDT, P., *Kunststoffe*, **42**, 142 (1952).
63. TOUCHETTE, N. W., SEPPALA, H. J. and DARBY, J. R., *Plast. Tech.*, **10**(7), 33 (1964); *Brabender Inf. Bull. No. 193*.
64. ARENDT, W. D., *Plast. Engng.*, **35**(9), 46 (1979).
65. SCHULER, E. W., *Plast. Engng.*, **34**(2), 18 (1978).
66. HESS, K.-M., *Kunststoffe*, **69**, 199 (1979).
67. HAMMOND, R., *Trans. J. Plast. Inst.*, **26**, 49 (1958).
68. DYER, B. S., *Trans. J. Plast. Inst.*, **27**, 84 (1959).
69. MATTHEWS, G. A. R., *Advances in PVC Compounding and Processing*, Chapter 5, Kaufman, M. (Ed.), Maclaren, London (1962).
70. SCHNEIDER, A., *Kunststoffe-Rundschau*, **7**(10), 333 (1963); **8**(6), 324 (1964).
71. MCKINNEY, P. V., *J. Appl. Polym. Sci.*, **9**, 3359 (1965).
72. UNO, T., *Japan Plast. Age*, February, 51 (1968).
73. PENN, W. S., *PVC Technology*, 3rd edn., Titow, W. V. and Lanham, B. J. (Eds), Applied Science Publishers, London (1971).
74. BOULTON, A. J., *Developments in PVC Technology*, Chapter 6, Henson, J. H. L. and Whelan, A. (Eds), Applied Science Publishers, London (1973).
75. RICE, P. and ADAM, H., *Developments in PVC Production and Processing–1*. Chapter 5, Whelan, A. and Craft, J. L. (Eds), Applied Science Publishers, London (1977).
76. TANAKA, S., *Japan Plast. Age*, May/June, 27 (1977).
77. ANON, *Mod. Plast. Intl.*, **7**(7), 18 (1977).
78. HESS, K-M., *PRI Int. Conf. on PVC Processing*, Eng. Royal Holloway College, PRI, London, pp. 13.1–13.10 (1978).
79. PERRY, N. L., *Encyclopedia of PVC*, Vol. 2, Chapter 17, Nass, L. L. (Ed.), Marcel Dekker, New York (1976).
80. ANDERS, D., *Kunststoffe*, **69**, 194 (1979).
81. DOMINGHAUS, H., *Plastverarbeiter*, **12**, 775 (1963).
82. ANON, *Intl. Plast. Engng.*, **6**, 14 (1966).
83. GALE, G. M., Paper 8, *PRI Conf. on Plastics Rheology in Polymer Processing*, PRI, London (1969).
84. HEMSLEY, D. A., KATCHY, E., LINFORD, R. J. and MARSHALL, D. E., *PRI Int. Conf. on PVC Processing*, Eng. Royal Holloway College, PRI, London, pp. 9.1–9.10 (1978).
85. FLATHERS, N. T., JOHNSON, R. E., PALLAS, V. R. and SMITH, W. M., *Mod. Plastics*, **38**, 210 (1961).
86. GALE, G. M., *RAPRA tech. Rev.*, No. 28, (1966); *RAPRA Bull.*, **5**, 78, (1967).
87. DANIEL, T. J. and MATTHEWS, D., *RAPRA Res. Rep.*, No. 163 (1967).
88. JONES, D. R. and HAWKES, J. C., *Trans. J. Plast. Inst.*, **35**, 120. 773 (1967).
89. HUMPHREYS, J. W., *Developments in PVC Technology*, Chapter 7, Henson, J. H. L. and Whelan, A. (Eds), Applied Science Publishers, London (1973).
90. GUIMON, C., *SPE 23rd ANTEC meeting*, May, 1085, (1967).
91. MOROHASHI, H., *Japan Plast.*, **2**(4), 27 (1968).
92. BAJAJ, J. K. L., *Plast. Tech.*, **22**(10), 34 (1976).
93. ANON, *Adhesives Age*, **20**(2), 26 (1977).
94. BURKE, G. H. and PORTINGELL, G. C., *Brit. Plast.*, **36**(5), 254 (1963).

95. KHANNA, S. K., and POLLITT, W. F. O., *J. Appl. Polym. Sci.*, **9**, 1767 (1965).
96. DOWRICK, D., *Plastics*, **30**, 63, 328 (1965).
97. MOORE, D. R., *PRI Int. Conf. on PVC Processing*, Eng. Royal Holloway College, PRI, London, pp. 11.1–11.10 (1978).
98. MORRELL, S. H., *Progress of Rubber Technology*, **36**, 57 (1972); **42**, (1978).
99. FUNT, J. M., *Mixing of Rubbers*, RAPRA, Shrewsbury (1977).
100. ALLEN, P. W., *Natural Rubber and the Synthetics*, Crosby Lockwood, London (1972).
101. GEHMAN, S. D., *Rubb. Chem. Tech.*, **35**, 819 (1962).
102. CLAXTON, W. E. and CONANT, F. S., *Rubber Age*, **97**(10), 80 (1965).
103. ONUFER, R. J., BLAKE, W. T. and SCHMITZ, A. O., *Predicting Rubber Processability with the C. W. Brabender Plastograph*, Information Bulletin No. 196, Brabender OHG, Duisberg (1964).
104. BEACH, K. C., COMPER, L. F. and LOWERY, V. E., *Rubber Age*, **85**, 253 (1959).
105. ONUFER, R. J., *Discovering the Keys to Processing Better Rubber Compounds with the C. W. Brabender Plastograph*, Brabender OHG Bibliography No. 247.
106. SCHRAMM, G., *The Use of the Brabender Plastograph in the Rubber Industry*, Paper to Swedish Inst. Rubb. Tech. Ann. Mtg (1967).
107. ROTHENPIELER, A., *Rheotron-Vortrag anl. der Ronneby-Tagung*, Sweden (1975).
108. BOONSTRA, B. B. and MEDALIA, A. I., *Rubber Age*, **92**, 82, 892 (1963); *Rubb. Chem. Tech.*, **36**, 115 (1963).
109. BOONSTRA, B. B., (Ed.) *Rubber Technology and Manufacture*, Chapter 7, Blow, C. M., (Ed.) Newnes-Butterworths, London (1977).
110. HOLCOMB, K. L. and STUDEBAKER, M. L., *The Use of the Brabender Plasti-Corder to Study the Mixing Operation, Carbon Black-Rubber Interactions*, Brabender OHG Bibliography No. 485 (1976).
111. JONES, H. C. and SNYDER, E. G., *Ind. Engng. Chem.*, **43**(11), 2602 (1951).
112. KERN, N. V., PALMER, J. W. and KRON, R. B., *Rubber Age*, **100**(1), 66 (1968).
113. HEPNER, I. L., Thesis, University of London (1955).
114. WELDING, G. N., Private Communication to J. R. Scott (1955).
115. SCOTT, J. R., *Applied Science of Rubber*, Chapter 5, Naunton, W. J. S. (Ed.), Edward Arnold, London (1961).
116. TOKITA, N., and WHITE, J. L., *J. Appl. Polym. Sci.*, **10**, 1011 (1966); **12**, 1589 (1968).
117. COLM, H., *Rubber World*, **158**(5), 67 (1968).
118. CROWTHER, B. G. and EDMONDSON, H. M., *Rubber Technology and Manufacture*, Chapter 8, Blow, C. M. (Ed.), Newnes-Butterworths, London (1971).
119. BRICHTA, A. M., *Plast. Rubb. Processing*, **2** (2), 49 (1977).
120. BRICHTA, A. M. and WELDING, G. N., *Plast. Rubb. Processing*, **2** (2), 53 (1977).
121. ROBERTS, M. R., *Eur. Rubb. J.*, **159**(9), 22 (1977).
122. GARVEY, B. S., Rubber Compounding and Processing, in *Encyclopedia of Polymer Science and Technology*, Vol. 12, Mark, H. F. and Gaylord, N. J. (Eds), (1970).

123. BRICHTA, A. M. and WELDING, G. N., British Patent 1209467 (1970).
124. SCHEUERMANN, W., *Gummibereifung*, **48**(9), 56 (1972).
125. CROWTHER, B. G. and MORRELL, S. H., *Progress of Rubber Technology*, **36**, 37 (1972).
126. PEAKMAN, M. G., *J.I.R.I.*, **4** (1), 35 (1970).
127. COMES, R. N., *Rubber World*, **135**(4), 565 (1957).
128. EVANS, C. W., *Rubber Age*, **101**(9), 61 (1969).
129. FREAKLY, P. K. and WAN IDRIS, W. Y., *Rubb. Chem. Tech.*, **52**, 134 (1979).
130. STUDEBAKER, M. L. and BEATTY, J. R., *Science and Technology of Rubber*, Chapter 9, Eirich, F. R. (Ed.), Academic Press, New York (1978).
131. DERRINGER, G. C., *Rubber World*, **167**(6), 33, 58; **168**(1), 49; **168**(2), 43; **168**(3), 40 (1973).
132. TOPCIK, B., *Rubber Age*, **105**(7), 25; **105**(8), 35 (1973).
133. KOCH, H., *Rubber Age*, **105**(5), 53 (1973).
134. BARBOUR, A. L., *Rubber Age*, **108**(4), 43 (1976).
135. STUDEBAKER, M. L., and BEATTY, J. R. *Rubber Age*, **108**(5), 21; **108**(6), 21 (1976).
136. ELLWOOD, H., *Eur. Rubb. J.*, **159**(8), 15 (1977).
137. ANON, *Eur. Rubb. J.*, **159**(8), 27 (1977).
138. SCHWARZ, G., *Eur. Rubb. J.*, **159**(9), 28 (1977).
139. MEDER, A. and MAY, W., *Rubb. J.*, **146**, 39 (1964).
140. EINHORN, S. C., *Rubber World*, **148**(5), 40 (1965).
141. TOKITA, N. and PLISKIN, I., *Rubb. Chem. Technol.*, **46**, 1166 (1973).
142. VAN BUSKIRK, P. R., TURETZKY, S. B. and GUNBERG, P. F., *Rubb. Chem. Technol.*, **48**, 577 (1975).
143. MILLS, W., YEO, C. D., KAY, P. J. and SMITH, B. R., *Rubber Industry*, **9**, 25 (1975).
144. TURETZKY, S. B., VAN BUSKIRK, P. R. and GUNBERG, P. F., *Rubb. Chem. Technol*, **49**, 1 (1976).
145. SMITH, B. R., *Rubb. Chem. Technol.*, **49**, 291 (1976).
146. BRYDSON, J. A., *Developments in Rubber Technology—2*, Chapter 2, Whelan, A. and Lee, K. S. (Eds), Applied Science Publishers, London (1981).
147. ANON, *Plast. Rubb. Wkly.*, 17 May, 23 (1980).
148. PENN, W. S., *Synthetic Rubber Technology*, Maclaren, London (1960).
149. BRITISH GEON LTD, *Breon Nitrile Rubbers* (1964).
150. BROWN, J., *Rubb. Plast. Age*, **37**, 6 (1956).
151. GOSHORN, T. R. and WOLF, F. R., *Rubber Age*, **97**(2), 77 (1965).
152. ZEPPERNICK, F., *Kautschuk Gummi*, **18**, 231, 313, 806 (1965).
153. GOSHORN, T. R., JORGENSEN, A. H. and WOODS, M. E., *Rubber World*, **161**(1), 66 (1969).
154. MARSHALL, S., *Rubber World*, **162**(9), 49 (1970).
155. WARDLE, H. A. and SERCOMBE, M. G., *PRT Polymer Age*, **4**(2), 62 (1973).
156. WOODS, M. E., MORSEK, R. J. and WHITTINGTON, W. H., *Rubber World*, **167**(6), 42 (March 1973).
157. WOODS, M. E. and KROSKY, R. P., *Rubber Age*, **105**(4), 33 (1973).
158. WIDMER, H. and MILNER, P. W., *Rubber Age*, **106**(1), 41 (1974).
159. NORDSIEK, K. H. and BERG, G., *Polymer Age*, **6**(55), 60 (1975).
160. WOODS, M. E. and Whittington, W. H., *Rubber Age*, **107**(9), 39 (1975).
161. EVANS, C. W., *Rubber Age*, **108**(8), 19 (1976).

162. PYNE, J. R., *Plast. Rubb. Intl.*, **3**(5), 195; **3**(6), 258 (1978).
163. EVANS, C. W., *Powdered and Particulate Rubber Technology*, Applied Science Publishers, London (1978).
164. SMITH, L. P., *Elastomerics*, **110**(1), 32 (1978).
165. E. I. DU PONT DE NEMOURS AND CO., Wilmington, *Future Rubber Processing*, Delphi Report (1971); ANON, *Rubber Age*, **104**(11), 66 (1972).
166. MORRELL, S. H. and PYNE, J. R., *Eur. Rubb. J.*, **158**(2), 12 (1976).
167. LEHNEN, J. P., *Eur. Rubb. J.*, **159**(1), 10 (1977).
168. LEO, T. J., *Rubber Age*, **108**(1), 35 (1976).
169. WHITEHOUSE, A. A. A., PRITCHETT, E. G. K. and BARNETT, G., *Phenolic Resins*, Iliffe, London (1967).
170. THYSSEN HENSCHEL, Kassel, *Henschel Mixers—Special Information*, Technical Bulletin (1978).
171. VALE, C. P. and TAYLOR, W. G. K., *Aminoplastics*, Iliffe, London (1964).
172. GROVE, S. A., *Plast. Des. Process.*, **17**(7), 55 (1977).
173. ANON, *Plast. Rubb. Wkly.*, 29 June, 14 (1979).
174. HIEMER, A., *Kunststoffe*, **69**, 444 (1979).
175. ANON, *Eur. Plast. News*, **7**(1), 48 (1980).
176. GEE, G., *Qu. Rev. Chem. Soc.*, **1**, 265 (1947).
177. STARITA, J., *Trans. Soc. Rheol.*, **16**, 339 (1972).
178. VAN OENE, H., *J. Colloid Interface. Sci.*, **40**, 448 (1972).
179. HAN, C. D., KIM, Y. W., and CHEN, S. J., *J. Appl. Polym. Sci.*, **19**, 2831 (1975).

BIBLIOGRAPHY

ANON, *Eur. Plast. News*, **8**, 6, 9, 12 (1981).
WEBBER, T. G. (Ed.), *Coloring of Plastics*, Wiley Interscience, New York (1979).

Appendix 1: Guide to Mixing Equipment

Type	Design principle	Main uses
1. Vibratory or reciprocating		Powder blending Liquid dispersing
2. Tumble (i) Drum		Dry-blending powders and granules Reducing batch to batch variations
(ii) Eccentric		As (i) but with increased cross-mixing
(iii) V		Laboratory blending
(iv) Double-cone		As 2. (ii)
(v) Cube		As 2. (ii)
(vi) Ball mill		Comminution and dry-blending of agglomerates and thermosetting resins

251

Table A1—*contd.*

Type	Design principle	Main uses
3. Stirrer (i) Paddle		Polymerisation Dry- and wet-blending of powders with additives.
(ii) Propeller		As 3. (i); mainly liquid systems'
(iii) Disperser		Emulsifying Dispersing solids in liquids
(iv) Turbine		As 3. (iii)
(v) Planetary		Dry- and wet-blending of powders with additives; especially plastisols
4. Intensive non- fluxing		Dry-blending, especially powders and powders with liquids, e.g. plasticised PVC powders, plastisols
5. Ribbon (i) Trough		Blending powders, and powders with liquid additives
(ii) Cone and screw		As 5. (i)
(iii) Cone and ribbon screw		As 5. (i)
(iv) Vertical auger		As 5. (i)

Table A1—*contd.*

Type	Design principle	Main uses
6. (i) Z-blade Sigma-bladed, etc.		Dispersion of solids in liquids, especially high viscosity systems.
(ii) Claw-bladed		As 6. (i)
(iii) With extruder discharge		As 6. (i)
7. Plough		Blending powders with liquid.
8. Air and fluidising	air→	Dry-blending of powders.
9. Toroidal		Similar to 4.
10. Continuous turbine		Production of solutions, suspensions and emulsions up to $1000\,Ns/m^2$ viscosity
11. Colloid, disc and pin mills.		Dispersing solid powders in liquids.
12. Bead mills		As 11.

Table A1—*contd.*

Type	Design principle	Main uses
13. Mullers and pug mills		As 11., particularly with agglomerating solids and high viscosity systems.
14. Roll mills		Dispersion of solids in liquids
15. Electrostatic		Powder or liquid blending

TABLE A2
BATCH COMPOUNDING MACHINES (CHAPTER 4)

Type	Design principle	Main uses
1. Roll mills		Rubber, thermosetting and thermoplastic compounding
(i) Strip cutter		Removal of milled hide or crepe for granulation
(ii) Mixing ploughs		Improvement of cross-mixing
(iii) Stock blender		As 1. (ii)
2. Internal mixers		Compounding rubbers and thermoplastics

TABLE A3
CONTINUOUS COMPOUNDING MACHINES (CHAPTER 5)

	Type	Design principle	Main uses
1. (i)	Single-screw Two-section screw		Polyolefin and PVC compounding
(ii)	Smear-head		Polyolefin compounding especially for good pigment dispersion
(iii)	Increased helix angle		Rubber compounding
(iv)	Eccentric cams		Polyolefin compounding
(v)	Slotted screws		As 1. (iv)
(vi)	Two-channel screws		Thermoplastic especially PVC compounding
(vii)	Convergence- divergence		Rubber compounding; colour concentrates; carbon black master- batches Compounding sensitive materials, e.g. glass- filled, cross-linkable or foamable
(viii)	Lozenge kneaders		Polyolefin and polystyrene compounding.
(ix)	Triangular kneaders		Polyolefin, polystyrene and plasticised PVC compounding
(x)	Shear cone		Plasticised PVC compounding

Table A3–*cont'd.*

Type	Design principle	Main uses
(xi) Pin extruders		Rubber compounding
(xii) Reciprocating slotted screw		Polyolefin, polystyrene and PVC compounding; most other plastic compositions
(xiii) Separate channels		Thermoplastics compounding
(xiv) Bidirectional		As 1. (xiii)
2. Twin-screw (i) Tapered screw		Thermoplastics compounding
(ii) Reversed threads		General compounding especially where venting required
(iii) Roll mill section		As 2. (ii)
(iv) Internal mixer section		As 2. (ii)
(v) Continuous internal mixer		General compounding

Table A3–*cont'd.*

Type	Design principle	Main uses
(vi) Eccentric, kneaders		As 2 (ii)
(vii) Lozenge kneaders		General compounding especially where low shear required, e.g. glass-filled compositions
(viii) Triangular kneaders		General compounding especially where high shear required
(ix) Dual feed		General compounding
3. Miscellaneous		
(i) Planetary, gears		Thermoplastics, especially PVC compounding. Carbon black dispersion in polyolefins
(ii) Bihelicoidal gears		Low viscosity melt compounding
(iii) Roll mill extruder		Rubber compounding
(iv) Spiral disc		Thermoplastics compounding
(v) 'Diskpack'		General compounding

Table A3—*cont'd.*

	Type	*Design principle*	*Main uses*
(vi)	Cascade		Compounding shear-sensitive compositions
(vii)	Integrated mixing, venting extrusion		General compounding
(viii)	Motionless or static		Dispersion of colourants Polymer/polymer blending

Appendix 2

The following companies have given permission to reproduce illustrations and have provided information used in the compilation of this book. Their cooperation is gratefully acknowledged.

Apollo Machinery Sales Ltd, Maple Cross, UK.

Atlas Chemical Industries (UK) Ltd, Leatherhead, UK.

Baker Perkins Chemical Machinery Ltd, Hanley, Stoke-on-Trent, UK.

Battagion S.p.A., Bergamo, Italy.

Battenfeld (England) Ltd, Chesham, UK.

Bayer UK Ltd, Richmond, UK.

Beken Engineering Ltd, Barking, UK.

Berstorff Ltd, Lancaster, UK.

Bone Cravens Ltd, Sheffield, UK.

Thomas Borges & Partners Ltd, Stalybridge, UK.

Buss–Hamilton Ltd, Cheadle Hulme, UK.

Carter Bros. (Rochdale) Ltd, Rochdale, UK.

Churchill Fluid Heat Ltd, Uxbridge, UK.

Colormax Ltd, Telford, UK.

Comerio Ercole S.p.A., Busto Arsizio, Italy.

Coudenhove (UK), Kettering, UK.

Glen Creston Ltd, London, UK.

Croda Chemicals Ltd, Goole, UK.

Demag Hamilton Plastics Machinery Ltd, Gerrards Cross, UK.

Dierks & Sohne Maschinenfabrik, Osnabruck, West Germany.

Engelmann & Buckham Machinery Ltd, Alton, UK.

Esde Maschinenfabrik GmbH, Bad Oeynhausen, West Germany.

Peter Evans Associates, Highbridge, UK.

Farrel Bridge Ltd, Rochdale, UK.

T. K. Fielder Ltd, Eastleigh, UK.

Fishburn Printing Ink Company Ltd, Orpington, UK.

Floataire Ltd, Leicester, UK.

Foscolor Ltd, Wigan, UK.

Hubron, Ltd, Manchester, UK.

Iddon Brothers Ltd, Leyland, UK.

Krauss–Maffei (UK) Ltd, Warrington, UK.

Leesona Plastics Machinery Ltd, Burtonwood, UK.

Liquid Controls Ltd, Wellingborough, UK.

Maillefer S. A., Lausanne, Switzerland.

Manchem Ltd, Manchester, UK.

The Mastermix Engineering Company, Ltd, Redditch, UK.

Meccaniche Moderne, Busto Arsizio, Italy.

Metallgesellschaft AG., Frankfurt, West Germany.

Mortimer Plastics Machinery Ltd, London, UK.

Morton Machine Company Ltd, Wishaw, UK.

MTI-Mischtechnik Industrieanlagen GmbH., Detmold, West Germany.

Nautamix (UK) Ltd, Macclesfield, UK.

Oaktree Equipment Ltd, Faringdon, UK.

OBS Machines Ltd, Milton Keynes, UK.

Pilamec Ltd, Bournemouth, UK.

Plasten Engineering Ltd, Warley, UK.

Premier Colloid Mills Ltd, Walton-on-Thames, UK.

George Reffold, Preston, UK.

Regis Machinery (Sales) Ltd, Bognor Regis, UK.

Samafor, La Courneuve, France.

Francis Shaw & Company (Manchester) Ltd, Manchester, UK.

T. A. Shore Company Ltd, Nottingham, UK.

Silverson Machines Ltd, Chesham, UK.

Sisis Equipment (Macclesfield) Ltd, Macclesfield, UK.

E. A. Thorne & Sons Ltd, Bromsgrove, UK.

Thyssen Plastik Maschinen GmbH., Munchen, West Germany.

UPM Machinery Sales Ltd, Slough, UK.

Vac-U-Max Ltd, Stockport, UK.

Victor International Plastics (London) Ltd, London, UK.

Webster Griffin Ltd, Tunbridge Wells, UK.

Welding Engineers Inc., King of Prussia, Pennsylvania, USA.

Werner & Pfleiderer (UK) Ltd, Stockport, UK.

Willinger Machinery Company Ltd, London, UK.

Winkworth Machinery Ltd, Staines, UK.

Index